STO

ACPL ITEM
DISCARDED

D1092726

JUN 29 '66

MATERIALS TECHNOLOGY

in Steam Reforming Processes

MATERIALS TECHNOLOGY

in Steam Reforming Processes

Proceedings of the Materials Technology Symposium

held on October 21-22, 1964

Organised by the Agricultural Division

Imperial Chemical Industries Ltd.

Edited by

C. EDELEANU

SYMPOSIUM PUBLICATIONS DIVISION

PERGAMON PRESS

OXFORD · LONDON · EDINBURGH · NEW YORK

TORONTO · PARIS · FRANKFURT

Pergamon Press Ltd., Headington Hill Hall, Oxford
4 & 5 Fitzroy Square, London W.1
Pergamon Press (Scotland) Ltd., 2 & 3 Teviot Place, Edinburgh 1
Pergamon Press Inc., 44–01 21st Street, Long Island City, New York 11101
Pergamon of Canada Ltd., 6 Adelaide Street East, Toronto, Ontario
Pergamon Press S.A.R.L., 24 rue des Écoles, Paris 5e
Pergamon Press GmbH, Kaiserstrasse 75, Frankfurt-am-Main

Copyright © 1966
Pergamon Press Ltd.

First edition 1966

Library of Congress Catalog Card No. 65-20478

PRINTED IN GREAT BRITAIN BY ADLARD AND SON, LTD.,
BARTHOLOMEW PRESS, DORKING
(2347/65)

1358339

CONTENTS

PREFACE

SINCE the war a great deal of technical effort has been devoted to materials and the demands of the new industries such as aircraft, electronics, nuclear power and now space, have been so heavy and, in some ways, technically glamorous that the progress made in other fields is perhaps less well documented. Older industries such as the chemical industry have also progressed rapidly during this period and, although naturally a great deal of the progress is due to new chemistry and better chemical engineering, developments in materials of construction and ways of using materials have made a considerable contribution. The number of people involved in these developments is comparatively small and the apparent "scientific" content of their work may appear pedestrian to those accustomed to industries based on more sophisticated engineering but their productivity has been remarkably high. Given sufficient time and money, problems can always be solved elegantly, and scientifically explained, but it is also possible to take short-cuts if you know your technology and have sufficient common-sense.

This book contains a number of papers by some of the people involved in the development of one particular process as well as some people who are now helping its further development. The process involving some relatively high temperatures has made severe demands of material and the main purpose is to record what was done and why, and to draw attention to some of the mistakes and how these have been dealt with. Naturally, I hope that the book will also be some use to people not particularly interested in chemical plant but who are, nevertheless, interested in high temperature technology.

If I may be allowed a personal view, I feel that there is also a message in the book for those people normally concerned with apparently more sophisticated technology and especially for those, and I was one of them a few years ago, who believe that all worthwhile jobs require a big effort, a great deal of time and, most important, a fundamental understanding of every scientific detail. Naturally, the thorough approach has great merits and is frequently absolutely necessary but we must also accept that success may be attainable by shorter methods arising from inspired guesses made by people having a thorough knowledge of their subject. The time available for decisions in this case is referred to in some of the papers and, in general, was very short. Much of the experimental work had, in fact, to be done after the decisions were made and was aimed at confirming their correctness and hence the likely reliability of the plant. There is perhaps a lesson here. For example, much as rupture data is necessary to make predictions on reliability, it is quicker, cheaper and more effective to take an indirect approach and develop a tube isolation technique which positively increases reliability.

The papers do not give sufficient credit to work done in connection with the development of the pressure natural gas reforming process but very little of this is documented and available. Credit should be given to many people not in the industry who are not cited in these pages.

C. EDELEANU

THE ICI NAPHTHA REFORMING PROCESS

S. P. S. Andrew

INTRODUCTION

During the past four years the catalytic reforming of naphtha has become the preferred route for the production of synthesis gas and forms a major additional supply of town gas in the United Kingdom. For countries that have no sources of natural gas, this simple continuous process, which was developed by the Agricultural Division of Imperial Chemical Industries Limited, has completely transformed the economics of producing town gas and of ammonia and of chemicals based on hydrogen. The catalytic steam reforming process is markedly lower both in production cost and in capital investment than processes based on coal and, being very flexible, is capable of producing either high calorific value town gas, rich in methane, or almost pure hydrogen. Reformers are now in operation for a wide range of product gases: hydrogen, methanol synthesis gas, ammonia synthesis and lean town gas (380 Btu/ft³) and, very recently, the ICI has developed the naphtha reforming process so that it is capable of producing a full town gas having a calorific value of 500 Btu/ft³.

As with all new processes a number of material problems had to be overcome in design. Reformers operate at high pressures and high temperatures. The development of high-temperature alloys and methods of fabricating them have, therefore, substantially contributed to the success of the process. Techniques for the internal insulation of large high-pressure vessels and their connecting pipework had also to be developed. The high temperatures and pressures of the process fluids could result in various forms of corrosive attack on the material of construction and careful testing and selection of these materials were needed to avoid such difficulties.

APPLICATION OF THE PROCESS

The reaction between naphtha and steam over a nickel-based catalyst is capable of producing a wide range of possible product gases depending upon the conditions of operation of the reformer. The factors involved may most readily be appreciated from a consideration of the effects of operating pressure and temperature and the steam ratio (the ratio of moles of steam to atoms of carbon in the feed gas to the reformer) on the conversion products

A   1

of the reformer, Fig. 1. Provided the light distillate is completely reformed to molecules containing only single atoms of carbon, two limiting possibilities exist. Either the whole of the carbon is reformed to give oxides of carbon together with hydrogen in the product gas or else the reforming proceeds to the limit where no hydrogen is present in the product gas and the maximum

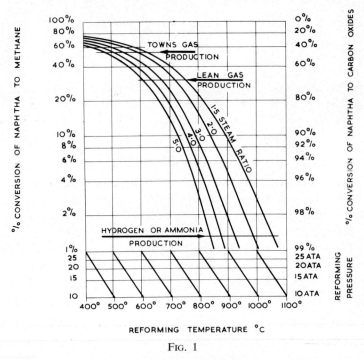

FIG. 1

Diagram showing variation of equilibrium conversion of naphtha with steam ratio, reforming temperature and pressure.

amount of carbon is reformed to methane. These two limits correspond respectively to the equilibria attained at very high temperatures, low pressure and high steam ratios and the equilibria attained at very low temperatures, high pressures and low steam ratios. The variation of these parameters is, therefore, the primary means used in design to enable naphtha reforming to be employed for the production of different gas streams.

For *hydrogen production*, the process flow diagram is generally as shown in Fig. 2 and the overall reaction taking place over the reformer and water gas shift reactor is, ideally:

$$CH_{2\cdot1} + 2\cdot0\ H_2O \longrightarrow CO_2 + 3\cdot05\ H_2$$
$$+\ 49\ kcals$$

In practice, only some 98 to 99 per cent conversion of the light distillate to carbon oxides is attained in the reformer (Fig. 1) under commercially attractive conditions.

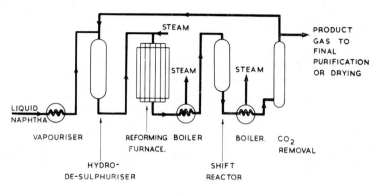

FIG. 2

Flow diagram for hydrogen or lean gas production.

For *ammonia synthesis gas production*, the process flow diagram is generally as shown in Fig. 3, the necessary nitrogen content being introduced as air into the secondary reformer, a catalyst filled vessel in which the oxygen of the

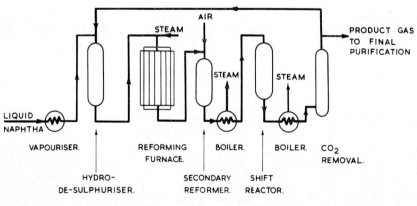

FIG. 3

Flow diagram for ammonia synthesis gas production.

air is burnt liberating heat and raising the temperature of the product gases from the primary reformer thereby bringing about a secondary reformer product gas equilibrium at a temperature some 150° to 200°C higher than that of the product gases from the primary reformer. The overall reaction taking place over both reformers and the water gas shift reactor is, ideally:

$$CH_{2\cdot 1} + 1\cdot 54\, H_2O + 1\cdot 1\, Air \longrightarrow CO_2 + 0\cdot 86\,(N_2 + 3H_2) \\ + 17\cdot 7\ kcals$$

Again, of course, only some 99 to 99·5 per cent conversion of the light distillate to carbon oxides is attained in actual plants.

The flow diagram for *lean gas production* is generally similar to that for hydrogen (Fig. 2) although the operating conditions markedly differ. For lean gas production a gas is required which, after partial CO_2 removal and butane enrichment, is a satisfactory town gas. A typical stoichiometry for an ICI lean gas reforming plant is:

$$CH_{2\cdot 1} + 1\cdot 30\, H_2O \longrightarrow 0\cdot 1\, CO + 0\cdot 6\, CO_2 + 1\cdot 75\, H_2 + 0\cdot 3\, CH_4 \\ + 31\cdot 5\ kcals$$

Conversion of the light distillate to carbon oxides is only some 70 per cent complete to produce this gas (Fig. 1) so that a lean gas reformer operates at a markedly lower temperature than a hydrogen reformer.

For *town gas production,* a gas having a calorific value of about 500 Btu/ft³ is required. ICI has recently developed a reforming process which eliminates the need for butane enrichment. The flow diagram for this process is shown in Fig. 4. Typical stoichiometry for the overall process is:

$$CH_{2\cdot 1} + 0\cdot 85\, H_2O \longrightarrow 0\cdot 05\, CO + 0\cdot 40\, CO_2 + 0\cdot 80\, H_2 + 0\cdot 55\, CH \\ 16\cdot 9\ kcals$$

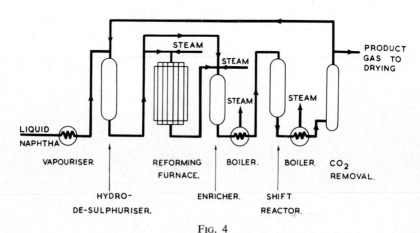

FIG. 4

Flow diagram for towns gas production.

Conversion of the light distillate to carbon oxides is now only 45 per cent complete and the required equilibrium reforming temperature is even lower than for lean gas production (Fig. 1).

TECHNOLOGICAL ASPECTS OF REFORMING

The Construction of the Primary Reformer

The general constructional arrangements of most, though not all, of ICI's reforming furnaces are sketched in Fig. 5. On the left is shown a typical vertical section through the furnace looking along its length. A photograph of the reformers at Billingham is shown in Fig. 6. The furnace is of rectangular

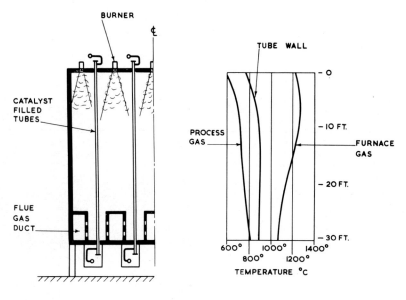

FIG. 5

Diagram showing layout of and temperature in typical reformer furnace.

construction lined with refractory brickwork on all sides and the reacting gases pass downwards through catalyst filled tubes, of about 4 in. bore and 30 ft heated length, suspended in rows in the furnace. Oil burners fire downwards from the roof of the furnace into lanes between the tube rows and the flue gases are removed through ducts built up on the floor of the furnace. A typical furnace might have one hundred tubes arranged in four rows of twenty-five. There is, however, a large variation in the size and numbers of tubes, depending on the output, between different plants.

In reforming furnace design, the metallurgical limits set by tube materials frequently set an upper limit to the possible operating pressure of the reforming process. From Fig. 1 it can be seen that reformer equilibrium temperatures generally lie in the range of from 650°C, for town gas production, to over 1000°C for ammonia synthesis gas production. As the tube wall temperature must exceed the reformed gas temperature by some 100°C to permit reasonably rapid heat transfer, it is evident that tube wall temperatures must lie in the range 750°C upwards. At such temperatures the tube metal creeps under stress. The relative magnitudes of the effects of stress and

FIG. 6

temperature on tube life may be seen in Fig. 7, which shows the theoretical life of a reformer tube as a function of operating pressure and temperature. This graph has been calculated from the results of creep tests on cast 25/20 CrNi alloy extrapolated for lives of over one year. The steepness of the constant pressure lines shows the importance of operating temperature on tube life and reveals the necessity for reformer furnace designers to be able to predict accurately the tube wall temperature profiles in a projected furnace. A prediction that was 50°C too low would result in changing an expected tube life of ten years into an actual life of one and a half years.

A prediction that was 50°C too high would have increased the tube thickness unnecessarily by 40 per cent and the cost of the tubes by nearly as large a factor. As the tubes in a large reformer might cost around £100,000 the installation of excessively thick tubes is clearly not financially desirable. It is also undesirable from a structural viewpoint as the thermally induced stresses in the tube on start up and shut down of the reformer are increased in proportion to the tube thickness.

The manner in which tube metallurgy affects the design of the reforming process is shown in Fig. 8, which has been drawn for the same alloy as Fig. 7. Superimposed on the tube strength limit are curves giving equilibrium conversion of light distillate to carbon oxides derived from Fig. 1 for a fixed

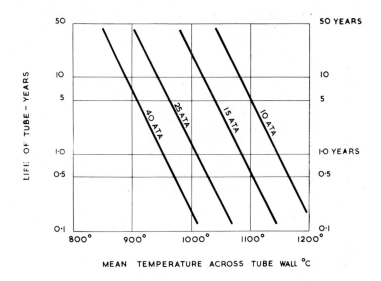

FIG. 7

Diagram showing influence of internal pressure and wall temperature of tube life for typical naphtha reformer tube made of cast 25/20 Cr Ni Alloy.

steam ratio of $3 \cdot 5$. A tube life of 10 years has been assumed together with a temperature difference of 100°C between tube wall and reformer equilibrium temperature in drawing up Fig. 8. From this figure it can be seen that when a high percentage conversion of the light distillate is required, as for hydrogen production, reforming pressures in excess of about 20 atm are difficult to attain with the particular tube alloy and temperature approach chosen for consideration.

Reformers for ammonia synthesis gas production are not limited in operating pressure by metallurgical considerations as much as are hydrogen producing reformers. The final reforming is effected in the adiabatic secondary reformer after the addition of the necessary nitrogen in the form of air which, by its combustion, supplies further heat to the partially reformed gases leaving the reforming furnace. Being adiabatic, no metallurgical limits exist in the design of the secondary reformer as the vessel walls can be protected from the heat by internal insulation. With a rise in temperature of 150° to 200°C from the partially reformed gases leaving the primary furnace to the completely reformed gases leaving the secondary reformer, it can be seen from Fig. 8 that a 98 to 99 per cent conversion to carbon oxides is metallurgically practicable at pressures as high as 35 atm for ammonia

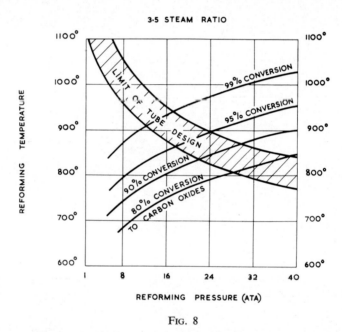

Fig. 8

Diagram showing metallurgical limitations to the operation of reforming furnaces.

synthesis gas reformers, corresponding temperatures being 810°C leaving the primary reformer and about 1000°C leaving the secondary reformer.

For lean gas and town gas manufacture, the reforming equilibrium temperatures required are markedly lower than for hydrogen production or ammonia synthesis gas production. Operating pressures in excess of 35 atm therefore pose no severe metallurgical difficulties.

The Construction of the Secondary Reformer

The most important process consideration in designing the secondary reformer is ensuring a uniform mixing of the air with the primary reformer exit gases. If poor mixing occurs then that part of the mixture which is rich in air is heated, by combustion of the air, to a very high temperature which can damage the catalyst. The most important engineering consideration is the insulation of the pressure vessel shell from the high internal temperature which can exceed 1300°C in the combustion zone. Cast *in situ* refractory internal linings have been successfully employed for this duty.

Corrosion Problems

The constructional materials employed in the primary and secondary reformers in the transfer lines and in the heat recovery equipment such as water heat boilers and feed heaters which cool the process gas must all resist attack by the process gas. The reformer tubes must also resist attack by the furnace flue gases. The high temperatures and high partial pressures of steam in the secondary reformer would result in the extraction of silica from refractory materials containing this component which the process gas would attack by the formation of volatile silica hydrates. The deposition of this silica in the colder parts of the heat recovery train would rapidly cause a serious fall off in performance and finally choking of the equipment. The extraction of nickel as nickel carbonyl both from the catalysts in the primary and secondary reformers and from nickel containing alloys was a further problem which needed investigation, particularly in connection with the use of reforming for manufacturing town gas where the nickel would deposit in the gas burners. Investigations, however, showed that, fortunately, at high temperatures the equilibrium is not in favour of nickel carbonyl formation and at low temperatures, where the equilibrium is favourable, the rate of formation of the carbonyl is very slow indeed.

Only fuels containing very low amounts of vanadium can be burnt in the primary reformer furnace otherwise vanadium attack would take place on the very hot reformer tubes. Usually a distillate fuel identical to that processed is used.

Corrosive attack by hot carbonic acid solutions in the condensing regions of the make-gas heat recovery train must be avoided by a suitable choice of materials of construction coupled with careful design of the equipment so as to avoid high impingement velocities.

DEVELOPMENT OF THE PROCESS

The first light distillate reforming plants operating at pressure and producing gas for ammonia synthesis came into operation at the ICI Works at Heysham in 1961, at Billingham in 1962, and Severnside in 1963. Since then the process has been developed for the production of lean gas and for town gas. The use of the process for all purposes has developed with great rapidity,

Fig. 9, and has spread to India, Finland, Germany, Spain, Japan, Austria, Portugal, Australia and Holland, and at present there are over 100 reformers either in operation or under construction capable of processing over 500 tons/hr of naphtha in total.

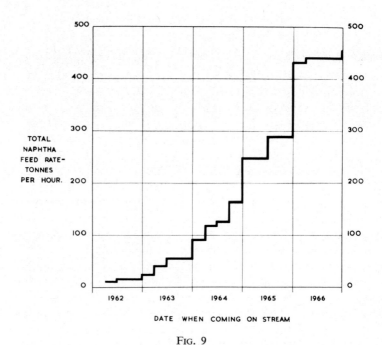

FIG. 9

Graph showing increasing use of ICI raphtha reforming processes

SOME FUNDAMENTAL ASPECTS OF THE
CREEP DEFORMATION OF METALS

J. Nutting

CREEP is one of the many manifestations of the plastic behaviour of metals. It is not surprising, therefore, that the concepts which have been developed for the understanding of the plastic behaviour of metals and alloys at relatively low temperatures and at relatively high stresses should find immediate application to the study of creep. Yet at the same time it is to be expected that some new concepts will have to be introduced to account for the elevated temperature mechanical behaviour of materials. From these considerations it follows that if we are to develop new materials to meet the challenge for operation over long periods at high temperatures and high stresses we shall have little hope of success if we do not first give serious considerations to the behaviour of these materials at lower temperatures, before thinking about their high-temperature behaviour.

In metallic systems it is possible to define a low temperature as less than $\frac{1}{3} T_m$, where T_m is the melting-point in °K of the metal. For all practical purposes below this temperature the strain which will occur in a metal will be dependent only upon the applied stress, and not upon the time for which the stress is applied, provided that this stress does not exceed $0 \cdot 1$ to $0 \cdot 2$ per cent of the shear modulus. Plastic deformation occurs under these conditions by the movement and multiplication of dislocations within the metal lattice. With annealed metals the dislocation density is about 10^6 cm^{-2} and as the plastic strain is increased by increasing the applied stress the dislocation density will increase up to a maximum of 5×10^{10} cm^{-2} at a total plastic strain of 10 per cent. Further strain beyond this gives no increase in the dislocation density and how the metal accommodates strains greater than this is not fully understood at the moment.

As the temperature at which a metal is deformed is increased above $\frac{1}{3} T_m$ the total strain, which occurs as a result of applying a load, becomes more and more dependent upon the time for which the load is applied; that is to say creep occurs.

The amount of creep extension which can be tolerated at what are thought to be reasonable working stresses depends upon the engineering design criterion adopted. Within certain limitations alloys can be produced which will meet these design criteria. But it is perhaps interesting to note the wide range of the maximum technological working temperatures of alloys based on different systems. For conventional aluminium* and titanium based alloys temperatures greater than $0\cdot4$–$0\cdot5$ T_m cannot be tolerated yet with nickel based alloys temperatures of $0\cdot75$ T_m can be achieved. This difference in relative maximum working temperature is to some extent a measure of the metallurgist's skill in developing alloys and it might well be asked what is the limit? Just how close to the melting point can a successful alloy be used? Taking into account the problems associated with fabrication into technologically useful articles then an upper estimate would be $0\cdot80$ T_m if lives of greater than a few minutes are required.

As the operating temperatures for industrial plant are increased the metallurgist responds to the challenge in two ways. Firstly he may seek to modify the composition and heat treatment of an alloy in an attempt to make it more creep-resistant; alternatively, he may change to alloys with an entirely different base which have an increased melting-point. It is for this latter reason that the refractory metals Nb, Mo, W with melting-points of 1950°, 2620°, 3570°C respectively are finding application for very high-temperature service in rocket motors. 1500°C is only $0\cdot45$ T_m for the metal molybdenum, and as has been pointed out this is a relatively low temperature for obtaining creep resistance.

MODES OF CREEP DEFORMATION

Experiments have shown that when a metal is deformed at a constant load and at temperatures of $0\cdot5$ T_m and above, an increase in dislocation density occurs with time. This increase is associated with the primary creep region where the rate of creep extension decreases with time to a steady constant value corresponding to the onset of the secondary stage of creep.

The increase in dislocation density and the changes in dislocation distribution obtained during primary creep are similar to those found during plastic deformation at temperatures below $0\cdot3$ T_m when work hardening occurs. In fact the whole phenomenon of primary creep can be looked upon as very similar to work hardening. If, therefore, it is desired to control primary creep the factors which are thought to influence work hardening capacity at a lower temperature give some indication of the measures to be adopted. Changes in the grain size, changes in the size, shape and distribution of precipitates and in the case of face-centred cubic (f.c.c.) alloy systems, changes in stacking fault energy will all bring about changes in the amount of primary creep. As a result of these variations and of changes in the test conditions primary creep extensions of $0\cdot1$–1 per cent can be obtained.

It is during the secondary stage of creep that changes occur which are not

* One of the most successful creep-resistant alloys S.A.P. has an aluminium base. This material is discussed later.

characteristic of low-temperature deformation first make their appearance. At temperatures of $0 \cdot 5 \, T_m$ vacancy movement occurs readily and as a result dislocations can move out of their slip planes by climb. They may meet other dislocations of opposite sign and be annihilated or they may link with other dislocations to form a three-dimensional wire netting. This process generally referred to as recovery occurs during the whole of the secondary stage, but at the same time the processes which lead to dislocation generation during primary creep will continue to operate. As a result we may look upon the secondary stage as a condition of dynamic equilibrium between work hardening and recovery process.

At low temperatures the grain boundaries in a metal are a source of strength. At high temperatures they become a source of weakness. At temperatures above $0 \cdot 5 \, T_m$ boundary shearing can occur, but the strain at the boundaries must be accompanied by general plastics flow, that is dislocation movement within the grains. Therefore if measures are taken to impede dislocation movement these measures will also have the effect of lowering the boundary sliding. Changes in grain size do, however, influence the creep rate, and although it is customary to think that these changes are associated with changes in the total grain boundary area available for sliding, it is more likely that the increased creep rate found by decreasing the grain size is associated with the increased availability of vacancies, generated at the grain boundaries and with the shorter distances these vacancies will have on average to migrate before they condense on dislocations. Together with these effects the grain boundaries play an important role in the influence on creep ductility.

The creep rate that is established will depend upon the temperature since the higher the temperature, the greater the concentration of vacancies and the more frequently will the vacancies jump. These views have been confirmed by measurements of the activation energy for creep which have been found to be equal to those for self-diffusion. Thus where recovery (i.e. vacancy movement) is the controlling process we may expect a doubling of the creep rate for every 10-degree rise of temperature.

The applied stress will also influence the creep rate. Provided the stress is large enough to bring about dislocation movement the creep rate varies as the fourth to eighth power of the stress. This type of relationship is a consequence chiefly of the dislocation velocity being dependent upon the applied stress and to a lesser extent upon the dislocation density increasing with the applied stress. An equation relating the creep rate to stress and temperature can be devised and is of the form given below:

$$\dot{\varepsilon} = AG^{-M}\sigma^{n}e^{-Q(\sigma)/KT} \tag{1}$$

where A is a constant

$ \ G \ =$ the grain diameter

σ is the applied stress

$M =$ constant having a value of $0 \cdot 8$ at high stresses and 2 at low stresses

n varies between 4 and 8 for high stresses and is equal to 1 for low stresses

Q is the activation energy for creep (this may be stress-sensitive in some cases)

T is the temperature.

At very high temperatures and very low stresses where vacancy movement occurs readily and the dislocations may not be activated a form of creep may occur by the preferential diffusion of the vacancies away from the direction of the applied stress. This is called diffusion creep. The creep rate is low and it varies directly with the applied stress. In some cases diffusion creep can be of technological consequence.

CREEP FRACTURE AND CREEP DUCTILITY

In most cases of creep failure, the metal comes apart at the grain boundaries. Although some authors have associated the onset of creep failure with the tertiary stage of the creep curve, that is when the creep rate starts to increase, more recent work indicates that the basic mechanisms which lead to creep failure are operative from the moment the metal is put under load at the elevated temperature.

The fracture initiating mechanisms are thought to be of two types. At high stresses the grain boundaries may shear and then, particularly at the grain edges of those boundary planes which are perpendicular to the direction of the applied stress, cracks are initiated. These cracks slowly spread along these boundary surfaces as the adjacent boundaries shear more. Consequently, under a constant load creep test, the internal areas of metal carrying the load decreases, the boundaries shear faster and the cracks open up faster. There is therefore acceleration in the failure mechanism; it is this rapid stage which is associated with tertiary creep.

At lower stresses a somewhat different mechanism operates. As a result of shearing along the grain boundaries holes are formed at ledges on the boundary surfaces. These holes spread by further shearing and by the condensation of vacancies at them until the holes along the surfaces coalesce to give cracks which accelerate in growth as before, eventually to give fracture.

In some cases creep failure may occur after the specimen has necked down to a great extent whilst in others failure may be associated with macroscopic elongations of less than 1 per cent. Because the failure is eventually intercrystalline it is sometimes thought that any explanation of differences in creep ductility must be sought in changes of structure at the grain boundaries. It is now beginning to be realized that there may be other explanations. If the body of the grains resists deformation, the strain to be accommodated at the region of the grain boundaries for a given macroscopic strain, may be relatively large and as has been pointed out the more strain there is at these regions the more likely are cracks to form. Therefore by changing the structure within the grains in such a way that the grains are more readily deformed the macroscopic elongation may be increased, although the total movement at the grain boundary may be the same as in the specimen failing with a low macroscopic elongation.

These arguments are supported by the fact that creep life is related to the creep rate as follows:

$$\dot{\varepsilon}t = R \tag{2}$$

where $\dot{\varepsilon}$ = creep rate
    t = time to failure
    R = constant.

In general it may be said that the lower the applied stress the lower will be the creep ductility. This generalization arises from the changes in the mode of creep failure with the applied stress. At low stresses provided a suitable cavity has been nucleated by shear the cavity will grow chiefly by vacancy condensation, and by the time these cavities have coalesced to give cracks of a size which will propagate under the applied load, little overall elongation has had chance to occur, i.e. the specimen has a low creep ductility. In some alloy systems the creep ductility is found to increase again as the stress is decreased still further. This type of behaviour can usually be associated with changes in the microstructure within the grains where, with the prolonged heating required to produce failure at low stresses, coarsening of dispersed phases may occur so allowing plastic flow within the grains. It is significant in this respect that pure metals and single-phase alloys do not show increases in creep ductility at these low stress levels.

THE STRUCTURE OF CREEP-RESISTANT ALLOYS

In order to achieve technologically useful creep properties at temperatures greater than $0 \cdot 4 \, T_m$ it is essential to add alloying elements to metals. The basic principles for alloying to obtain creep resistance are now well understood and underlying ideas are very simple. Since creep involves the movement of dislocations to stop creep we must stop dislocation movement, or if we cannot stop them we must hinder their movement as much as possible.

In the transient stage we have seen that the dislocation density increases very rapidly. Almost the whole of transient creep can be accounted for by the movement over very short distances $\sim 10^{-4}$ cm of the newly generated dislocations. Therefore if we could make it more difficult for dislocations to be generated and then limit the distances they move we can lower the amount of transient creep. The sources of dislocations are the grain boundaries, so by increasing the grain size the amount of transient creep at a given stress will be reduced. Similarly by putting in dispersed phases which act as dislocation barriers we shall limit the distance the dislocations can move. By suitable heat treatment of supersaturated solutions dispersions having spacings of 10^{-5} to 10^{-6} cm can be obtained so shortening the distance of dislocation travel by a factor of 10 to 100. However, the role of the dispersed phase may be complex in that the particle matrix interface may then act as a dislocation source. It is therefore essential to obtain a dispersed phase in which there is good matching between the lattices of the matrix and the dispersed phase so lowering the ease with which the interface can act as a dislocation source.

To move a dislocation through a metal requires a force to be exerted. The greater the force above this limiting value the greater will be the velocity of the dislocation through the lattice. The addition of alloying elements which go into solid solution have the effect of lowering the dislocation velocity for a given applied stress, but this effect is relatively small. However, the solute elements may segregate to the dislocations and this will have the effect of raising the stress to make the dislocation move. If the velocity of movement is low so that solute elements always have time to diffuse to the dislocation then an increase in the creep resistance will be obtained. A special case of this type of behaviour is found with the f.c.c. solvents. Here the dislocations are dissociated and segregation of solute to the associated stacking fault can greatly improve the creep resistance. This is partly the reason why f.c.c. base alloys have better creep resistance than those based on b.c.c. systems. A further possibility is that in systems where extended solid solutions can be formed improvement in creep resistance is associated with the compositions around which ordering occurs. In ordered structures the dislocations are confined to their slip planes, cross slip is difficult, therefore the stress for deformation is raised.

However, the formation of solid solutions is not a very satisfactory method of improving creep resistance. At temperatures above $0 \cdot 5$ to $0 \cdot 6$ T_m the strengthening effects disappear because the thermal agitation is so great that the solutes boil off from the dislocations, and unless other barriers are put in their way the dislocations move unhampered through the lattice.

The most successful method of improving the creep resistance is to produce a stable dispersed phase within the matrix. The dispersed phase particles act as barriers to dislocation movement and if the barriers are strong enough, i.e. if the binding energy of the dispersed phase structure is large, the only way the barriers can be overcome is by the dislocations climbing over them. The climb process involves the movement and condensation of vacancies on the dislocations. Therefore to obtain a given creep strain at a given stress a higher temperature or a considerably longer time will be required to obtain the necessary vacancy generation and movement. If climb is to be the rate-limiting process it follows that there are critical dispersion sizes for obtaining good creep resistance. If for a given volume fraction of dispersed phase the particles are very small then the distance the dislocations have to climb is small, and the particles are soon by-passed. On the other hand, if the particles are large and the spacing between them correspondingly large, the dislocations may by-pass the particles by a bowing mechanism. Between these two limits there is a range in which good properties is to be expected. The critical interparticle spacings for creep resistance are thought to be about 200–2000 Å. Within this spacing range, the creep properties will be improved by increasing the volume fraction of the dispersed phase.

The particles also exert other effects. The climbing dislocations link together to form subgrain boundaries and with pure metals creep occurs by rotation at the subgrain boundaries. But where dispersed phases are present the subgrains do not form so readily and when they are formed, the subgrain boundaries are anchored by the particles.

In the same way, particles which are formed at grain boundaries hinder grain boundary sliding and grain boundary migration. The boundary particles may, however, become the sites for cavity nucleation. It is now thought that cavities are more readily nucleated if the interfacial energy between the particle and the matrix is low since decohesion could then easily occur along the interface. But so little is known about the factors influencing the energy of incoherent interfaces, that it is difficult to make useful suggestions about suitable alloying additions for lowering the susceptibility to grain boundary cavitation.

The ideal microstructure for creep resistance would show the following features:

1. A large grain size.

2. Particles along the grain boundaries, but which should be large and have a high interfacial energy with respect to the matrix.

3. A dispersion of precipitates throughout the grains; the spacing of the precipitates should be about 1000 Å and the volume fraction of the precipitates should be about 50 per cent.

4. In order to obtain high-temperature stability of the structure, the interfacial energy between the precipitate and the matrix should be as low as possible; the specific volume of the matrix and the dispersed phase should be the same, so that if thermally induced precipitate growth does occur, it will not lead to vacancy generation.

5. There should be very strong bonding in the structure of the dispersed phase. This will enable the particles to resist shearing by moving dislocations.

6. The matrix should contain many elements in solid solution. If the structure is f.c.c., the lower the stacking fault energy the better, whilst a composition should be aimed at which gives the greatest amount of ordering.

Some of the above requirements are mutually incompatible. It is difficult to see how an alloy could be made having particles at the boundaries having a high interfacial energy, and particles within the grain having a low interfacial energy.

It should also be pointed out that one of the most successful creep-resistant alloys, S.A.P., has a very small grain size. But with this material special considerations apply. The grain size is about 1 µ, that is it is less than the subgrain size. The boundaries are stabilized by the presence of Al_2O_3 particles and because of the short lengths of boundary dislocation nucleation can only occur at high stresses. In almost all the other creep-resistant materials the grain size is considerably larger than the subgrain size.

Knowing these requirements it may be possible to improve slightly some of the existing alloys. But to develop new alloys to operate in the range $0 \cdot 8 \, T_m$ would appear to be very difficult. It would seem that the conventional methods of melting and casting, followed by some fabrication and then heat treatment it is bound to lead to structural compromises which have the effect of lowering the creep resistance. Even if newer methods of initial fabrication, using powder metallurgical techniques, are introduced as a means of obtaining compositions not feasible by melting and heat treatment, there are still the problems posed by the final fabrication requirements, particularly if conventional welding is involved. Reluctantly, but nevertheless realistically, the conclusion must be drawn that unless changes in the design and modes of fabrication of large engineering structures operating at high temperatures are forthcoming, it will not be possible to utilize fully the potential of creep-resisting alloys.

SOME OTHER FACTORS INFLUENCING THE BEHAVIOUR OF METALS AT HIGH TEMPERATURES

In all the previous discussion it has been assumed that the basic modes of operation of a metal structure are those of a constant load applied at a constant temperature with environmental conditions which bring about no changes at the metal surface, i.e. the conditions of a creep test in an inert atmosphere.

In practice such idealized conditions are rarely encountered. The load and temperature may fluctuate during starting up, shutting down, or change of running conditions; in the very nature of the design there may be fluctuating loads, that is a superimposed fatigue condition; the loads may not be uniaxial and almost certainly the environment will not be inert with respect to the metal.

(a) *Environmental Effects*

If the atmosphere is oxidizing and the alloy not sufficiently oxidation-resistant metal wastage will occur. In some cases alloy additions made to improve oxidation resistance, also improve the creep resistance, but in many cases the creep resistance may be lowered.

There is some evidence to suggest that the presence of oxide films on a metal surface will improve the creep properties, but this may only be of minor technological consequence.

The adsorption on to a metal surface of carbon, nitrogen or hydrogen from the surrounding atmosphere and its subsequent diffusion into the metal may greatly modify the creep properties. The general type of behaviour is that the diffusing element will react with other elements in the alloys bringing about changes in the microstructure usually in the form of fine precipitates within the grains. These precipitates may confer added creep resistance to the body of the grains, and as a result the local strain at the grain boundaries could be increased, leading to earlier failure. Alternatively the diffusing element may give rise to new precipitates at the grain boundaries, lowering the grain boundary cohesion and again leading to failure with a low overall ductility. It could be that the newly formed precipitates lower the creep rate and improve the creep ductility, but as might be expected such cases are rare.

(b) *Multi-axial Stressing*

Although tests have shown that different modes of creep loading, e.g. the superposition of tensile and torsional loading, influences creep rates, it is not thought that there is any significant change in the modes of creep deformation under these more complex loading conditions. But in some cases of multi-axial loading the creep ductility may be increased since cavitation can be hindered.

(c) *Temperature Fluctuations*

Apart from the known and measured variation of creep behaviour with temperature, there are other effects worthy of consideration which could be introduced by temperature fluctuations during service. In restrained systems thermal contraction can lead to stress increases. Although the metal may be able to tolerate these, new forms of dislocation distribution may be developed particularly at high stresses and low temperatures which could then lead to enhanced creep on reheating. Such difficulties can be overcome by designs which avoid restraint. However, a more subtle form of the same effect may occur which cannot be overcome by good design. If the alloy contains dispersed phases which have very different coefficients of thermal expansion than the matrix, then on cooling internal contraction stresses are developed which may be relieved by dislocation generation at the interface between the dispersed phase and the matrix. Again, the newly generated dislocations would affect the creep behaviour on subsequent reheating. Most of the non-metallic inclusions found in metals have lower coefficients of thermal expansion than metals and are therefore likely to produce these effects. The effects are also likely to be more marked the larger the inclusions. There is, therefore, much to be said for keeping the inclusion content of creep-resistant alloys as low as possible.

(d) *The Combined Effects of Fatigue and Creep*

Under the action of reversed stresses dislocation interactions are such that vacancies are generated. It is not surprising therefore that reversed stressing may accelerate the creep rate since as we have seen the rate-controlling process for secondary creep is the generation and subsequent condensation of vacancies on dislocations. Experiments have also shown that reversed stressing may give rise to precipitate shearing more readily than a steadily applied load, and again this would give a lowering of the creep rate, under fluctuating load. The small amount of experimental evidence that is available indicates that modes of creep failure under fluctuating load are the same as under the steady load condition. But much further work is required for a fuller understanding of these complex conditions.

FACTORS AFFECTING CHOICE OF MATERIALS AND DESIGN OF UNITS FOR PRESSURE STEAM REFORMING

W. D. CLARK and A. W. ELMES

ALTHOUGH the steam-reforming project was perhaps of larger importance than many which arise, it was typical in many ways. The process was a considerable development on existing chemistry and engineering processes; research work had been carried out and feasibility had been proved on the laboratory and pilot plant scale; flow sheets had been devised and preliminary costings carried out which showed that the whole was commercially attractive. The materials specialists first became involved in the work when it was on the pilot scale, and valuable experience was accumulated that was of vital importance in the design of the full-scale plant. Other experience was available also; there was a long history of the related low-pressure methane-steam process and some knowledge of plants that operated at modest pressures using natural gas. The synthesis of ammonia, the second stage in the process, had been carried out in Billingham Division over many years and experts and technicians were available accustomed to plant working at high pressures.

The time available to design and construct the integrated full-scale unit on the basis of the experience with the simple pilot units was very short by the standards of some other advanced techniques, and a number of factors affecting the choice of materials were unknown. It was decided as a policy to use the simpler and readily available materials where these had a reasonable chance of giving satisfactory service, even though some other more "advanced" material could well have been considered. A major factor in this decision is that the "better" material is almost certainly not only more expensive but is more difficult to get, and perhaps has fabrication problems. The early acquisition of full-scale operating experience was vital. Again, though it was necessary to consider all the troubles which might arise, it was important not to incur delay or expense over difficulties which might prove to be imaginary. Thus, in the design of some items some degree of ignorance about materials was accepted: this particularly applied where the possible consequences were not hazardous and where the deterioration could be measured periodically so that a replacement could be scheduled, or the item could be by-passed for a period.

Like most plants, a steam-reforming plant consists of a series of units. Some of these units could be eliminated from detailed consideration at once. They are the common currency of chemical engineering; they are the boilers, reboilers, the air coolers and so on which are available from commercial firms and can readily be designed to fit into the system. As other papers will show, we have not always been justified in the assumption that such standard units necessarily fit the process, but the difficulties when they have arisen have usually pointed the way to a remedy, and these remedies are available for future plants. We must not learn the same lessons more than once.

Most serious consideration had therefore to be given to a series of plant items which stood out when these various simplifications, assumptions and plain guesses had been made. Of these, clearly the most important and the one closest to the frontiers of available materials was the choice of alloys for the headers and the tubes and the various connections to them which form part of the primary reforming furnaces. The solution which was adopted for this problem and for other problems which were foreseen or have arisen is discussed briefly in the section below in which the various units shown schematically in Fig. 1 are dealt with in numerical sequence. Separate papers give more detail on the major problems.

1. After removal of the bulk of the sulphur in a liquid phase washing unit the naphtha passes through a feed pump to the steam heated vaporizer. This has given some trouble through fouling on the naphtha side and mild steel tubes have corroded where they were immersed in the sludge.

2. The naphtha vapour is superheated (by steam), a small portion of hydrogen added, and passed through the hydrodesulphurizer where organic sulphides are reduced to H_2S and absorbed. This vessel is made of 1% Cr–Mo steel with a generous corrosion allowance; very little attack has taken place.

3. An excess of steam is then added to the naphtha vapour, and the mixture enters the inlet header of the primary reformer from which it is distributed to the individual reformer tubes through inlet pigtails which give sufficient pressure drop to ensure even distribution. In the reformer tubes the naphtha breaks down to form hydrogen. In the existing ICI furnaces the gases leave the tubes to the exit header via exit pigtails.

This primary reformer furnace and header involves a number of problems depending on the design adopted—e.g. the support of tubes at top or bottom, whether the tubes are welded to the exit header or have a blank flange at the bottom to facilitate removing catalyst, whether the header is inside the furnace chamber which makes expansion problem different, etc., but the major decision is the choice of material. The tubes have to contain the pressure— say 200–500 lb/in.^{2}—with an internal temperature up to 850°C and a skin temperature some 30°C higher. When reviewing the available data on possible materials it rapidly became clear that, with a few exceptions, high temperature rupture testing had been carried out for only short periods and the long-term

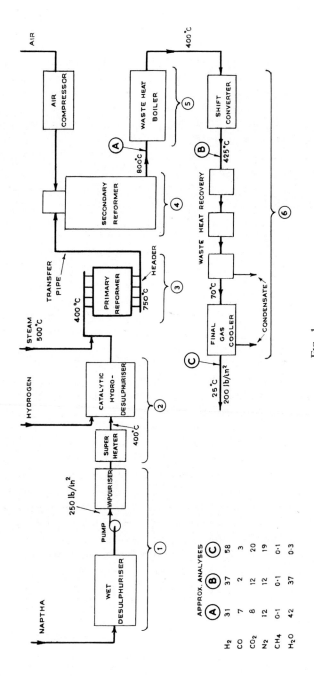

FIG. 1

Units in a pressure naphtha reforming plant producing ammonia synthesis gas.

design stresses suggested were usually based on gross extrapolation and guesswork. At this time the operating temperature was thought to be higher than later proved the case, and rupture strength seemed a major limitation. The data for cast alloys appeared less reliable than that for wrought alloys, but it appeared that 18/37 alloys were stronger than 25/20 Cr–Ni alloy, that cast tube was stronger than wrought tube and that high carbon perhaps added to the strength. Centrifugally cast tube was judged to be altogether superior as regards soundness to sand castings, and such tube was readily available, and incidentally very much cheaper than wrought tube which was on long delivery. It was decided to use spun cast 18/37 Cr–Ni tube because of the extra strength, and also relative freedom from sigma formation to which wrought 25/20 is very prone. Because of ignorance about welding, it was decided to keep the carbon down to about 0·15 per cent and to use design stresses based on data for 100,000 hr rupture of wrought 18/37 in the expectation that there would be a considerable margin in hand. In the event, as detailed by Estruch,[1] it was found that high carbon was valuable and did not reduce weldability, but cast 18/37 was weaker than cast 25/20. The 18/37 alloy has some advantage over 25/20 as regards ductility and is still used for headers where failure due to low ductility would be serious, but 25/20 is now preferred for tubes. Hahn[2] discusses the welding techniques involved.

The reformer tubes are connected to the exit header by 1 in. diameter Incoloy tubes which are called exit "pigtails". Hahn[3] gives details of the welding problems associated with these pigtails, the use of which was found to have an incidental advantage. If a furnace tube splits the gas leaking out causes local overheating of adjacent tubes, and it is necessary to shut down and blank off (by welding) the failed tube, losing some 36 hr production. No valves are available which can be fitted in the exit pigtails. It has been found safe, however, to squeeze the exit pigtail flat and thus seal it even while the plant is on line (and treat inlet pigtails the same way). This "nipping" technique, described by Estruch[4] was very valuable in the case of the first furnaces built where for various reasons a number of tubes have split, but with better tubes and more experience in operation failures of tubes are much less likely and the ability to nip pigtails is perhaps not a sufficient reason for requiring the design to include them. Another factor influencing design in this region is that if pigtails are used, the furnace tubes can be closed at top and bottom by blank flanges, which facilitate charging and discharging catalyst.

The furnace chamber used was of orthodox suspended refractory construction. Detailed consideration was given to heat losses in relation to the cost of extra insulation. The furnaces are cased as far as possible to minimize air leakage, and a major difficulty was found at the bottom where all the tubes project through. Because of thermal expansion they move about 6 in. vertically when going on line, there is also some lateral movement because of expansion of the header, and it is difficult to get a seal which can accept these movements. Steps taken to minimize the difficulty are described by Cooper.[5]

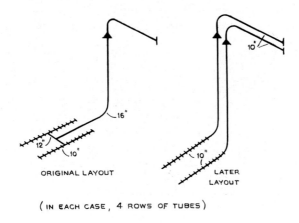

ORIGINAL LAYOUT

LATER LAYOUT

(IN EACH CASE, 4 ROWS OF TUBES)

Fig. 2

Layout of primary furnace header and transfer pipe.

Figure 2 shows the basic layout of the headers and transfer lines in the early (Heysham) and later furnaces designed by Agricultural Division: the later design avoids the large sand cast tees and is easier to deal with as regards expansion. In both cases they are anchored at the inlet to the secondary reformer and all other supports are sprung or counterbalanced. Much of the weight is taken at the top of the vertical leg and difficulties at this point are detailed by Hahn.[6] At other places, support via pieces of sand-cast matching alloy plate welded to the header tube has given no trouble.

The header itself with the pigtails was enclosed in a box and can be inspected from the end. The transfer lines are insulated externally with a form of calcium silicate which was shown to be particularly temperature resistant, and they were clad with aluminium sheet so that the insulation could not get wet and perhaps cause stress corrosion cracking.[5]

4. The connection between the hot alloy steel transfer line and the cold mild steel shell of the secondary reformer is of the form indicated in Fig. 3. The refractory lining at this point and for the whole of the secondary reformer was required to withstand severe conditions, thus:

(i) It must resist the process gas.
(ii) It must resist flame impingement coupled perhaps with a minor amount of erosion.
(iii) It must resist changes in pressure without spalling.

B

(iv) It must conform closely to the shape of the reformer under all conditions of operation, both hot and cold.

(v) It must be virtually impermeable to the process gas.

Simulative service tests were devised for all these circumstances and a
refractory concrete based on Secar cement filled with calcined china clay
aggregate was chosen for the purpose. The pilot plant itself was a useful
location for trials.

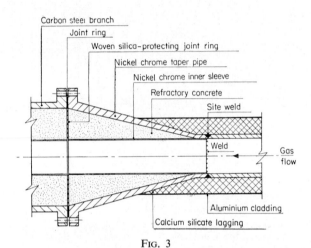

FIG. 3

Connection between hot alloy steel transfer line and the cold mild steel shell of
the secondary reformer.

The vessel was of mild or low alloy steel and a thickness of lining was
designed sufficient to maintain the shell temperature at an acceptable value
if no by-passing of process gas occurred behind the refractory lining. The
lining was placed by casting in panels on a chequer pattern. The aim was to
minimize shrinkage and to develop uniformity of conditions. This system is
cheaper than gunning, is much less wasteful, and has produced very durable
linings that are in first-class condition after up to three years' operation.[7]
However, in the first unit to be started, some by-passing did occur, and,
rather than risk overheating of the shell on this and subsequent vessels,
simple water jackets were included on all Billingham-designed secondary
reformers. Later vessels have an inner lining of brickwork designed to
facilitate repairs without disturbing the lining proper.

The inner lining in the upper cone of later vessels is of high alumina
material to minimize the risk of silica transfer from this location where the
highest temperature conditions apply. Transfer of SiO_2 to a later stage of
the process by the reduction/oxidation mechanism had been considered in the
design and flow sheet stage. In fact, silica deposition in boilers and in CO

conversion units did occur but was proved to have its origin in the alumino-silicate refractory used to support the catalyst bed[8] and substitution by fused alumina material has cured this trouble. The presence of alumino-silicate in the main body of the reformer lining is only of minor importance because the contact with the main stream of process gas is relatively insignificant. Investigation has shown that solution of silica in superheated steam occurs even at modest pressures.

5. From the secondary reformer the gas is passed to a waste heat boiler at about 900°C. The boiler is of mild steel with the inlet channel and tube plate protected by a layer of refractory which carries austenitic steel ferrules which project into the tubes to minimize thermal stresses in the tubeplate. The inlet to the boiler and the connection between the boiler and the secondary reformer is lined with refractory concrete of the same kind as that used in the reformer proper. Dismountable joints are essential between these units and a simple system has been devised[9] based upon the fact that refractory material can be used to contain high temperature and that flanges operating at a lower temperature can make a gas-tight seal in a mild steel structure.

6. At the exit from the boiler, the gas temperature has been reduced to approximately 450°C and passes by way of the shift converter to a heat recovery train which may involve more boilers, feed heaters, and perhaps heat exchangers directly associated with the process, for example, CO_2 removal plant reboilers. No trouble has occurred in these items (which are all basically of mild steel) until the temperature has fallen below the dew point of the gas (150–200°C). As soon as droplets of condensation appear suspended in the gas, serious erosion problems can occur, to an extent depending upon the exact layout of the plant, the gas velocities and the catchpot efficiencies. These are discussed by Hines and Neufeld.[10] The gas is finally cooled to about 30°C prior to compression, and air coolers may be economic. Hall and Erskine[11] describe corrosion of air coolers and its avoidance.

7. The large air compressors (e.g. 5000 h.p.) which are a necessary part of the process, and which are used to inject air into the secondary reformer, must operate in an atmosphere that will contain traces of SO_2. Under these circumstances, if interstage coolers are used for efficiency, the condensed gases may be corrosive to the compressor casing and may in consequence deposit corrosion products on impellers. More serious, the impellers themselves may be damaged because of corrosion or hydrogen embrittlement. This particular difficulty had not been anticipated, but the remedial steps which have been taken are described by Erskine and Hall.[12]

The materials specialist can anticipate many of the major difficulties that are likely to occur in plant operation though it is not possible to be certain how serious they will prove. He cannot, however, foretell the whole story and the actual working of the process itself on an industrial scale is certain to turn up further problems. It is important to recognize the nature of such problems at an early stage and to be prepared to take remedial action even if it runs counter to some preconceived ideas. In the case of the steam reforming process the situation has now been reached in which reliable operation is the normal state of affairs, but there is no suggestion that we have reached the end of development. In the future there lies the aim of working at higher temperatures and at higher pressures, and it may be necessary to solve assembly problems arising from the use of totally new materials such as, for example, silicon carbide of the type described by Professor Roberts. None of the methods of construction that has been used is held to be in any sense sacred, and an excellent case could be made out, for example, for substituting mild steel transfer pipes lined with refractory for the present type of construction. The purpose of discussion is to pool the experience of designers and operators with the aim that all shall profit. The greater the degree of cooperation, the better for all.

REFERENCES

1. B. Estruch and C. Lyth, High-temperature alloys for use in reformer furnaces, This volume, p. 29.
2. F. P. Hahn, The welding of high alloy materials relevant to pressure steam reforming of naphtha. This volume, p. 239.
3. F. P. Hahn, Fabrication of pigtail assemblies. This volume, p. 255.
4. B. Estruch and S. Gill, Blanking-off reformer tubes during plant operation. This volume, p. 259.
5. D. Cooper and R. C. Hall, Thermal insulation for steam reforming plants. This volume, p. 329.
6. F. P. Hahn, Failures of header support bracket assemblies. This volume, p. 249.
7. L. G. Huggett, Lining of secondary reformers. This volume, p. 305.
8. L. G. Huggett and L. Piper, Transfer of silica in the pressure steam reforming process. This volume, p. 335.
9. L. G. Huggett and W. Green, Joints between refractory lined pipes. This volume, p. 327.
10. J. G. Hines and P. Neufeld, Corrosion of mild steel due to impingement in the make-gas stream. This volume, p. 357.
11. A. F. Hall and R. Erskine, Corrosion problems on finned air-cooled heat exchanger tubing. This volume, p. 377.
12. R. Erskine and A. F. Hall, Corrosion in centrifugal air compressors. This volume, p. 369.

HIGH TEMPERATURE ALLOYS FOR USE IN REFORMER FURNACES

B. Estruch and C. Lyth

1. INTRODUCTION

The background against which the original selection of tube materials for the ICI pressure reformers was made has been dealt with by Clark and Elmes.[1] Data on high temperature properties contained in a paper by Skinner and Moran[2] influenced decisions at the time. This paper summarizes some of the results of the testing programme which was initiated at the design stage to amplify the rather scanty amount of information available.

2. CREEP-RUPTURE OF 18/37 CR–NI ALLOYS

2.1. *Experimental Procedure*

All the rupture tests reported were done with specimens of 0·1785 in. diameter and 1 in. gauge length. The blanks from which the specimens were machined were cut parallel to the axis of the tube. The method of casting should give identity of structure and properties in all directions perpendicular to a tube radius. Thus, the strength in the longitudinal direction should be the same as that in the direction of the hoop stress, which is usually the highest stress in a tube under internal pressure.

The tests were carried out in platinum-wound furnaces the temperature of which was maintained to within $\pm 6°C$ of the desired value. During the test no precautions were taken to prevent access of air to the specimens. Heating to temperature and application of stress were done in accordance with B.S. 3082.

In some cases an accurate determination of the elongation at rupture was obtained by direct measurement of the specimen after rupture. In many instances, however, this was impossible because of multiple fracture or excessive oxidation. In such cases an estimate is given based on the last reading before rupture, from a dial gauge attached to the lever arm of the testing machine.

2.2. *Materials Used*

Three different casts of 18/37 Cr–Ni have been studied. Each cast was supplied in the form of a centrifugally cast tube. All casts were obtained commercially and were tested in the as-cast condition. The compositions are given in Table 1.

TABLE 1

Analysis of Casts Tested

Cast	C %	Cr %	Ni %	Mn %	Si %	S %	P %	Cu %
MUR	0·54	16·5	35·0	0·9	1·3	0·02	0·01	0·05
MTH	0·12	19·0	34·2	0·71	0·82	0·02	0·03	0·09
MTZ	0·06	18·3	35·1	1·1	1·3	0·02	0·01	0·004

2.3. *Results*

The results of the rupture tests of cast MUR (0·54% C) are given in Fig. 1. In this diagram the rupture stresses have been plotted against life for the temperature range 825–1050°C. The bracketed figure adjacent to each point gives the elongation at the end of the test, whether or not the specimen broke. It is interesting to note that in general there is a tendency for the elongation at rupture to increase as the applied stress decreases. This is to be contrasted with the results on other materials where, as a rule, the elongation at rupture decreases with decreasing stress.

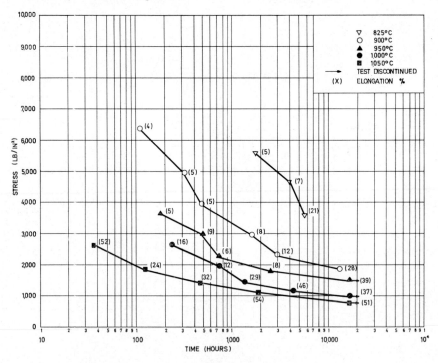

FIG. 1

Rupture stresses for cast 18/37 Cr–Ni alloy (0·54% C).

The results at 900°C which are typical of the tests on casts MUR, MTH and MTZ are given in Fig. 2. The effect of carbon content on strength at this temperature is shown. On average, the stress that MTZ (0·06% C) and MTH (0·12% C) can stand for any given life is about 60 and 75 per cent respectively, of that of MUR (0·54% C). This pattern also holds for the other temperatures. In general the elongation at rupture is highest for MTZ (0·06% C) and lowest for MTH (0·12% C) at all temperatures.

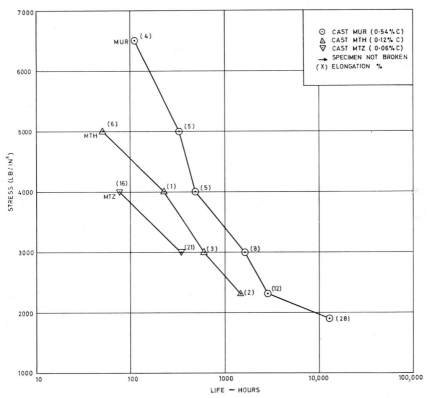

FIG. 2
Effect of carbon on the rupture strength of cast 18/37 Cr–Ni alloy at 900°C.

2.4. Interpolation and Extrapolation of Results

Visual inspection of log stress versus log time curves at different temperatures suggested that the experimental points could be fitted by an equation of the form:

$$\log \sigma = (a + bT) + (c + dT) \log t \tag{1}$$

where $\sigma =$ stress in lb/in.^{2}
$T =$ temperature in °C
$t =$ life in hr
and log indicates $\log_{10}$.

The constants of this equation were determined by the method of least squares for casts MUR (0·54% C) and MTH (0·12% C) with the results given in Table 2.

TABLE 2

Coefficients of Stress/Time/Temperature Equation for Two Casts of 18/37 Cr–Ni

	a	$b \times 10^3$	c	$d \times 10^3$
MUR	+7·8989	−3·9745	−0·5672	+0·3441
MTH	+7·500	−3·76	−0·568	+0·372

The number of experimental points on MTZ was insufficient to calculate the constants.

The equation for MUR has been obtained with data based on tests lasting up to 16,000 hr over the range 825–1050°C and provides a reasonable basis for interpolation within the experimental range and for extrapolation up to 10^5 hr. The extrapolation factor is only ≏6 as compared with a factor of 50–100 involved in estimating the figures on which the initial Billingham design was based.

2.5. Scatter

Creep results are always affected by a certain amount of scatter which, on testing a large number of specimens from the same cast, gives a scatter band width equivalent to a factor 2–3 in life. A larger scatter band is to be expected if different casts are tested; 14 different commercial casts tested by the International Nickel Company (Mond) Ltd.[4] showed a scatter approaching a factor 10 in life. This means that tubes with a wall thickness calculated using a design stress equal to the mean rupture stress for a 10-year life will mostly fail within a period spanning the third to the thirtieth year, 50 per cent should be expected to fail during the first 10 years. It is reasonable to expect that the scatter would be reduced by restricting the range of carbon content and other variables but, at present, material supplied by various manufacturers differs to this extent.

Incidentally, if the equation for cast MUR (0·54% C) and the Mond results are plotted on the same graph, it will be seen that the plot of the equation falls approximately in the centre of the Mond scatter band. The equation for cast MUR can therefore be considered to represent the average rupture properties of spun cast high carbon 18/37 Cr–Ni.

2.6. Calculation of Equivalent Lives

Because of operation difficulties in the early life of the first plant, many tubes were overheated and some failed by creep rupture. A method was developed by which an estimate could be made of the extent to which operation at excessive temperature had "used up" the design life of individual tubes.

The stress/time/temperature equation for MUR discussed above (2.4.) has been used to calculate the factor by which operating at an increased temperature increases the rate of progression of a tube towards failure. These factors are shown in Table 3 for a normal temperature of 850°C and five stress levels.

TABLE 3

Factors for the Calculation of Equivalent Lives

Temp. °C	Stress lb/in.²				
	677	762	869	1006	1189
800	0·48	0·47	0·46	0·44	0·43
810	0·55	0·54	0·53	0·52	0·50
820	0·64	0·63	0·62	0·61	0·59
830	0·74	0·73	0·72	0·71	0·70
840	0·86	0·85	0·85	0·84	0·84
850	1·00	1·00	1·00	1·00	1·00
860	1·2	1·2	1·2	1·2	1·2
870	1·4	1·4	1·4	1·4	1·5
880	1·6	1·7	1·7	1·7	1·8
890	1·9	2·0	2·0	2·1	2·1
900	2·3	2·4	2·4	2·5	2·6
910	2·7	2·8	3·0	3·1	3·2
920	3·3	3·4	3·6	3·8	4·0
930	4·0	4·2	4·4	4·7	5·0
940	4·9	5·1	5·4	5·8	6·3
950	5·9	6·3	6·8	7·3	8·0
960	7·3	7·8	8·4	9·2	10
970	9·0	10·0	11	12	13
980	11	12	13	15	17
990	14	15	17	19	22
1000	18	20	22	25	29
1010	23	25	28	32	38
1020	29	32	37	43	50

As a practical example, reference to the table would indicate that running a tube for ten months at 980°C under a stress of 1000 lb/in.² is equivalent to 150 months $= 12\frac{1}{2}$ years at 850°C under the same stress.

If the tube has run at two or more different temperatures the problem is complicated by the fact that there is no experimental evidence showing how creep at one temperature affects subsequent creep at a second temperature. The simplest assumption is, of course, to assume additivity, e.g. if a tube has operated under stress of 1000 lb/in.² for 6 months at 940°C, and 4 months

at 1000°C, the equivalent life at 850°C under the same stress would be
$6 \times 5 \cdot 8 \times 4 \times 25 = 134 \cdot 8$ months $\simeq 11$ years.

The above concept of equivalent life has been applied to tubes which have
not failed but have been subjected to overheating, to decide whether such
tubes should be replaced during a scheduled shut down. The effect of deliber-
ately overrunning a reformer on tube life can also be calculated in this way.

2.7. *Comparison of Present Results with Published Data for Cast and Wrought 18/37 Alloys*

The rupture stresses calculated by means of equations in Section 2.5 for
MUR (0·54% C) and MTH (0·12% C) are given in Table 4 together with
the values published by A.C.I. [3] for cast alloys HT (0·35–0·70% C, 13–17%
Cr, 33–37% Ni) and HU (0·35–0·70% C, 17–21% Cr, 37–41% Ni) and
by the International Nickel Company for wrought alloy Incoloy 800 (0·1% C
max., 19–23% Cr, 30–35% Ni).

TABLE 4

Rupture stresses for 18/37 Cr–Ni alloys

Temp. °C	Life hr	Stress for rupture (lb/in.²)				
		MUR	MTH	HT[3]	HU[3]	Incoloy 800[6]
871	10	14,800	9570	11,000	—	—
871	10²	7980	5460	8500	8000	—
871	10³	4310	3110	7000	6000	3500
871	10⁴	2330	1775	—	—	2300
871	10⁵	1260	1010	—	—	—
982	10	5840	4030	5800	—	—
982	10²	3445	2520	4500	4500	—
982	10³	2030	1580	3700	2900	1700
982	10⁴	1200	990	—	—	1200
982	10⁵	710	620	—	—	—

For lives of the order of 10^3 hr, the rupture stresses given for HT and HU
are *c.* 50 per cent higher than the corresponding values for MUR, which
extensive testing has shown to represent the average properties of the 18/37
type of alloys. Reference to the original data shows that the extrapolation of
the A.C.I. values to 10^5 hr would lead to design stresses more than 100 per
cent higher than the values extrapolated from ICI's long time tests.

By comparing columns 3, 4 and 7 it can be seen that the strengths of cast
low- and high-carbon alloys are respectively slightly lower and slightly
higher than those of wrought alloys of similar composition.

2.8. *Structural Changes during Creep*   1358339

In the as-cast condition the 18/37 Cr–Ni alloys possess an austenitic structure. Since in general they contain more carbon than can be held in solution, the austenite grains are surrounded by a carbide network. The amount of intergranular carbide varies with the carbon content, but was observed even in cast MTZ (0·06% C). X-ray diffraction analyses of electrolytic extracts has shown that these precipitates consist mainly of $(Fe, Cr)_7C_3$.

Except for difference in the time scale, the structural changes follow a similar pattern at all temperatures in the range studied. The interior of the grain is free from precipitate in the as-cast condition. After very short time at

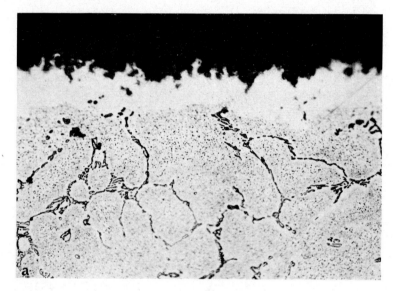

FIG. 3 (a)

MUR (0·54% C) after 1760 hr at 825°C and 5600 lb/in.^{2} ($\times$ 300).

temperature, a precipitate begins to appear inside the grains. As would be expected the size of the particles increases with time and when specimens treated for the same time at different temperatures are compared, the particles in the specimen treated at the higher temperature are coarser (Figs. 3(a) and (b)). The intergranular precipitate, which initially has the lamellar structure typical of many eutectics, becomes spheroidal and coarsens with time (Fig. 3(b)).

At high temperatures and after long times the carbide particles become less numerous. This process of solution of carbide from the smaller particles and re-precipitation on the larger ones leads eventually to the complete disappearance of the intragranular precipitate and large rounded intergranular particles are the only ones left.

The formation of a decarburized layer near the metal surface in contact with the atmosphere has been observed in all the specimens (e.g. Fig. 3(a)) and is characterized by the absence in it of intragranular carbides. Regions

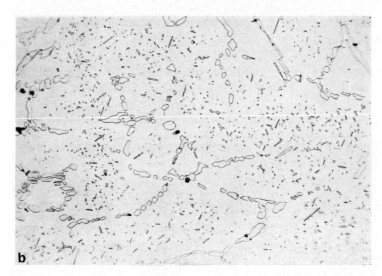

FIG. 3 (b)
MUR (0·54% C) after 1402 hr at 1000°C and 1500 lb/ in.² (×300).

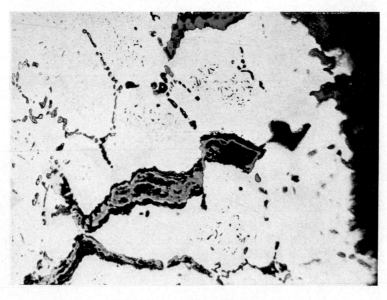

FIG. 4
Cracks between oxide and decarburized regions after 257 hr at 1000°C and 2700 lb/in.² stress (×300).

depleted of carbides are also present on both sides of the network carbide. Whether this depletion is the result of the formation of the intergranular network when the alloy cools down after casting, or to direct precipitation from the supersaturated matrix on the intergranular carbide particles instead of on fresh nuclei during the test, is not clear. However, the net effect is the formation of areas with a low carbide content and therefore of lower strength.

After some time at temperature the interdendritic carbides near the surface are oxidized; actual contact of the carbides with the atmosphere is not necessary for oxidation to occur, and the reaction progresses along the interdendritic network. In the regions where the network carbides have been oxidized, cracks tend to form between the resultant oxide inclusions and the

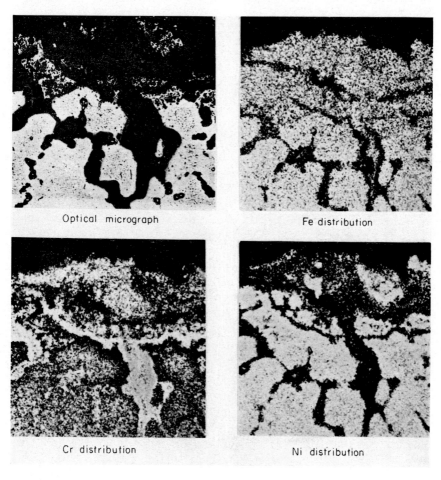

Optical micrograph

Fe distribution

Cr distribution

Ni distribution

FIG. 5

Preferential oxidation of chromium as shown by X-ray microscan ($\times 126$).

low strength decarburized regions (Fig. 4). The cracks afford ready access for oxygen from the environment and its diffusion along grain boundaries causes the oxidation of more carbide with the subsequent formation of more cracks and leads eventually to the failure of the specimen along a plane roughly normal to the applied stress. Proof that the oxidation takes place preferentially in the chromium rich carbide particles and that the nickel-rich matrix is more resistant to attack is given by the micrographs of Fig. 5 obtained by means of the electron probe micro-analyser.

Besides the fast propagation of carbide oxidation and cracking along grain boundaries in the transverse direction, general oxidation in all directions takes place also although more slowly, by oxygen diffusion through the matrix. Similar diffusion of oxygen from the surfaces of the cracks open to the atmosphere produces general oxidation and decarburization in their vicinity.

When the stress is high the cracks propagate quickly and the specimen fails in a relatively short time after the initiation of the first crack. However, when the stress is low and the temperature is high, the rate at which oxidation progresses is high and the oxide, the strength of which is now high relative to that of the metal, fills the crack and acts as a cement. The crack now becomes stable and can only propagate at a slow rate. Under these conditions, new cracks form in other regions of the specimens and the process is repeated. This explanation is offered to account for the large number of cracks filled with oxide and absence of necking in the specimens tested at low stresses, the high elongations obtained in comparison with the highly stressed specimens, and the stepped strain/time curves which in such cases are obtained

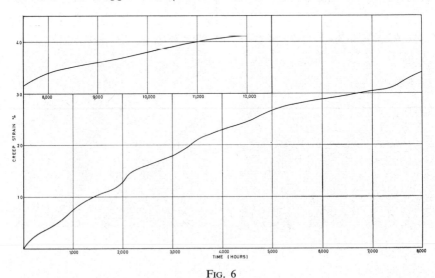

Fig. 6

Strain time curve for cast 18/37 Cr–Ni alloy (0·54% C) tested at 1050°C and 756 lb/in.^{2}

(Fig. 6). These steps can hardly be explained by a succession of phase transformations taking place during the test.

3. CREEP-RUPTURE OF 25/20 CR–NI ALLOYS

3.1. General

The tests on 18/37 highlighted two points: the superior rupture strength of
high-carbon alloys and the fact that the published rupture strengths of HT
and HU (high-carbon 18/37 alloys) were unrealistically high. Moreover, the
rupture strength of cast 18/37 alloy now appeared lower than the figures
published by A.C.I. for HK (cast 25/20 Cr–Ni), making 25/20 appear more
attractive as a reformer tube material. To obtain confirmation a number of
tests on 25/20 were carried out.

3.2. Materials Used

Specimens from four commercially spun-cast 25/20 tubes have been tested.
Their compositions are given in Table 5.

TABLE 5

Analyses of Casts Tested

Cast	C %	Cr %	Ni %	Mn %	Si %	S %	P %	Cu %
LYX	0·09	24·0	22·0	0·75	1·20	—	—	0·1
MAD	0·38	27·1	20·0	0·78	1·35	—	—	0·1
LYD	0·45	25·4	19·6	1·23	1·50	—	—	0·1
NXY	0·42	25·6	21·7	0·40	1·65	0·02	0·025	0·05

3.3. Experimental Procedure

The experimental procedure was identical to that described for the tests on
18/37 except that the specimen diameter was 0·357 in. instead of 0·1785 in.
Tests carried out beforehand had shown that the difference in life due to the
difference in diameter was negligible.

3.4. Results

The results for cast NXY (0·42% C) are shown in Fig. 7. The bracketed
figures indicate the elongation at the end of the test. Results for casts MAD
(0·38% C) and LYX (0·09% C) are given in Fig. 8. The effect of carbon on
strength is perhaps even more marked than in the case of 18/37.

Metallographic examination of as received material and creep-tested
specimens showed that the structures, and the deformation and fracture
mechanisms of 25/20 are similar to those found in 18/37.

3.5. *Interpolation and Extrapolation of Results—Scatter*

No attempt was made to fit an equation of the type given in Section 2.4 to any particular high-carbon cast. Instead, the experimental data on high-carbon casts from all available sources were collected and the parameters

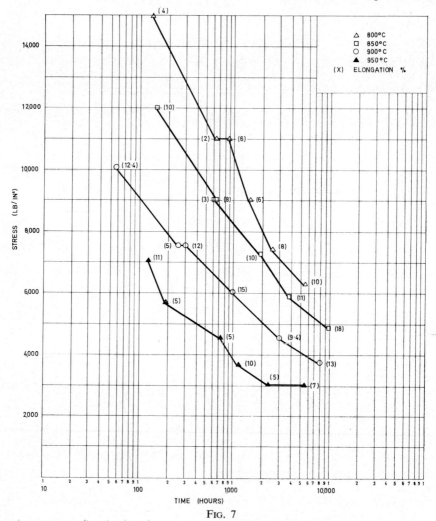

Fig. 7

Rupture stresses for cast 25/20 Cr–Ni alloy (NXY 0·42% C).

of the equation that would give the best fit to the whole set were calculated. The result was:

$$\log \sigma = (5 \cdot 8510 - 1 \cdot 8052 \times 10^{-3} \, T) \qquad (2)$$
$$+ \, (0 \cdot 1130 - 0 \cdot 3192 \times 10^{-3} \, T) \log t$$

where the symbols have the meaning given in Eq. (1).

The total number of points used approached 170, extending over the range 760–1090°C and including tests of over 10,000 hr duration. Tests carried by ICI accounted for 50 per cent of the points corresponding to lives longer than 1000 hr and 100 per cent of the lives longer than 5000 hr.

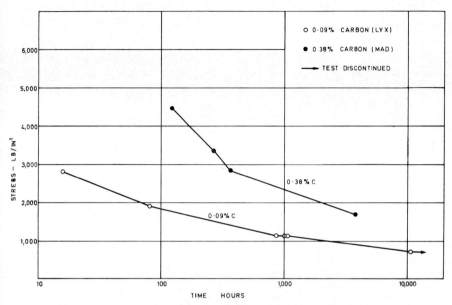

FIG. 8

Rupture stresses for cast 25/20 Cr–Ni alloy (MAD 0·38% C).

Both scatter and mean rupture stress are better shown in a Larson–Miller diagram (Fig. 9) based on the same experimental points. The least squares method was used to determine the values of the Larson–Miller constant $C = 15$, in $P = 10^3 \, T \, (C + \log t)$, and the constants of the equation

$$\log \sigma = 4\cdot9039 + 0\cdot03773 \, P - 0\cdot004447 \, P^2 \tag{3}$$

relating the mean rupture stress to the Larson–Miller parameter P.

TABLE 6
Cast 25/20 Cr–Ni Stresses for Rupture in 100,000 hr
(Extrapolated)

Temp. °C	Equation (2)	Equation (3)
800	4950	4625
850	3350	3225
900	2250	2200
950	1525	1450
1000	1025	960

In Table 6 are given two sets of values for the stress rupture of 25/20 calculated by means of Eqs. (2) and (3). The differences are small, but Eq. (2) tends to give higher values than (3). The latter is therefore safer and it is to be preferred for extrapolation.

Reference to Fig. 9 shows that the scatter is equivalent to at least a factor 10 in life. If values equivalent to ± 25 per cent of the mean rupture stress are plotted in the same graph, the curves obtained form a band which contains practically all the experimental points. Either the lower boundary or the mean curve may be used to define the design stress, according to the design philosophy adopted or, in other words, the proportion of failures that can be tolerated during the design life of the furnace.

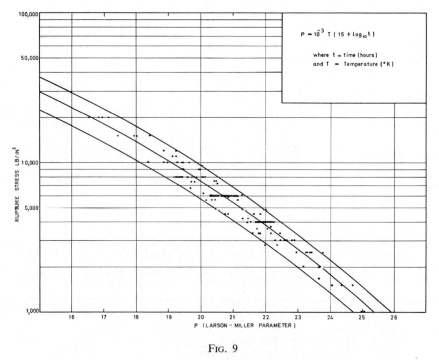

FIG. 9

Larson–Miller diagram summarizing the results of 170 rupture tests on 25/20 Cr–Ni alloy.

3.6. Comparison with Published Data for HK Alloy

Table 7 gives average rupture stresses calculated using Eq. (3) or the Larson–Miller diagram of Fig. 9 and the values published by A.C.I. Both sets of values are in reasonable agreement, and practically all differences can be explained in terms of normal scatter.

TABLE 7
Rupture Stresses for 25/20 Cr–Ni Alloys

Temp. °C	Life hr	Stress for rupture (lb/in.^{2})	
		HK^3	25/20 (Eq. 3)
760	10	23,000	20,500
	100	14,500	17,900
	1000	9000	13,500
871	10	11,000	12,700
	100	7800	9000
	1000	5000	6200
982	10	6500	7400
	100	4500	4800
	1000	3000	3100
1093	100	2500	2400

4. AGE-HARDENING OF CAST 18/37 CR–NI ALLOYS

4.1. *Introduction*

In recent years serious failures have occurred in power plants due to cracking of tube assemblies fabricated in 18 Cr/12 Ni/1 Nb and 18 Cr/9 Ni/ ½ Ti, respectively.[7, 8] The cracking took place at the heat-affected zone near the welds, after heating for stress relieving or during normal service, due to embrittlement caused by the formation of a strain induced precipitate in the heat-affected zone.

In the construction of steam reforming furnaces, extensive use is made of T.I.G., metal arc and/or flash butt welding. Whichever technique is used, in the finished tubes and headers there is always a heat-affected zone which has gone through a thermal cycle similar to the one responsible for the formation of the cracks which have caused serious trouble in power plants.

In Section 2.8 it has been mentioned that a phase transformation takes place in 18/37 Cr–Ni when held at temperatures within the range of normal plant operation. The possibility of formation of cracks, especially in highly restrained areas, should not be dismissed. It is conceivable that the precipitate would be effective in reducing ductility only below a certain critical temperature. If such was the case the danger would be restricted to shut down and start up periods. But even in these conditions the consequences could be catastrophic if the part affected was a main header, which is precisely a part where, during heating and cooling, localized stresses due to restraint can reach very high levels. Failures of headers in embrittled 25/20 steels are known to have occurred in similar circumstances in U.S.A. and France.

With these things in mind, it was decided to carry out an investigation on the effect that holding 18/37 Cr–Ni specimens in the relevant range of temperatures has on their structure and mechanical properties.

4.2. Materials Used

Five different casts of 18/37 Cr–Ni have been studied. The chemical analysis of three of these casts (MUR, MTH and MTZ) were given in Section 2.2. The composition of the other two is given in Table 8.

TABLE 8
Analysis of Casts NXN and NUF

Cast	C %	Cr %	Ni %	Si %	Mn %	S %	P %	Cu %
NXN	0·43	17·7	38·2	0·79	0·88	0·02	0·02	0·05
NUF	0·50	17·4	38·3	1·8	0·44		—	—

4.3. Experimental Procedure

The study of the effect of time at temperature on structure and properties has been mainly made with small specimens which were introduced cold into a furnace at a set temperature. After a predetermined time, the specimens were removed from the furnace and cooled in air. A section was then prepared for micrographic examination and hardness testing. Tensometer and bend specimens were also treated in a number of cases.

4.4. Results

4.4.1. *Cast MUR* (0·54% C). The effect on hardness of ageing this alloy initially in the as-cast condition is shown in Fig. 10. The maximum increase in hardness is obtained at 700° and 750°C. The increase produced by ageing at higher temperatures becomes progressively smaller with increasing temperature up to 1000°C but the peak hardness is attained in a shorter time. Above this temperature, i.e. at 1150° and 1250°C there is a decrease in hardness after heat treating for only 2 hr. At 600°C the hardness increase was less than at 700–750°C, but this may be only because 40 hr at 600°C is insufficient for full ageing to occur.

The results of bend tests on a number of aged specimens showed that the hardening or softening which occurs during heat treating is associated with a decrease or increase in ductility, respectively. They justify, therefore, the assumption that the effects of ageing on ductility can be predicted from the associated hardness variations.

Micrographic examination of specimens treated at temperatures in the range 600–1250°C showed that at the lower temperatures a fine precipitate

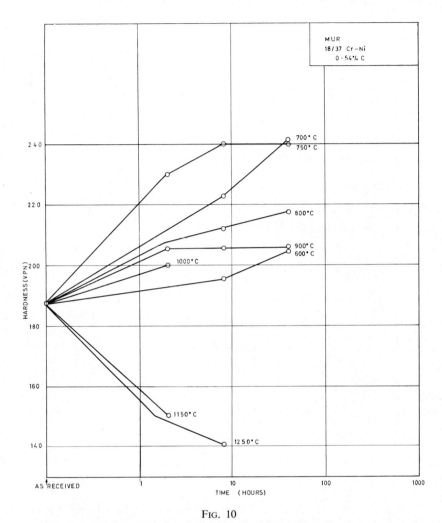

FIG. 10

Effect of ageing and solution treatment on hardness of cast 18/37 Cr–Ni alloy
(MUR 0·54% C).

forms within the grains whereas at the higher temperatures the only change
is a slight spheroidization and coarsening of the carbides present in the as-cast
structure.

4.4.2. *Cast MTH* (0·12% C). The carbon content of this cast places it in the
higher region of the "low carbon" range. Ageing at 750° and 900°C results
in an increase in hardness although less pronounced than in the case of cast
MUR (0·54% C). Treating at temperatures at and above 1000°C softened
this alloy, although formation of a precipitate was observed at 1000°C.

4.4.3. *Cast MTZ* (0·06% C). No increase in hardness was observed after ageing as-cast specimens of this alloy for 40 hr in the range 600–900°C. Two hours at temperatures at or above 1000°C were sufficient to produce an appreciable degree of softening.

4.4.4. *Cast NXN* (0·43% C). The age hardening of this alloy followed a pattern similar to that of alloy MUR. Besides small specimens for micrographic examination and hardness tests, a number of tensometer specimens from this alloy were aged at 700°C for time up to 800 hr. The results (Fig. 11)

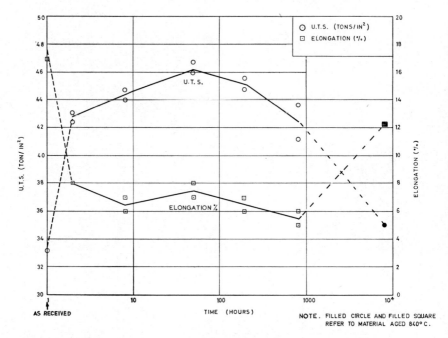

FIG. 11

High carbon 18/37 Cr–Ni alloy (NXN 0·43% C). Effect of ageing time at 700°C on room temperature U.T.S. and elongation.

show a drop in the room temperature elongation from 17 to 8 per cent after ageing for only 2 hr; the elongation dropped further to 5–6 per cent when the ageing time was increased to 800 hr. The effect of ageing on the U.T.S. is to increase it from 33 tons/in² for the as-received material to a peak of 46 tons/in² after 40 hr. With longer times the U.T.S. decreases. In the same graph have been plotted the results obtained from specimens machined from a tube that had been in service for 8000 hr in the semi-technical plant. The analysis of this material (NUF) is very similar to that of NXN. The semi-technical plant operated in the range 700–950°C, and it has been estimated that the average temperature was about 840°C. The elongation, U.T.S. and hardness of these specimens, as well as their microstructure show that after 8000 hr at temperature, high carbon 18/37 Cr–Ni has over-aged completely and that its mechanical properties have returned to values approaching those of the as-cast material.

The effect of holding the specimens at a higher temperature before ageing has also been studied. A number of specimens were solution-treated at 1100–1250°C and aged at 700–900°C for times up to 160 hr. After the solution treatment at 1250°C their behaviour was very similar to that of the as-cast material. After solution treating at 1100°C ageing for 40 hr at either 700° or 900°C results in a slight decrease in hardness. After 160 hr the hardness seems to increase. These changes are, however, small and it is doubtful whether they are significant.

4.5. *Hot Tensile Tests*

The results reported so far give an idea of how the phase changes that occur within a wide range of temperatures can affect the mechanical properties at room temperatures. However, from the practical point of view it is important to know how ductility, as measured by the elongation in a tensile test, varies with temperature. To that effect three sets of tensile tests were done at temperatures up to 750°C with specimens in the following conditions:

(i) As-cast.
(ii) Aged for 72 hr at 660°C and 24 hr at 750°C.
(iii) After 8000 hours of service in the range 700–900°C in a semi-technical plant.

The results are given in Figs. 12 and 13. In the as-cast condition the ductility is preserved up to 600°C; it goes through a minimum at $\simeq$700°C and rises again at higher temperatures. The aged specimens behaved in a completely different way. The ductility is lowest at room temperature (cf. Fig. 11) rises slowly up to 600°C and then rapidly to values similar to the room temperature elongation of the as-cast alloy. The ductility of the over-aged material from the semi-technical plant followed a pattern similar to that of the furnaced-aged specimens, from 600°C upwards. At room temperature the over-aged material was much more ductile.

4.6. *Ageing During Continuous Heating*

Work done on 18/12/Nb austenitic steels has shown that at 600°C the maximum hardness attainable by ageing the heat-affected zone is much higher than at 750°C and above, but that on the other hand the time necessary to reach the peak hardness at 600°C is much longer. It has also been found that over-ageing at 900–1000°C is relatively fast. A result of this is that by heating the welds to 1000°C at a rate in the range 50–200°C/hr it is possible to obtain a low final hardness without the material ever going through a dangerously hard condition. With 18/37 the highest hardness may be obtained

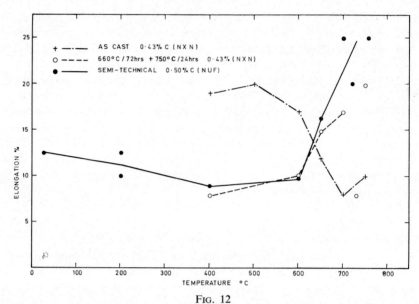

FIG. 12

Effect of heat treatment on hot ductility.

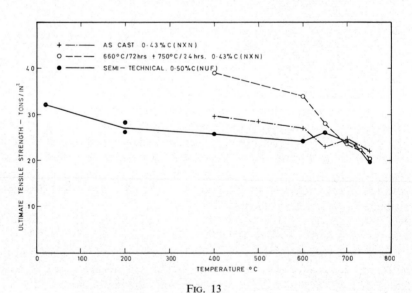

FIG. 13

Effect of heat treatment on hot tensile strength.

at a higher temperature (700–750°C) and the time for over-ageing at 800–1000°C seems to be longer than for 18/12/Nb. It seemed doubtful whether rapid heating would prevent hardening of 18/37 but it was tried. Three sets of specimens were heated at 50°, 100° and 200°C/hr, respectively, and in each case individual specimens were cooled in air from different temperatures between 650° and 900°C. The hardness of the specimen cooled from 900°C, was 225–230 VH when heated at 200°C/hr and reached 225 VH for 50°C/hr. This last heating rate is possibly the fastest rate that could be tolerated in a reformer furnace and it still does not prevent hardening.

5. HOT STRENGTH OF WELDING MATERIALS USED IN REFORMER FURNACES

The materials and techniques developed for welding the materials used in reformer furnaces have been discussed elsewhere.[15, 16] It is obvious that apart from developing suitable techniques it is essential to know how welded joints will behave in service and especially whether such joints will have the required strength.

A certain amount of work on the rupture strength of weld metal has been done by some manufacturers of welding products.[9, 10, 11] The results of rupture tests with specimens prepared from all-weld metal deposits of five different compositions are summarized in the form of a Larson–Miller diagram (Fig. 14). The difference in strength between the five types of weld metal is small and, on the existing evidence, it is difficult to assess whether the difference is a real one or if it is only the result of the scatter normally found in creep-rupture testing.

The mean rupture strength of cast high carbon 25/20 Cr–Ni alloy and the scatter band for this material (cf. Fig. 9) are shown in the same graph (Fig. 14). On the left-hand side of the diagram, corresponding to low values of temperature and/or life the strength of all the weld metals is comparable with the strength of cast high carbon 25/20 Cr–Ni alloys. On the other hand, at high values of the temperature/time parameter which correspond to the temperature region in which reformer plants operate, the strength of the weld metal is only about one-half of the strength of the 25/20 parent metal.

The fact that the strength of the weld metal is, say, 70 per cent of the strength of the parent metal does not necessarily mean that the welded assembly as a whole will have only 70 per cent of the strength of a non-welded tube. In pressure plants where the maximum stress in a tube is likely to be the hoop stress, the weld will be afforded a certain degree of reinforcement by the adjacent parent metal. Furthermore, the weld can be made thicker than the wall of the parent tube and this provides additional strength. The argument is supported in a semi-quantitative way by the results (Table 9) of the rupture tests carried out with specimens containing either a longitudinal or a transverse weld. Further supporting evidence is provided by operating experience on ICI semi-technical plants with 18/37 Cr–Ni tubes welded with Inconel 92 wire and Incoweld A electrodes where all the failures have occurred so far in the parent metal. In low pressure plants the maximum stress will, in general, be the longitudinal stress but because this is not very high, the strength of the weld metal is unlikely to be a limiting factor.

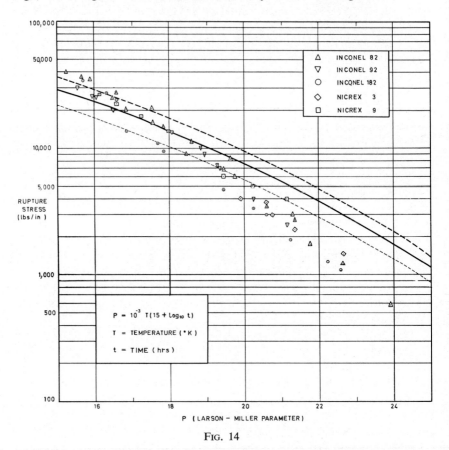

FIG. 14

Rupture stresses of weld metal and scatter band for cast 25/20 Cr–Ni alloy steel.

Although the difference between the rupture stresses of metals used in the fabrication of reformer tubes is appreciable at the operating temperature, there is no doubt that welded joints of satisfactory strength can be obtained.

6. METALLOGRAPHIC EXAMINATION OF TUBES AFTER SERVICE

6.1. Introduction

A number of tubes have been metallographically examined after service in a reformer furnace. The reason for removing tubes was mainly failure in service, but unfailed tubes were also removed during a shut down when it

TABLE 9
Stress Rupture Tests on Welds (900C°, 6,000 lb/in.^{2}).

Material	Type of weld	Life (hr)	Elongation (%)
Parent metal	No weld	217	3·8
		199	5·7
Inconel 82	Longitudinal	174	6·7
Inconel 92	Longitudinal	115	5·1
Inconel 182	Longitudinal	166	4·2
Incoweld "A"	Longitudinal	83	3·6
Inconel 82	Transverse	69	3·4
Inconel 92	Transverse	47	3·5
Inconel 182	Transverse	7	6·0
Incoweld "A"	Transverse	49	3·1

was suspected that, because of severe overheating, they were near the end of their useful life. Finally, on a few occasions, tubes were cut out and examined simply to find out how normal operating conditions affected structure and properties. All the tubes examined had a machined outside surface, but "as-cast" bores.

6.2. Types of Failure

There have been two different types of failure. The first type, which accounts for the best part of the total, takes the form of a longitudinal split. The position of the split is not related to the welds and is the result of overheating. The second one is circumferential cracking at a weld. This type of failure has been readily explained as the result of faulty flash butt welds and will not be discussed further here.

6.3. Longitudinal Failures due to Overheating

6.3.1. *Visual appearance.* Examination of longitudinal failures has shown that the split is always the result of the coalescence of a number of smaller longitudinal cracks. A cross-section of the failure shows that its first stage is the initiation of several intergranular cracks at the bore which propagate towards the outside. When these cracks reach approximately the middle of the wall, small cracks begin to form and propagate from the outside, and the final failure, i.e. leakage of hot gas, occurs when the two sets of cracks meet. The longitudinal orientation of the cracks is consistent with the fact that the maximum stress is the hoop stress.

The cracks start generally from a zone where casting porosity is above average (Fig. 15). These zones are usually associated with longitudinal bands of bore roughness already present in the tube in the as-received condition. The number of longitudinal bands may vary from one to six and, when there is more than one, they are evenly spaced. It is not uncommon to see tubes

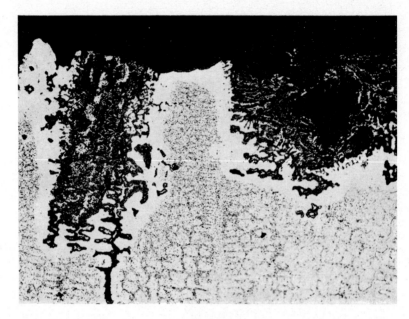

FIG. 15
Cracks propagating from porosity at bore of reformer tube ($\times$ 50).

where the cracks starting at the rough bands have already propagated through three-quarters of the wall thickness before cracks appear in the smooth parts of the bore. The cause of these bands of roughness and porosity is obscure but it may be that standing waves set up in the liquid metal by vibration of the mould during casting is partly responsible.[14]

After service the tube bore is covered with a layer of scale. The thickness of this layer is variable and it is always thicker below the rough bands and inside the cracks. The scale consists mainly of oxidation products.

6.3.2. *Micrographic examination*. Micrographic examination has confirmed that in the areas where the first cracks initiate the interdendritic porosity is above average. The scale that covers the bore and the crack faces is of the type that has been described as "green rot" and consists of a mixture of oxide richer in chromium than the original material and metallic particles richer in nickel (cf. Fig. 5).

There is evidence that oxidation is always preceded by heavy carburization and the amount of carbide present is often greater near the cracks and zones of porosity. It appears that this is because diffusion of carbon is easier in these regions.

6.3.3. *Mode of failure*. The mode of failure is a combination of creep and intergranular oxidation followed by general oxidation.

Initially, the matrix has a fairly high resistance to oxidation due to the chromium that it contains. The chromium in the matrix reacts with the carbon in the hydrocarbons to form chromium carbides which can be oxidized more easily than the matrix as a whole. Oxygen (which is present in equilibrium with steam at the operating temperature) diffuses faster along grain boundaries and preferentially oxidizes the carbide particles at the boundaries. Once the carbide particles have been converted into oxide the carbide-denuded metal is weaker and creeps faster and small cracks begin to form. Through these cracks oxygen has more ready access to the carbide particles lying ahead, which are thus oxidized more easily. This cracking-oxidation process proceeds until a crack of sufficiently large size to cause gas to leak has been formed.

6.4. *Tubes Removed from Furnace before Failure*

Examination of normal tubes has shown that, as expected, the same process is taking place in them but at a much slower rate. A low carbon tube, removed from one of the Heysham units during a shut down because it had no history of overheating and its external appearance was good, on examination was found to contain cracks which would have eventually led to failure.

6.5. *Structural Transformations in Tubes during Service: Effect of Environment*

It has already been mentioned (Section 2.8) that the structure of both high and low carbon 18/37 Cr–Ni spun cast tubes consists of an austenitic matrix and a carbide precipitate. Carbides precipitate during manufacture when the tube cools from the melting point down to a temperature in the region 1200–1100°C. On further cooling to room temperature no further precipitation takes place, and in a tube in the as-received condition the matrix is super-saturated with carbon.

In Section 4, it was shown that if a tube is reheated and maintained at temperatures above 600°C in a neutral atmosphere, the excess of carbon in the matrix will precipitate both at the grain boundaries and inside the grains. This structural change in the alloy is associated with an increase in hardness and a decrease in ductility which does not adversely affect the performance of the tubes.

As previously discussed by Edeleanu and Estruch,[14] heating in a steam reforming furnace gives rise to other changes. On the outside, the tube is exposed to the hot flue gases which contain a large proportion of nitrogen, and some excess oxygen. Nitrogen reacts with the chromium in the alloy to form chromium nitride which shows as an acicular precipitate. At 600–700°C the nitriding rate is slow and becomes obvious only after several years' service. At 900–1000°C, the reaction is fast and precipitation can be observed after a few weeks. Oxygen diffuses in austenite more slowly than nitrogen and its effects on the alloy, i.e. formation of an oxide layer, denudation of the matrix of carbon and nitrogen, and the oxidation of carbides and nitrides, can be seen to follow the precipitation of nitrides (Fig. 16).

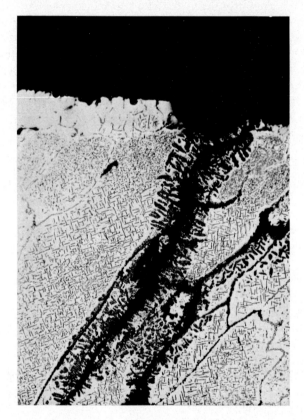

FIG. 16

Formation of acicular nitrides followed by oxidation at the outer surface of a severely overheated tube ($\times 100$).

At the bore, the material is in contact with a gas mixture in which steam has an oxidizing effect whereas that of the hydrocarbons and carbon monoxide is carburizing. Examination of tubes after service shows always that there has been an increase in the number and size of the carbide particles near the bore. A certain amount of decarburization and oxidation, usually to a larger extent than at the outer surface, is also present (Fig. 17). It is not clear whether carburization and carbide oxidation occur simultaneously or whether these two processes alternate as a result of changes in plant operating conditions. The simultaneous nitriding and oxidation occurring at the outer surface can hardly be explained as the result of fluctuating conditions and since carburization and nitriding are rather similar reactions it is conceivable that oxidation of carbides may take place simultaneously with the carburization of the matrix. If the fine details of the relevant solid state processes were known, it would be possible to explain these apparent anomalies.

The net effect of these conditions on the composition of a reformer tube is shown schematically in Fig. 18.

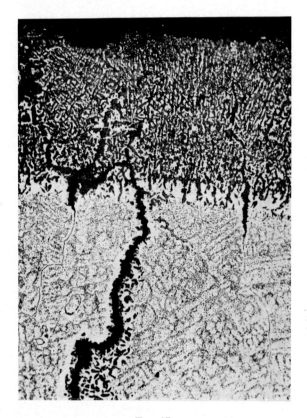

FIG. 17

Carburization and oxidation at the bore of a severely overheated tube ($\times 100$).

7. MATERIAL SPECIFICATIONS

The experimental work described in previous sections, coupled with the experience gained during fabrication and operation of the plants, has increased considerably our knowledge of the properties and behaviour of the materials used in the construction of steam reformer furnaces. The selection of materials can now be made on a much sounder basis and this is, of course, reflected in present-day specifications.

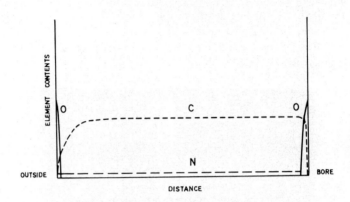

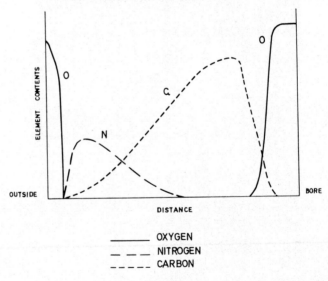

Fig. 18

Schematic representation of the variation of the concentrations of O, C and N across the wall in a tube after service and in the as-cast condition.

7.1. *Tubes*

7.1.1. *Chemical composition.* For reformer tubes the chemical composition adopted is given by Table 10. This analysis is basically that of A.C.I. HK alloy, but contains some modifications.

The carbon content has been limited to the range $0\cdot35$–$0\cdot45$. There are two reasons for this limitation. First, it appears that both rupture and creep strength attain a maximum at about 0.40%C, although the decrease in strength is small until the carbon content drops below about 0·25 per cent. Second, low values of the Si/C ratio are advisable in order to decrease the risk of cracking during welding[12] and to avoid embrittlement due to sigma phase precipitation during service. One obvious way of keeping the Si/C ratio low is by bringing the carbon content up. For these same reasons the maximum Si content has been reduced to 1·5 per cent. Care should, however, be exercised, for it has been stated that too low a Si/C ratio can also lead to trouble by increasing the risk of cracking.

With regard to the tramp elements which may find their way into the final product if scrap is added to the charge, there is as yet no clear evidence on their effect on the mechanical properties of alloys of the 25/20 Cr–Ni type. However, work on high nickel alloys[13] has shown that reducing the concentration of lead below 0·001 per cent may increase the life to rupture by a factor of four. In the absence of more detailed knowledge it seems wise to try to keep elements which may adversely affect the hot mechanical properties to a level as low as possible.

TABLE 10
Chemical Composition of 25/20 Cr–Ni
Alloy for Steam Reforming Tubes

Element	%
C	0·35–0·45
Mn	2·00 max.
Si	1·50 max.
Cr	24 27
Ni	19–22
S	0·04 max.
P	0·04 max.
Mo	0·5 max.
Pb	0·001 max.

7.1.2. *Mechanical properties at room temperatures.* It is customary to ask for a minimum value for the U.T.S. and elongation at room temperature as part of the acceptance tests for spun cast tubes. This is not because the figures have any direct relevance to design for high temperature conditions, but because the tensile properties at room temperature are an indication of casting quality. The presence of casting porosity, which reduces room temperature elongation, also adversely affects the life of a tube in the creep range.

Section 4 discusses the ductility of 18/37 Cr–Ni spun cast material and how it is affected by ageing in the 600–1100°C range. The ageing of alloys of the 25/20 type follows a similar pattern. It must be borne in mind, however, that age hardening will occur not only on reheating but also during manufacture

C

if cooling through the range 600–1100°C is too slow. In this case, however, the U.T.S. will increase, whereas in the case of poor casting quality U.T.S. and elongation will both fall. Attempts to improve the ductility of age-hardened material by means of a "softening" treatment at 1050°C will only make matters worse. In fact, all treatments below $\simeq 1200$°C will either be ineffective or further reduce the ductility. Generally speaking, in spin casting with metal moulds the tubes cool fast enough and elongations of 15 per cent or higher are usually obtained in the as-cast condition.

7.1.3. *Porosity and other casting defects.* Present manufacturing techniques and inspection by the foundries have improved product quality so much that, as far as the user is concerned, manufacturing defects such as cold shuts, excessive localized porosity, circumferential cracks due to contraction, etc., are a thing of the past. The modern tendency towards using bore machined tubes besides eliminating unwanted material which does not contribute to the tube strength and would impede heat transfer, allows a better assessment of tube quality by dye penetrant checking of the tube bore and ends.

When tubes with as-cast bore are used the best way of assessing the depth of porosity is by examining a polished and macroetched ring at $\times 25$ cut off one of the tube ends.

7.1.4. *Macrostructure.* The effects of the large variation of macrostructure from tube to tube has been discussed by Edeleanu and Estruch.[14] A small amount of work has been done on the rupture strength of the different types of macrostructure encountered but the results are inconclusive and, for this reason, no preference has been stated in the specification.

TABLE 11
Chemical Composition of 18/37 Cr–Ni
Alloy for Header Components

Element	%
C	0·25–0·50 (0·35 preferred)
Cr	16–19
Ni	33–37
Mn	1·5 max.
Si	1·5 max. ($< 1·0$ preferred)
S	0·03
P	0·03
Cu	0·5

7.2. Headers and Transfer Lines

7.2.1. *Chemical composition.* Headers and transfer lines in the existing ICI plants were made to the composition given in Table 11.

As it was the case with the tubes, the initial selection of 18/37 Cr–Ni for headers and transfer lines was made because this material appeared to be necessary from strength considerations, and the chances of embrittlement by sigma precipitation were smaller than for 25/20 Cr–Ni. Moreover, 18/37 has also a lower coefficient of expansion and this makes it less prone to cracking under the effect of bending stresses due to thermal gradients set up during start-up or shut-down.

Although the material becomes brittle during service, this has not prevented successful repair welds whenever this has been necessary.[17] It may be relevant here to mention that through failure of one of the counterbalancing systems while the furnace was in operation, one of the Billingham headers came to rest on the ground, and the assembly was bent back to the original shape.

7.2.2. *Tensile properties at room temperature.* With the massive components used for headers and transfer lines, it is not always possible to attain the elongation specified for tubes. This is specially relevant to sand castings like tee pieces, elbows, cone reducers, etc. Too-low values for the elongation may lead to difficulties during fabrication and figures below 4–5 per cent should be avoided. At the manufacturing stage the aim should be to increase the cooling rate after casting to the highest possible value compatible with the production of a defect-free product. Heat treatment below 1200°C should be avoided completely. Softening at temperatures much above this figure, apart from the inherent difficulties, brings the risk of grain boundary fusion and permanent damage to the casting.

7.2.3. *Inspection.* In view of the dangerous implications of a header failure, the inspection of header components has to be much more stringent than inspection of tubes. Machining of all surfaces, (outside, inside and ends) followed by a careful dye penetrant check is therefore recommended. Any suspicious areas should be ground down and if complete removal of the defect encroaches on the designed minimum wall thickness, the material should be rejected. In spun cast components, repair of the defective material by welding should not be allowed. In the case of sand castings, radiography should be used for the detection of internal defects in zones where, due to changes in section, etc., flaws are more likely to be present.

REFERENCES

1. W. D. CLARK and A. W. ELMES. This volume, p. 21.
2. E. N. SKINNER and J. J. MORAN, Furnace tube alloys for hydrocarbon pyrolysis and steam methane reforming, 12th Petroleum and Mech. Eng. Conference, Sept. 1957.
3. A.C.I. Data Sheets, Alloy Casting Institute, Mineola, N.Y., U.S.A., 1957.
4. C. J. COX, The International Nickel Company (Mond) Ltd., Private communication.
5. Engineering Properties of Incoloy Alloy 800, Tech. Bull. T-40, Huntington Alloy Products Division, Huntington, West Virginia, U.S.A., p. 17, 1961.
6. Incoloy 800 Alloy Extruded Tubing, Hy. Wiggin & Co., Ltd., Hereford, p. 6, 1962.
7. F. E. ASBURY, B. MITCHELL and L. H. TOFT, *Brit. Weld. Jnl.*, **7**, 667–78, 1960.
8. K. V. Lynbavsii and Y. M. Nikitin, *Automatic Welding* (B.W.R.A. Translation). July 1960.
9. Incoweld "A" Welding Electrode and Filler Wire, Hy. Wiggin & Co. Ltd., Birmingham, p. 8, 1960.
10. Inconel Welding Electrode 182—Inconel Filler Metal 82, International Nickel Co., Inc., Huntington, West Virginia, U.S.A., pp. 3, 5, 1962.
11. M. C. J. BYSTRAM, Murex Welding Process Ltd., Private communication.
12. D. ROZET, H. C. CAMPBELL and R. D. THOMAS, *Jnl. Am. Weld. Soc.*, **27**, 481s, 1948.
13. D. R. WOOD and R. M. COOK, *Metallurgia*, **63**, 109–17, 1963.
14. C. EDELEANU and B. ESTRUCH, *Proceedings Joint B.I.S.R.A.—I.S.I. Conference*, I.S.I. Special Report 86, p. 220, 1964.
15. F. P. HAHN, The welding of high alloy materials relevant to pressure steam-reforming of naphtha. This volume, p. 239.
16. F. P. HAHN, Fabrication of pigtail assemblies. This volume, p. 255.
17. F. P. HAHN, Failures of header support bracket assemblies. This volume, p. 249.

THE RESEARCH BACKGROUND OF THE THERMALLOY GRADES OF CHROMIUM – NICKEL – IRON HEAT-RESISTING ALLOYS

H. S. Avery

1. INTRODUCTION

This paper is intended to give a glimpse of the background of the alloys that are becoming popular in hydrogen reformer service as well as related types that are widely used in the United States for industrial applications. It does not pretend to cover them comprehensively. This would require much more space than is available here. However, it is hoped that by providing some insight it will lead to more effective utilization of the cast high-temperature alloys.

An explanation is given of how the Thermalloys differ in some respect from common wrought and other cast alloys and information is given, particularly on alloys, of interest to steam reforming plant.

The more popular grades standardized by the American Alloy Casting Institute are shown in Table 1. The generally available specifications for these are ASTM A297 (13 grades for general application), A447 (26–12 CrNi), A448 (15–35 CrNi) and A362 (centricast tubes); A362 is currently being revised and in its present version (A362–63) it may be considered obsolete.

As will be observed, these alloys differ from the common stainless steels, specifically as far as carbon is concerned; *cf.* A296 which deals with corrosion-resistant alloys.

The A.C.I. designation uses the prefixes of C and H to indicate suitability for corrosion and heat-resistant service, respectively. The second letter is arbitrarily assigned to show alloy type, with a rough alphabetical sequence as nickel content rises (see Table 1). Though it has been little used, there is provision for showing carbon content of the H grades, the numbers following the two letters being the mid-point of the carbon specification (Table 2). The corrosion grades have used such suffixes for years, but in that case the numbers designate maximum carbon contents.

The function of the various alloying elements differ; for instance, chromium increases oxidation resistance and corrosion by hot gases. Manganese and silicon are added for steel-making purposes, but silicon does influence carburizing resistance. Nickel confers the austenitic structure associated with

TABLE 1

Cast Heat Resistant Alloys for Industrial Applications

Cast alloy Designation	Wrought Alloy Type	Composition—per cent (balance Fe)							
		C	Mn max.	Si max.	P max.	S max.	Cr	Ni	Other elements
HA	—	0·20 max.	0·35-0·65	1·00	0·04	0·04	8-10	—	Mo 0·90-1·20
HC	446	0·50 max.	1·00	2·00	0·04	0·04	26-30	4 max.	Mo 0·5 max.†
HD	327	0·50 max.	1·50	2·00	0·04	0·04	26-30	4-7	Mo 0·5 max.†
HE	—	0·20-0·50	2·00	2·00	0·04	0·04	26-30	8-11	Mo 0·5 max.†
HF	302B	0·20-0·40	2·00	2·00	0·04	0·04	19-23	9-12	Mo 0·5 max.†
HH	309	0·20-0·50	2·00	2·00	0·04	0·04	24-28	11-14	Mo 0·5 max.† N 0·2 max.
HI	—	0·20-0·50	2·00	2·00	0·04	0·04	26-30	14-18	Mo 0·5 max.†
HK	310	0·20-0·60	2·00	2·00	0·04	0·04	24-28	18-22	Mo 0·5 max.†
HL	—	0·20-0·60	2·00	2·00	0·04	0·04	28-32	18-22	Mo 0·5 max.†
HN	—	0·20-0·50	2·00	2·00	0·04	0·04	19-23	23-27	Mo 0·5 max.†
HT	330	0·35-0·75	2·00	2·50	0·04	0·04	13-17	33-37	Mo 0·5 max.†
HU	—	0·35-0·75	2·00	2·50	0·04	0·04	17-21	37-41	Mo 0·5 max.†
HW	—	0·35-0·75	2·00	2·50	0·04	0·04	10-14	58-62	Mo 0·5 max.†
HX	—	0·35-0·75	2·00	2·50	0·04	0·04	15-19	64-68	Mo 0·5 max.†

hot strength, but it also confers resistance to carburization and to some extent oxidation resistance. High nickel alloys, however, are vulnerable to sulphur attack, especially under reducing conditions. Carbon is the most potent element for controlling hot strength, but it also affects structure and especially the amount of ferrite; nitrogen is also important for strength.

In partially ferritic alloys (HD, HE, HF and HH) the alloy balance can be estimated by magnetic permeability testing and this is described in A.S.T.M. Specification No. A447–50, which sets limits for acceptance.[1]

2. THE CURRENT STATUS OF CAST ALLOYS

2.1. *A Current Image*

As an introduction to this, a recent paper by Drs. Edeleanu and Estruch will be quoted. In this paper a generally favourable experience with centrifugally cast tubes was reported, and it was remarked that "in practice they have proven surprisingly well behaved". However, they also state that "very little is known about the detailed metallurgy of the alloys used" and that "by wrought alloy standards these cast alloys are completely undeveloped".

2.2. *American Background and Resources*

There are, of course, a number of foundries that lack technical personnel who are familiar with the complexities of Cr–Ni–Fe alloy metallurgy and who have had no experience with the determination and control of high-temperature load-carrying ability. There are others that presumably can benefit from Alloy Casting Institute sponsored research in this field but that practically, because of only brief A.C.I. membership or of shifting technical personnel, have only a limited familiarity with this useful background. The Alloy Casting Institute has spent nearly a million dollars on cast heat-resistant alloy research during the past 27 years. In addition, it has benefited from many unbudgeted contributions of material and services. Furthermore our Company has carried forward an independent research programme of comparable size since 1934.

Some of the results of these programmes have been published. Others are accessible only as internal reports that are used by consultation. Our associate in the U.K., by agreement, has access to both of these reservoirs of technical information as well as the important production experience and knowledge with which it is coordinated. Therefore, it is suggested that the comment previously quoted be modified to say that "not enough is known about the subtle relations of metallurgy, plastic flow, and mechanical properties".

TABLE 2

Chemical composition ranges of designated grades

Grade	C%	Mn%	Si%	Cr%	Ni%	N%	P%	S%	Others
HC30	0·25 0·35	0·5 1·0	0·5 1·7	26 30	4·0 max.	0·30 max.	0·03 max.	0·03 max.	0·5 max.
HD50	0·45 0·55	1·5 max.	0·5 1·7	26 30	4 7	0·06 0·16	0·03 max.	0·03 max.	0·5 max.
HE35	0·30 0·40	1·5 max.	0·5 1·7	26 30	8 11	0·06 0·16	0·03 max.	0·03 max.	0·5 max.
HF30	0·25 0·35	1·5 max.	0·5 1·5	19 23	9 12	0·06 0·16	0·03 max.	0·03 max.	0·5 max.
HH30	0·25 0·35	1·5 max.	0·5 1·7	24 28	11 14	0·06 0·16	0·03 max.	0·03 max.	0·5 max.
HH33*	0·28 0·38	1·5 max.	0·5 1·7	24 28	11 14	0·06 0·16	0·03 max.	0·03 max.	0·5 max.
HI35	0·30 0·40	1·5 max.	0·5 1·7	26 30	14 18	0·06 0·16	0·03 max.	0·03 max.	0·5 max.
HK30	0·25 0·35	1·5 max.	0·5 1·7	24 28	18 22	0·06 0·16	0·03 max.	0·03 max.	0·5 max.
HK40	0·35 0·45	1·5 max.	0·5 1·7	24 28	18 22	0·06 0·16	0·03 max.	0·03 max.	0·5 max.
HK50	0·45 0·55	1·5 max.	0·5 1·7	24 28	18 22	0·06 0·16	0·03 max.	0·03 max.	0·5 max.
HL40	0·35 0·45	1·5 max.	0·5 1·7	28 32	18 22	0·06 0·16	0·03 max.	0·03 max.	0·5 max.
HN40	0·35 0·45	1·5 max.	0·5 2·0	19 23	23 27	0·02 0·12	0·03 max.	0·03 max.	0·5 max.
HT50	0·40 0·60	1·5 max.	0·5 2·0	13 17	33 37	0·02 0·12	0·03 max.	0·03 max.	0·5 max.
HU50	0·40 0·60	1·5 max.	0·5 2·0	17 21	37 41	0·02 0·12	0·03 max.	0·03 max.	0·5 max.
HW50	0·40 0·60	1·5 max.	0·5 2·0	10 14	58 62	— —	0·03 max.	0·03 max.	0·5 max.
HX50	0·40 0·60	1·5 max.	0·5 2·0	15 19	64 68	— —	0·03 max.	0·03 max.	0·5 max.

* Manufacturing control must ensure that this grade has a maximum magnetic permeability of 1·08 after 2000°F–24 hr W.Q.

These grade designations follow the Alloy Casting Institute System.

3. HIGH-TEMPERATURE EVALUATION

3.1. *Creep-Rupture Practice*

Material from both Companies are creep-rupture tested at our Research Center at Mahwah following the general practice described in "Precision in Creep Testing",[1] "Creep and Rupture Test Pyrometry",[2] and the A.S.T.M. Recommended Practice for "Conducting Creep and Time for Rupture Tension Tests of Materials—E139–58T".[3]

Test casting design of static sand castings and specimen dimensions are described in "Cast Heat Resistant Alloys of the 15% Cr:35% Ni Type"[4] and related publications.[5, 6, 7]

British and American practice may vary somewhat; three descriptions are pertinent: the standard American practice as embodied in A.S.T.M. E139–58T; the tentative British Standards Institution method as embodied in a draft (dated 25 July 1961) of "Creep and Rupture Testing of Metals—Part 3—Uninterrupted Tensile Creep Testing"; and the procedures used at the American Brake Shoe Co. Research Center. The last of these has improved with time, but for many years was aimed at and largely attained a precision that has only recently been formalized in the A.S.T.M. Standards. The earlier A.S.T.M. E22–41 permitted $\pm10°F$ latitude in temperature above 1600°F (871°C), for example, whereas since about 1938 this laboratory has recognized that control should be closer than this. Our 1956 report[6] of performance indicates that 96·4 per cent of the observed deviations from a nominal 1800°F (982°C) were within $\pm3°F$ ($\pm1·7°C$).

3.2. *Short- versus Long-term Creep-Rupture Tests*

For many years our laboratory has been interested in the relationship between short- and long-term tests. There is no question that they are related, but it is important to recognize the limitations of the shorter tests. We have encountered examples where the correlation is excellent and others where the short tests can be misleading. In general our survey and exploration work is limited to tests of not much more than 1000 hr, but for some of the important grades tests have been run for about a year in our laboratory and to above 13,000 hr at Battelle Memorial Institute in a cooperative programme with the Alloy Casting Institute.

For engineering materials it would be desirable to have at least a few tests that extend to the limit of the design life. However, if this is 100,000 hr (a not uncommon value that is used) it should be recognized that a single test of this duration may cost $40,000 and require $11\frac{1}{2}$ years to complete. A specification can easily become obsolete in this time. Thus very strong economic motivation is necessary before such tests are undertaken, and for the alloy casting industry has not yet appeared.

The best alternative to such long tests is identification of the pattern of

C§

creep rates and rupture times over a practical time range. This involves a recognition of normal behaviour and also of the disturbing factors that can invalidate extrapolation. Thus the identification and evaluation of variables is quite important. This area has received considerable attention in our laboratory. Detail on several alloys will be provided later.

3.3. *Acceptance Tests*

While it is, not practicable to use full-term tests to evaluate a material being purchased, it is nevertheless very desirable to make some estimate of an alloy's probable performance in service before it is accepted. The simple uniaxial tensile test at room temperature is the most common tool, even though there is rather general recognition that it merely provides a rough index of uniformity and has a very poor correlation with high-temperature load-carrying ability. Early recognition of this status led our laboratory to study a variety of other possibilities, including hot tensile tests, stress-rupture tests, hot hardness, metallographic structure, and magnetism. In special cases the last gives a good enough correlation with creep strength to justify general use. The details were developed in our laboratory and the magnetic permeability test was eventually adopted as an acceptance test in A.S.T.M. Specification B190, now changed to A.S.T.M. A447. We are also able to derive suitable minimum stress-rupture values for those that wish to use this relatively expensive technique as an acceptance test. Each of the other possibilities has some merit, which we have explored, but as a matter of experience we find very few users of the alloys that are interested in the more expensive acceptance tests.

3.4. *The Study of Minor Elements*

Proper understanding of the role of each minor element is necessary if an alloy is to be produced under good quality control. This will be illustrated in this paper by showing the effect of carbon on several of the alloys. Our laboratory has also pioneered on determining the effect of nitrogen.[1] Its potency should be well known by now, but despite this it is doubtful if more than a few of the some 76 alloy foundries in the United States make nitrogen determinations on the materials they produce. At this point it is pertinent to point out that a foundry interested in making a high quality product must know how the minor elements behave and control them by means of internal specifications. Since the end use can influence such specifications, there may be a number of them for a single alloy type.

4. RESEARCH FOR HIGH QUALITY

4.1. *Identification of Optimum Compositions*

After the role of major and minor elements in an alloy is well clarified, it is feasible to select an optimum composition as the foundry aim point in production. The optimum selected will depend on the criterion of excellence that is chosen. It will usually be some narrow range within the broad latitude of a type, such as the compositions detailed by the A.C.I. designations in Table 1. Sometimes it will involve additions of refractory elements, such as tungsten, molybdenum, or niobium. Many variations of the standard grades are possible and are justified for certain applications. As a matter of fact, the quite broad ranges of the A.C.I. types are so provided that a variety of variants can be made within their limits. This, of course, has the disadvantage that the properties given in the A.C.I. data sheets, especially those for hot strength, may be subject to considerable variation. The ranges from minimum to maximum creep-rupture strength for the alloys listed in Table 1 can be very great indeed.

The internal specification for an optimum alloy is usually guarded by the foundry as a proprietary matter. Certain aspects of this may eventually become common knowledge in the industry, frequently by imitation without insight, but other details may not.

The optimum specifications for hydrogen reformer alloys is a matter of concern to this symposium group. Pertinent information, some of which has not been previously published, will be provided here. When it is combined with other data presented at this symposium there will likely result generally accepted specifications for the HK40 and HT50. It is also probable that these will be very close to the internal chemical compositions specifications for Thermalloys 47 and 50 or 58 that have been in use for some years.

4.2. Weldability

Weldments have always been important to the alloy foundry industry. Despite this, there has not been industry-wide action in proportion to its importance. The availability of suitable electrodes and filler metals has lagged behind, so much so that our Electro-Alloys Division has at times had to develop and manufacture filler metals until they could be obtained commercially. The mistaken assumption that wrought grades, as generally used for filler metal, could be interchanged with the cast compositions is responsible for part of the lack of progress.

Some years ago the use of wrought 15% Cr:35% Ni electrodes resulted in such prevalence of weld fissures that failures could frequently be traced to the weld metal. This was largely a matter of carbon content, the casting being near 0·50 per cent and the electrodes near 0·15 per cent. It required only a scrutiny of charted creep-rupture results, plotted against carbon content, to reveal that there was a great difference in hot strength. As a result, the thermal stresses of welding caused plastic flow to concentrate in the weld metal because of its relative weakness. Moreover, the creep-rupture tests showed sometimes a surprising lack of hot ductility for the low carbon alloy; a result opposite to the usual opinion of low carbon alloys. The frequent fissures were thus readily explained and substitution of matching filler metal with 0·50 per cent carbon, solved the fissure problem. It did pose another, and for some years our foundry had to cast welding rods and weld them with atomic hydrogen or oxyacetylene methods. Eventually welding electrode manufacturers were persuaded to accept our specifications and suitable electrodes are now available in the United States for this grade.

Solving the other problems likewise requires a knowledge of the metallurgy and high temperature properties. Fortunately, the cast alloys are initially largely supersaturated solid solutions with ample ductility for welding in most cases. Thus the making of weldments in the producing works is probably the easiest of the welding situations. After carbide precipitation has occurred in service, and especially if carburization has also taken place, the ductility is lower and welding without fissures is more difficult. Careful consideration of all metallurgical aspects may be required if good welds are to be made after castings have been in service. Even so, if carburization has gone too far, it may be impractical to make satisfactory repair welds.

4.3. *Hindered Contraction Tests*

Our laboratory developed the hindered contraction test to help elucidate the matter of adaptation to unexpected overloads in service. This permits an interesting comparison of strength and ductility as safety factors. These tests also provide a quick and relatively inexpensive means of selecting temperatures for rapid stress relief of the alloys. The problem of thermal fatigue is a natural outgrowth of this and our laboratory developed a technique for studying this under relatively precise conditions. The results permit ranking alloys, evaluating the relative potency of service variables, and studying such variables as strength and ductility as they affect endurance to thermal cycling.

4.4. *Evaluation of Standard Grades*

Creep-rupture testing has been used as the primary evaluation of all of the standard Cr–Ni–Fe heat-resistant alloys, establishing base lines, and in many cases determining the range in properties that may be expected as certain variables operate. Most of this testing has been done in the 870–1090°C (1600–2000°F) temperature range. Noteworthy is the fact that only in a recent A.S.T.M. meeting was creep rupture data presented for the common wrought stainless steels at 1800°F (980°C.)

4.5. *Development of Premium Alloys*

The Thermalloy 40-A2, 50-CQ and 63WC (Supertherm) grades are examples of higher strength modifications of the standard types. The demand for such materials is not great, perhaps because the standard grades (provided minor elements are suitably controlled) have several types that are as strong as many superalloys. Since strength control by means of carbon content is relatively inexpensive, it has served most applications.

4.6. *Metallography and Alloy Index Formulae*

Metallographic structure and its relation to properties is an important tool for all metallurgical work on alloys. We constantly strive to gain a clearer understanding of these relations and when a good correlation develops, we have found an excellent quality control criterion. A rather well-known example is the combination of ferrite and austenite that occurs in certain grades, like the HD, HE, HH and HF types. An example will be provided, but comment will here be confined to various formulae that are used to estimate these metallographic tendencies.

Such formulae are desirable as a means of controlling production specifications, especially where the criteria of use call for various modifications of the standard grades. A well-known example is the Schaeffler diagram for estimating the amount of ferrite in stainless steel weld metal. Other simplified formulae are available for similar estimates of the presence of ferrite. We have developed our own formulae of this type, usually in a more complex form than those published because we have more information on the constituent elements, but we do not recommend them to customers even though they have a need to check the alloys.

4.7. *Carburizing Resistance*

As the potent effect of carbon in these alloys becomes more generally recognized it will be realized that carburization in service can have a profound effect on life expectancy. This is one factor that can badly distort the normal relation between long and short-term creep-rupture tests. Besides our routine survey of the effect of carbon content on an alloy, we consider it important to properly rank the material in terms of carburizing resistance. Several Alloy Casting Institute projects have studied various alloys in terms of behaviour in the common industrial carburizing furnace atmospheres, which are usually rather neutral carrier gases to which methane or another hydrocarbon is added to provide the carburizing potential. The conditions in the A.C.I. tests have been relatively mild and sometimes show almost no difference in the merit of the different Cr–Ni–Fe alloys. The contribution of silicon to carburizing resistance has been demonstrated, however.

Our laboratory has attempted to go beyond these mild tests to estimate the result of raising carburizing temperatures (now around 930°C (1700°F)) or of having more potent carburizing environments. The higher temperature (980°C or 1800°F is frequently employed) tends to produce an accelerated carburizing test. An atmosphere of 75 per cent hydrogen and 25 per cent methane may be used to approximate some petrochemical processing conditions.

It is suspected that the limitation on some future chemical processes may well be the resistance of the alloys to carburization rather than basic strength or scaling resistance.

5. HOT GAS CORROSION RESISTANCE

The preceding sections of this paper have aimed to give a glimpse of a few aspects of the development work that has been done on these alloys. Some of them will now be expanded with more detail that could be helpful in dealing with your material problems.

5.1. Scaling Resistance

Chromium is the mainstay of oxidation resistance. With nickel alone, or together with nickel in iron-base alloys, it forms oxide scale that is usually tightly adherent and protective. The available evidence indicates that this is almost purely a chemical effect, and thus the benefits of chromium and nickel are conferred on wrought and cast alloys alike. No difference is expected in the oxidation resistance of alloys of the same composition as made by different manufacturers, provided the product has physical integrity. (It can be shown that oxidation may be more severe at defects intersecting the surface, in weld fissures for example.) In general, the oxidation resistance is circumscribed when the alloy type is selected.

Fig. 1 shows the importance of chromium in reducing progressive oxidation.[8] Oxidation in terms of surface metal loss (of inches penetration per year) is plotted against chromium content, with and without nickel. Notice that metal loss is reduced to a low value if 25 per cent chromium is present. Also, that nickel has a protective effect. This explains why the higher nickel grades tend to have lower chromium contents. Nickel is roughly one-third as effective as chromium as a protective element, and since it is more expensive, the inclusion of nickel in one of these alloys is based on its other functions.

5.2. Nomographs

Fig. 2 permits estimation of the combined effects of chromium and nickel, with a quantitative evaluation of the protection provided. In using this nomograph[9, 10] the desirable rate of metal loss is below 0·05 in. per year, though some applications are satisfactorily served if the rate is no greater than 0·1 in. per year.

5.3. Behaviour of Standard Grades

There are a number of these nomographs available but since the alloy choice is usually from the standard grades the compilation in Table 3 may be more useful. Here the behaviour of eight A.C.I. types and two special

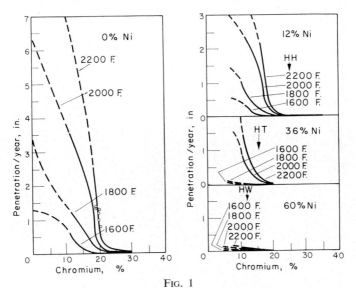

FIG. 1

The effect of chromium at various nickel levels on air oxidation of alloys at 1600°, 1800°, 2000° and 2200°F.

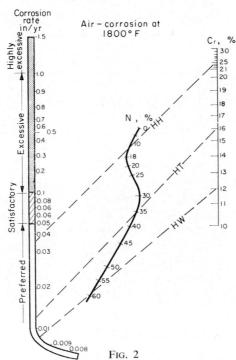

FIG. 2

Nomographic chart illustrating the relationship between nickel–chromium content and air-corrosion at 1800°F.

Thermalloys are shown under five different conditions. The behaviour in air and in oxidizing flue gases (with either 5 or 100 grains of sulphur per 100 ft³) is not much different. Sulphur dioxide does not seem to accelerate attack on

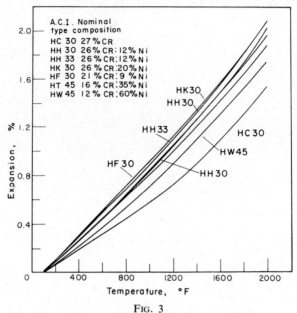

FIG. 3

Thermal expansion characteristics of cast heat-resistant alloys.

the surface. However, if hydrogen sulphide is present, as in reducing flue gases, the higher nickel alloys are quite vulnerable.[11] Note the higher rates of metal loss for the HT, HU and HW grades at 1090°C (2000°F) in reducing flue gas containing 100 grains of sulphur per 100 ft³. This behaviour is attributed to low melting sulphides that form with nickel, and becomes even more severe if the sulphur content of the gas is higher.

Temperature, nickel content, chromium content, sulphur in the gas, and reducing versus oxidizing conditions all influence the primary choice of a heat resistant alloy. Certain elements that can lead to catastrophic oxidation (e.g. molybdenum)[12] or can flux away the protective chromium oxide scale (e.g. sodium, lead and vanadium) should also be avoided where possible. There is a great deal of information in this field of scaling resistance, but the brief outline here will provide a logical basis for alloy type selection.

6. ENGINEERING PROPERTIES

6.1. *Thermal Expansion*

There is not a great difference among the austenitic heat-resistant alloys.

TABLE 3

Oxidation Resistance of Cast Alloys

(Expressed as inches per year metal loss)

Grade	Cr-Ni	In Air		Oxidizing Flue Gas		Reducing Flue Gas	
				2000°F		2000°F	
		2000°F	2200°F	5 g S	100 g S	5 g S	100 g S
HH	26-12	0·04-0·09	0·06	0·05-0·07	0·04-0·1	0·02-0·05	0·03
HI	28-15	0·03-0·05	0·06-0·1	0·02-0·05	0·04	0·02	0·03
HK	26-20	0·04	0·05-0·08	0·05	0·04	0·02-0·05	0·03
HL	30-20	0·04	0·06-0·1	0·05	0·04-0·05	0·02	0·03
HT	15-35	0·05-0·05	0·1-1·0	0·06-0·3	0·1-0·5	0·05-0·2	0·3-0·8
HU	18-38	0·04-0·05	0·1	0·04-0·06	0·04-0·1	0·02-0·05	0·02-03
HW	12-60	0·03-0·05	0·07-0·08	0·04-0·06	0·03-0·07	0·02-0·03	0·1-0·7
HX	18-65	0·03	0·06	0·03	0·03-0·04	0·02	0·02-0·05
T63	28-35	0·038	0·085	0·04-0·05	0·03-0·04	0·03	0·02-0·03
T63WC*		0·052	0·121				

* These values include subsurface effects as well as scaling.

Fig. 3 shows that the higher nickel grades have slightly lower expansion coefficients, but the largest difference is between the ferritic (e.g. HC or 27% Cr with below 3% Ni) and austenitic types. The ferritic alloys also have higher heat conductivity and where the low hot strength or the brittleness at room temperature are not a handicap they may be preferred in heat transfer applications or high sulphur environments.

6.2. *Property Variation in an HH Type Alloy*

The combination of 26 per cent chromium for oxidation resistance and 12 per cent nickel to provide an austenitic alloy with good hot strength have made the HH grade quite popular. Over a period of many years it will account for about 40 per cent of the cast heat resistant alloy production in the United States. This alloy, which is covered by A.S.T.M. specification No. A447, was the first that this laboratory studied in detail.

This can be used to show the sensitivity of a material to minor elements. In Table 4 are shown compositions from two specifications, together with an individual heat from the 1942 paper.[5] Our important contribution to this table is the 1000 hr rupture strength at 1800°F (980°C). Note that if the specification of A.S.T.M. A297 is used, the range of 1240 to 3600 psi is in prospect. This is a ratio of 1:3 in strength, and it does not necessarily include the weakest alloy that might be provided under this specification. The low value is merely from one heat that was obviously within the specification but was on the low side in carbon.

TABLE 4

The Role of Chemical Composition in Cast Heat-Resistant Alloys

Element	ASTM-A297 HH Grade	ASTM–A447 Spec. 25–12, Type II		Contribution of the element
		Specification	An example	
C%	0·20–0·50	0·20–0·45	0·32	Hot strength castability
Mn%	2·00 max.	2·50 max.	0·46	
Si%	2·00 max.	1·75 max.	0·45	Carb. resistance aust. instability
Cr%	24–28	23–28	25·9	Oxidation resistance
Ni%	11–14	10–14	11·5	Austenite Stability
N%		0·20 max.	0·16	Hot strength
Mo%	0·5 max.			
1000 hr LRS 1800°F	1240–3600 psi	2400–3500 psi	2400 psi	

The composition ranges under A.S.T.M. specification No. A447 are not much different. However, the minimum strength expected is about double the previous low of 1240 psi. This is not stated anywhere in the specification but was part of the intent when it was drafted. To attain this minimum requires an acceptance test that rejects the low strength compositions that might be supplied with the chemical limits shown. Either a stress-rupture test, a hot tensile test, or a magnetic permeability test can be used to reject the weak compositions. The specification also includes a room temperature tensile test after ageing 24 hr at 760°C (1400°F) because of insistence by some producers. Unfortunately, this test does not reject weak heats; it tends to accept them and may reject the strongest heat of an order.

Note the composition of the individual heat shown with a rupture strength of 2400 psi. From data presented in the original 1942 paper[5] it would be recognized that lowering of carbon, nickel or nitrogen; or raising of chromium or silicon would tend to result in strength below the 2400 psi level. A simple chemical specification that could prevent all of the adverse combinations would result in a more expensive alloy and one that is no longer of the HH type. With proper foundry control it is possible to provide HH alloys that have the minimum strength shown, and this is the intent of the Thermalloy 40B specification as used by our Companies.

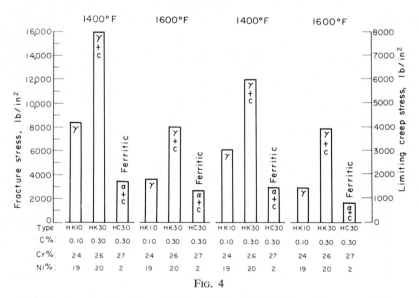

FIG. 4

Ferritic vs. austenitic alloys. 100 hr fracture stress limiting creep stress (from stress-rupture tests), (0·0001 per cent per hr min. rate).

As a matter of interest, the formulation of a relatively "foolproof" specification based on 26 per cent chromium leads to the HK or 26% Cr:20% Ni grade that has become the most popular reformer tube alloy in the United States.

6.3. *Ferritic versus Austenitic Alloys*

To further elucidate the relative hot strength of ferrite and austenite, and also to show the effect of carbon content, Fig. 4 compares HK10, HK30 and HC30 alloys in terms of 100 hr rupture stress and Limiting Creep Stress at two temperatures. Though there are minor differences at the temperatures of 1400°F (760°C) and 1600°F (870°C) the trends are the same. The HK10 alloy, with 0·10 per cent carbon, 26 per cent chromium and 20 per cent nickel is wholly austenitic but quite weak in comparison with its 0·30 per cent carbon companion. The HC30 alloy with only 2 per cent nickel is even weaker because of its ferrite matrix, even though it has the same carbon level as the HK30. Thus it is apparent that both carbon content and matrix character have an important influence on creep-rupture strength.

6.4. *The Effect of Carbon on the HH Alloys* (26% Cr:12% Ni)

Fig. 5 provides an answer to questions about the effect of carbon on the borderline alloys that can have a matrix with both ferrite and austenite. In this closely controlled experimental series carbon is the significant variable. As it increases the creep strength rises from 600 psi at 0·19 per cent carbon

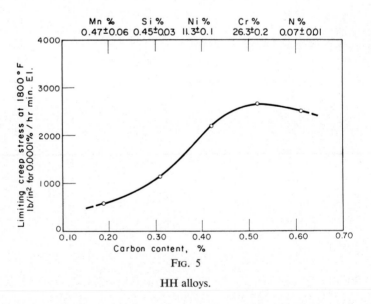

FIG. 5

HH alloys.

to 2700 psi at 0·52 per cent carbon; about a fivefold increase. The potent effect comes from both the tendency of carbon to inhibit ferrite formation and the strengthening effect of finely precipitated carbides. Though not shown on this graph imagine a point at 0·32 per cent carbon and 2100 psi. This is a real data item[5] and represents the effect of increasing nitrogen from 0·07 to 0·13 per cent.

6.5. *Ferrite in Austenite and Permeability*

Fig. 6 includes three photomicrographs that show the effect of carbon in decreasing the volume of ferrite in these alloys. These are three of the alloys shown in Fig. 5, etched to reveal the ferrite in outline.

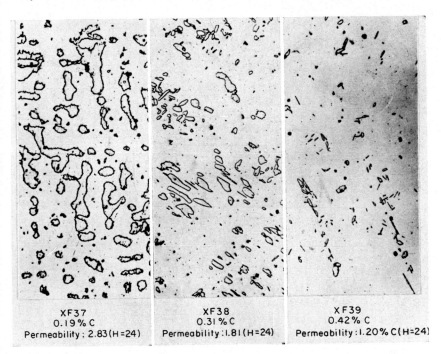

XF37
0.19% C
Permeability: 2.83(H=24)

XF38
0.31% C
Permeability: 1.81(H=24)

XF39
0.42% C
Permeability: 1.20% C(H=24)

FIG. 6

Ferrite distribution in 26·3% Cr:11·3% Ni alloys after creep testing at 1800°F.

The ferromagnetic quality of ferrite is the basis of the magnetic permeability test that was worked out for this grade and later incorporated in A.S.T.M. Specification No. A447. Fig. 7 is the 1942 correlation curve of magnetism and creep strength. The acceptance test level for a minimum Limiting Creep Stress of about 1700 psi at 1800°F (980°C) was set at a maximum permeability of 1·05 on this basis. The partially ferritic grade (I) with higher ductility (provided the sigma formation range is avoided) has a maximum permeability of 1·70. From the left-hand graph of Fig. 7 it can be concluded that the minimum Limiting Creep Strength on this basis is about half of the strength of the other grade (II). Engineers were thus given a rather clear-cut choice between hot strength and ductility. Subsequent orders indicate that they almost always choose strength (Grade II) under specification A447.

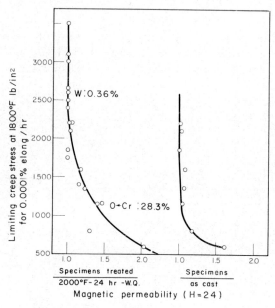

FIG. 7

Composition range: C% 0·19–0·49; MN% 0·40–1·31; SI% 0·40–1·18; NI% 11·1–12·8; CR% 24·9–28·3; N% 0·04–0·22.

It is important to appreciate that this permeability test is valid only for such borderline alloys. It does not have the same correlation with creep strength for those high nickel alloys in which the austenite itself is somewhat magnetic. This, coupled with the fact that such high nickel austenites may have Curie points near room temperature, and thus give very erratic permeability indications, has caused considerable confusion.

6.6. The Effect of Carbon on the HT (15% Cr:35% Ni) Alloys

Fig. 8 shows the short time creep rates for a group of 15% Cr:35% Ni alloys plotted against carbon content. Noteworthy are the very steep slope of carbon curve and the peak in creep resistance.

The shape of such curves as in Fig. 8 changes with stress and temperature. A list of rupture strength values is perhaps more informative where design guidance is sought. There is considerable interest in the 15:35 or 18:38 alloys for reformer service, the paper by Edeleanu and Estruch pointing out that the carbon range from 0·15 to 0·50 per cent was involved. In Table 5 the

results from six heats in the files of our laboratory are listed to show the
effect of carbon on the 15% Cr:35% Ni base, other minor elements being

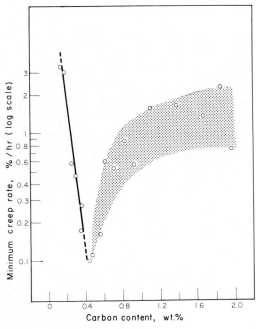

FIG. 8

The effect of carbon on the creep resistance of cast 16% Cr:35% Ni heat-
resistant alloys from stress-strain-rupture tests at 1400°F and 20,000 psi.

TABLE 5

The Effect of Carbon on HT (Cast 15% Cr:35% Ni) Alloys

	Limiting rupture stress in psi					
Grade . . .	HT14	HT18	HT25	HT29	HT35	HT50
C% . . .	0·14	0·18	0·25	0·29	0·35	0·50
100 hr rupture						
870°C 1600°F	3400	3900	6600	7300	8200	9100
925°C 1700°F	2200	2600	4500	5000	5800	6300
980°C 1800°F	1450	1700	3100	3400	4000	4400
1035°C 1900°F	940	1150	2100	2300	2800	3100
1000 hr rupture						
870°C 1600°F	2000	2350	4100	4500	5200	5800
925°C 1700°F	1300	1500	2700	3000	3500	4000
980°C 1800°F	820	980	1850	2000	2400	2750
1035°C 1900°F	530	650	1200	1350	1650	1900

closely controlled. The A.C.I. system is used to denote the actual carbon contents of the heats, and the range covered coincides with that reported by Edeleanu and Estruch. Note the wide range in hot strength that is involved. Though there are other considerations, from inspection of this table it is easy to understand why the carbon range for Thermalloys 50 and 58 is usually set at 0·40 to 0·60 per cent.

6.7. *The Potency of Carbon*

Fig. 9 shows the pattern for both the HK and HT alloys at two temperatures, and with the HH alloy at one temperature to supplement Fig. 5. The carbon level selected for a specification is not always the strongest; the level

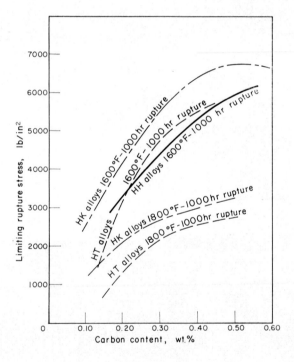

FIG. 9

used may reflect some compromise between strength and ductility. It is desirable to avoid steep parts of the carbon versus strength curve because where the curve is steep even a narrow carbon range can result in a considerable spread in properties.

7. METALLOGRAPHY

7.1. *Microstructures*

Metallographic evidence is so important that no discussion of these alloys should omit at least brief reference to certain salient features. Fig. 10a is a photomicrograph of a 15% Cr:35% Ni alloy with 0·44 per cent carbon (HT44). It reveals a matrix of austenite and a network of primary carbides

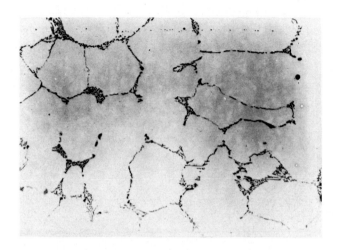

FIG. 10a

As-cast structure of HT-44 (16% Cr:35% Ni alloy at 250× magnification).

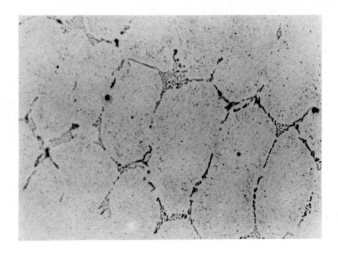

FIG. 10b

HT-47 alloy heated for 50 hr at 980°C (1800°F, 250× magnification).

that formed as the alloy solidified from the melt. The role of such carbides has been questioned; a quick answer, perhaps oversimplified, is that these carbides have little effect on either hot strength or ductility. The visible net is not a grain boundary pattern. In this alloy at this carbon level the grains are much larger than the austenite cells enclosed by the primary carbides and the grain boundaries are fine and inconspicuous. As carbon is lowered the volume of primary carbide diminishes, but the grain boundaries may become thicker and more prominent. Not enough is known about the composition of the grain boundary material, but there are hints that silicon may segregate here and especially in the lower carbon alloys may cause brittleness.[13]

7.2. Carbide Precipitation

Fig. 10b is an alloy of similar carbon content (HT47) that has been heated for 50 hr at 980°C (1800°F). Fine carbides have precipitated within the cells outlined by the primary carbides. Besides these visible carbides there are probably others too small to be resolved at this magnification of 250×. A closer look at such fine carbides is provided by the 50,000× electron micro-

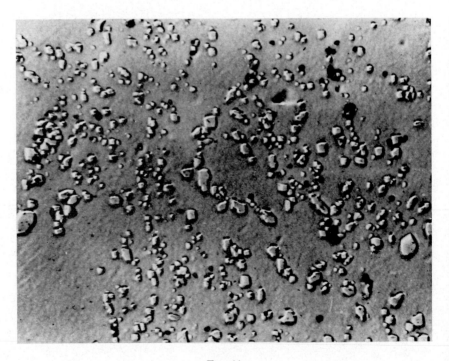

Fig. 11

Fine carbide in HT-55 alloy tested at 980°C. Electron photomicrograph at 50,000×.

graph of Fig. 11. These fine particles are responsible for much of the hot strength of the Cr–Ni–Fe heat resistant alloys. They also reduce ductility.

These particles were formed by combination of chromium present in the matrix with carbon that was dissolved in the austenite matrix just under the solidification point and that remained in supersaturated solution until the alloy was reheated. The "precipitation hardening" from their formation tends to dominate the behaviour of these alloys from the temperature where precipitation can begin (around 500°C) up to the range where they remain in solution or are redissolved (above 1050°C). At lower temperatures they are finer and form more slowly. With time they can slowly agglomerate, resulting in lowered strength and increased ductility. With lower carbon content the cells show more clearly the segregation pattern of non-uniform carbon distribution, the outer zones having a denser carbide dispersion.

It thus appears that these cast alloys have something like a honeycomb structure, the virtues of which are sometimes adopted for engineering structures. While research in this area has not been extensive, there is some evidence to indicate that the cellular structure is an asset and that in the stronger alloys with considerable carbon it provides a more favourable combination of hot strength and ductility than does the same alloy if the segregation pattern is erased by heat treatment or hot working.

7.3. *Homogenization*

The carbon concentration gradient can be destroyed by homogenization at say 1260°C and if precipitation is then induced by ageing at 980°C, the uniformity of the carbide precipitate is obvious. An alloy with this dispersion is usually stronger and less ductile than that of the same alloy as cast.

7.4. *Grain Size*

Whereas this kind of carbide solution and homogenization treatment is not considered worthwhile and is not employed with the cast alloys, for the wrought materials it may be necessary to gain adequate strength. Its history probably goes back to the work by Clark and Freeman[14] on the apparent influence of grain size in austenitic steels. In their experiments it was considered necessary to heat treat to achieve coarse grains for the desired comparison. The end result was an association of coarse grains with higher creep strength. This expectancy is still implied by certain design strength values, as in the A.S.M.E. Boiler Code tables. However, subsequent experience has revealed cases where the "grain size control" was not productive of the strength and life expectancy that were intended.

7.5. *Hot Ductility*

One result of increasing temperature is a compulsory trade of strength for ductility. In general it can be said that increasing temperature by 200°F

(111°C) tends to cut in half the rupture stress for a given life expectancy. At the same time there is an increase in tensile elongation that is best shown by quick tests, as in Fig. 12. Note that the lowest elongation tends to occur near 650°C (1200°F) where the finest precipitated carbide forms. Below this temperature the alloy is so sluggish that precipitation is scant or absent in short tests.

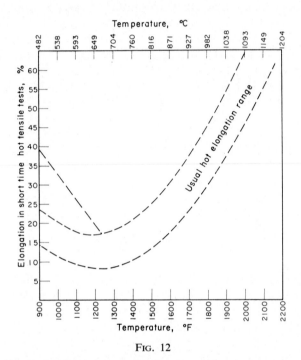

Fig. 12

The trend of hot ductility for Cr–Ni–Fe heat-resistant alloys.

7.6. Carbide Spheroidization

The rising ductility is associated with solution of the carbides or with their spheroidization because of easier diffusion. At quite high temperatures even the primary carbide networks tend to bead-like spheroids, as in Fig. 13, representing an HT56 alloy after creep testing 1001 hr at 2150°F (1180°C). This agglomeration pattern is sometimes helpful in estimating the temperatures reached by alloys in service, where more accurate measurements are lacking. Note that all of the fine carbides have been redissolved; their strengthening effect is gone, and the properties of the alloy are those of the austenitic matrix.

This discussion of metallography has been brief, without consideration of such matters as transformations, the sigma phase, and inclusions. If consideration is confined to the HT50, HK40 and HF30 alloys made under proper control, they need not be a matter of concern.

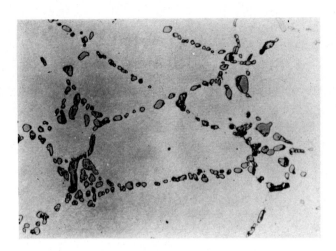

FIG. 13

8. LOAD-CARRYING ABILITY

8.1. *The Presentation of Creep-Rupture Data*

The volume of creep data is embarrassingly large and some means to make pertinent tests accessible is required. Besides various check lists and indices, we have adopted the Keysort card system standardized by the ASTM-A.S.M.E. Joint Committee on Effect of Temperature on Properties of Metals. A few of our completed cards are available in the ASTM packages that are compiled periodically, and it is expected that others will be contributed from time to time. However, complete publication is not contemplated.

8.2. *Parameters*

A parameter plot is very helpful at this stage. Parameters were discussed in considerable detail in the proceedings of the recent Joint International Conference on Creep. There exist many opinions about the best parameter to use, but from the discussions at this conference it might be concluded that the need is not for more and better parameters but for better data to evaluate those that we have. In the range of our interest we have found the Larson–Miller parameter to be the simplest and thus the most satisfactory. It seems to produce linear plots over the range in which we are most interested. For the departures from linearity below 760°C (1400°F) and above 1035°C (1900°F) there are not yet enough data points to show the pattern with assurance. In these somewhat doubtful zones we depend on empirical log–log plots of stress versus minimum creep rate and rupture time.

8.3. *Larson-Miller Treatment*

As an example of parameter treatment, ten rupture times available on an alloy are converted to Larson–Miller parameters by the formula $T(\log t + C)$ where T is the absolute temperature in degrees Rankine (obtained by adding 460°F to the Fahrenheit temperature, t is the rupture time in hours, and C is a constant that must be determined by experiment. To illustrate, parameters calculated for constants of 15, 20 and 25 are plotted against stress in Fig. 14. From inspection it is recognized that the constant of 20 gives the

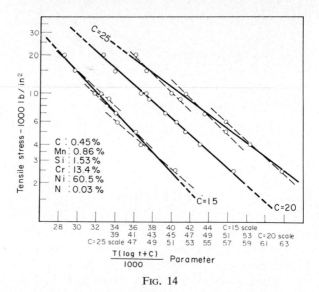

FIG. 14

HW-45 12% Cr:60% Ni cast heat-resistant alloy.

least dispersion about the central tendency line and that also the individual temperature lines make the smallest angle with the master rupture line.

8.4. *Trend Charts—HK40*

Values derived from this master rupture plot are drawn on both the log–log chart of minimum creep rates and rupture times and on a semi-logarithmic chart of stress versus temperature, as in Fig. 15. This chart is very useful for preliminary design estimates as it shows quickly the relation of life expectancy and dimensional stability, while interpolation of temperatures is easy. The conventional values from it are posted on a Keysort card. Note that Fig. 15 applies to an HK40 alloy rather than the HW45 alloy of Fig. 14. The Larson–Miller plot for Thermalloy 47 as made several years ago is shown in

Fig. 16. This was the basis of using this alloy in the United States, the original internal composition specification of the Electro-Alloys Division being gradually spread through the industry by customer action. A more recent

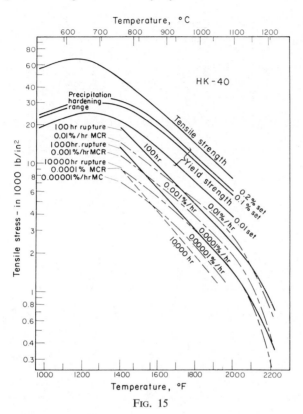

FIG. 15

Electro-Alloys heat has been extensively tested and found to confirm the earlier data within the limits of plus or minus 20 per cent that are shown. The confirming tests include fracture times of 6064 hr at 760°C (1400°F), 6830 hr at 980°C (1800°F) and 15,285 hr at 870°C (1600°F).

8.5. Trend Charts—Thermalloy 30 (HF30)

Fig. 17 is similar semilogarithmic chart for the HF30 alloy as made by Lloyds and the Electro-Alloys Division and that is frequently recommended for service between 650°C (1200°F) and 870°C (1600°F). This is based on tests up to 13,000 hr at 1400°F and 1600°F. The probability that extrapolations out to 100,000 hr (as shown on Fig. 17) will be good is now high.

8.6. Trends for the HT Alloy

Similar charts for the HT and HU alloys are not provided here. They are

available, and the trends can be seen in Table 5 but they are not validated
by long-term tests. A newer grade is becoming popular, a hybrid of HT and
HU, with about 18% Cr and 35% Ni. Short-term trends for this (to about

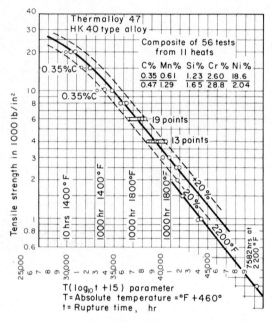

FIG. 16

High-temperature strength as affected by time and temperature.

1000 hr) are also available. The HT and HU alloys are considered carburizing
service materials in the United States. As such they are made in a great
variety of static castings, but these are not customarily designed on the basis
of creep-rupture data. Thus there has been no incentive for very long-term
creep tests.

A comment on the published values for the HT alloy is in order here. The
A.C.I. data sheets[15] give the 100 hr rupture stresses of 8500 psi at 1600°F
(870°C) and 4500 psi at 1800°F (980°C); and 1000 hr rupture stresses of
7000 psi at 1600°F and 3700 psi at 1800°F. Such figures are compiled from
data submitted from various sources, including our laboratory, the A.C.I.
sponsored work at Battelle Memorial Institute, and occasionally other
reports. They are examined by a committee and the published values selected.
Not having been on this committee, and knowing that the results have not
been confirmed by British creep testing, I inquired about the basis of the
selection, but evidently adequate notes of that work are not available, and
we could not determine how that committee arrived at the figures.

Based on Battelle data from A.C.I.-sponsored work, as reviewed in our

1947[4] paper the 8500 psi value at 1600°F is about right for HT or HU alloys between 0·40 and 0·46 per cent carbon. The same chart gives 6000 psi for the 1000 hr LRS. A.C.I. work had little data at 1800°F and the available information probably was that provided by our Electro-Alloys Division. Here again we confirm the 100 hr value but not that for 1000 hr. How the figures were derived or why they were boosted at the 1000 hr level to badly distort the long-term extrapolated picture is not known.

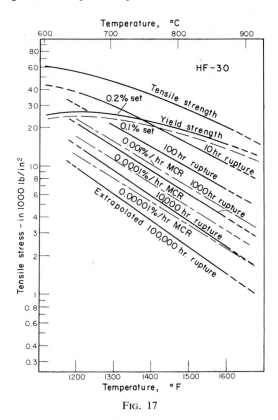

FIG. 17

8.7. *Manufacturing Variables*

Because manufacturing variables other than the simple chemical composition are involved, the data plots and design charts derived from testing a given product cannot be used with assurance for the products of other manufacturers without independent confirmation. It should be recognized that most of our testing has been done on statically cast specimens. By way of reassurance we can state that small specimens cut from our metal mould centrifugally cast tubes usually show somewhat longer rupture times than their statically cast companions from the same heat. However, it is suggested

D

that this favourable circumstance be used as a safety factor rather than as a justification for more optimistic design.

8.8. *Stability and Extrapolation*

Valid extrapolation of these data depends on the stability of the alloy. Known causes of instability are excessive surface attack by hot gases, intergranular oxidation, excessive carburization, and phase changes. Where these come into play after some time interval the usual log–log plot of rupture times tends to show a definite change in slope and excessive dispersion can develop on the Larson–Miller plot. Where they are normally present but vary only with time the plots are not disturbed and extrapolation is probably valid, even if study of the fractured specimens shows that the effect is present. Internal oxidation has received study because intergranular oxidation is the normal high temperature failure mechanism of these alloys when they carry loads. It has been recognized in many of the alloys after rupture, but in general it does not seem to disturb the rupture time plots of the austenitic alloys as it does those of the low-alloy ferritic steels.

9. CAST VERSUS WROUGHT HEAT-RESISTANT ALLOYS

The engineering use of heat-resistant alloys frequently calls for judgement in selection of the method of manufacture as well as the alloy type. The choice is usually between several standardized wrought forms and the infinite variety of sizes and shapes that castings can provide.

Sometimes there is no problem. Wire and thin sheets, for example, are used without hesitation where needed. On the other hand there is no availability of hot worked heat-resistant alloy for some items. Between such extremes there are many applications where both manufacturing methods, especially when supplemented by welding and machining, might be used. Availability, economy, and the adaptability of properties to engineering use then become important.

What is not generally recognized is the advantage in engineering properties provided by certain cast alloy grades.

9.1. *The A.S.M.E. Boiler and Pressure Vessel Code*

In the United States a strong influence on design strength values is exerted by the A.S.M.E. Boiler and Pressure Vessel Code Committee. It is appropriate to use details of this code as a reference base to clarify comparative engineering properties. Data are provided here that will be helpful if provisions of the code are extended in the future beyond the present limit of 1500°F. This code is concerned with ensuring the safety and reliability of the materials and the construction of engineering components that operate at high pressures and temperatures.

9.2. *Design Criteria*

The A.S.M.E. Code restricts design stresses for pressure vessels to 60 per cent of the average or 80 per cent of the minimum 100,000 hr rupture strength. This relation implies a range of plus or minus 20 per cent above the average. Not many 100,000 hr tests are available for defining such a range and thus the most quoted and used values are extrapolations. The maximum allowable stress values for a high-alloy plate material, as given in Code Table UHA-23, are partially reproduced in Fig. 18.

9.3. *Type* 310 *Stainless Steel*

Focusing attention on the 310 grade (wrought 25% Cr:20% Ni alloy) an ASTM compilation of data[16] provides values for 17 lots of 310. Of these, 10 include rupture stress for 1000 hr life at 1500°F, two include limiting creep stress (0·00001 per cent/hr MCR) at 1500°F, and nine permit extrapolation of the rupture stress to 100,000 hr. The 1000 hr rupture stresses of these and the Boiler Code limits are plotted together with some other data on Fig. 18. The 100,000 hr rupture stress of the nine 310 alloys averages 32 per cent of their 1000 hr values, with a range between 19 per cent and 45 per cent.

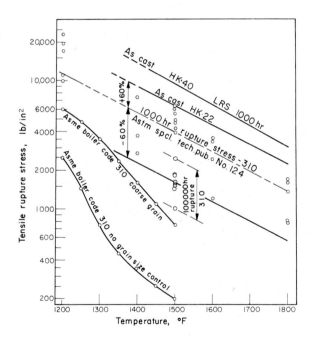

FIG. 18

Rupture strength and ASME design values for various 26%Cr:20%Ni heat-resistant alloys.

At 1500°F the design stress of 200 psi is 67 per cent of the 100,000 hr rupture stress, which in turn is 19 per cent of the 1000 hr value (1600 psi) for a 0·11 per cent carbon alloy air cooled from 1700°F in mill processing. This represents 310 stainless without grain size control.

The "controlled" material, which actually reflects water quenching from a solution heat-treatment between 1950°F to 2250°F, ranges up to 6300 psi (at 1500°F) for 1000 hr rupture. The broad scatter band for 310, established by plotting 1400°, 1400° and 1600°F points, suggests an average 1000 hr value of 3900 psi and a range of plus or minus 60 per cent. The lower edge of this band is about the midrange value for 100,000 hr rupture or for limiting creep stress (0·00001 per cent/hr) at 1500°F.

The Boiler Code allowable stress of 750 psi at 1500°F is 75 per cent of the lowest "controlled" 310, a 0·08 per cent carbon alloy water quenched from 1950°F, or 47 per cent of the midrange 100,000 hr stress (1600 psi). With the wide scatter of the data points on Fig. 18 the conservatism of the Boiler Code values is well justified.

9.4. *Comparative Strength of Castings*

However, greater material strength is readily available. The very top of the 1000 hr rupture range for wrought 310 also coincides with the central tendency of the cast HK22 alloy, which needs no heat treatment to develop its strength and is inherently coarse grained. The HK40 alloy is even stronger. Moreover, as Thermalloy 47 these properties of HK40 have been consistent within a range of plus or minus 20 per cent which is the latitude implied by the Boiler Code design criteria.

9.5. *The Scatter of Wrought Alloy Properties*

The wide scatter band for 310 stainless is due to the variety of processing variables that is involved. The wrought grades, because carbon adds hot strength and makes the higher carbon alloys more difficult to hot work, are characteristically made with low carbon, such as 0·04 to 0·10 per cent and seldom exceed 0·20 per cent. The cast alloys do not have this carbon limitation and can be freely specified at whatever carbon level is most desirable. Moreover, because their carbide distribution and habit are not disturbed, they have a superior uniformity.

9.6. *Cast HK40*

Compare the cast HK40 alloy with the 310 stainless steels in ASTM SP124.[16] This alloy provides extrapolated 100,000 hr rupture stresses of 6500 psi at 1400°F, 2900 psi at 1600°F, and 1270 psi at 1800°F. The wrought 310 stainless gives midrange properties of about 2640, 1290 and 650 psi. The HK40 is about twice as strong.

9.7. *Common Manufacturing Variables*

Some manufacturing variables are common to both wrought and cast products. Of course, the hot-worked materials are originally cast as an ingot. Ingots are subject to marked segregation of impurities, more so than castings because they are generally larger and cool more slowly. The normal shrinkage in cooling molten metal creates a pipe in the ingot top. After hot rolling, the billets from such ingots are cropped to discard the defective piped zoned and also eliminate much of the segregation, which is worst in the last metal to cool. The foundryman also uses this technique. Risers on a casting serve the same purpose as the top of the ingot; they are also cut off and discarded.

Directional properties represent a major difference between wrought and cast alloys. Hot rolling distorts inclusions, segregated zones and incompletely welded discontinuities to produce stringers, bands and seams in the metal. These ordinarily have little or no effect on tensile properties measured on longitudinal specimens, but they can cause a marked reduction in transverse properties. Since most reported properties are based on the longitudinal direction, this difference is frequently forgotten. With rods this may not be significant. However, with certain products it may be very important. A tube, subject to bursting stresses, is resisting destruction with its transverse strength. Castings are less likely to reveal directional properties. The relative merits in relation to this feature are closely related to the conditions of service and cannot be defined here with a simple generalization.

9.8. *Design of Castings*

With the important exception of centrifugally cast tubes, long simple shapes inhibit good directional soldification. A flat plate or a long rod is a difficult problem for the foundryman. The thinner the section the greater this difficulty. As a result, the foundry may recommend a minimum thickness for the casting design and will avoid rods and flat plates when possible. Add taper or detail to the simple shape and the part becomes more attractive to the foundry and less practical for hot working. Many parts are prohibitive in cost if the shape details must be produced by machining. This status is rather well known.

The design of castings for maximum economy is specialized and requires a background of experience and familiarity with many details of foundry practice. Many designs that reach the foundry are poorly adapted to casting without revision. Dissatisfaction with castings can sometimes be traced to this source. In other cases the cost to the user would have been lower if a foundry engineering department had been consulted on the original design. There are many technical details such as fillet sizes and locations, changes in section, and adaptability to moulding that are involved. Such things as controlled directional solidification may be of little concern to the average mechanical engineer who makes a drawing, but they are vital to the foundryman, and indirectly to the user who seeks a functional part with high quality and low cost.

9.9. *Tubing*

Tubing of the kind used for reformers is a product for which the wrought and cast grades are in direct competition. The wrought tubes of course can be produced with extremely thin walls, while the minimum desirable cast wall thickness is about $\frac{5}{16}$ in. For thick walls the ease with which sections can be controlled is a marked advantage for centrifugal castings, whose thicknesses are determined simply by accurate control of the amount of molten metal poured into the mould. The outside diameter is, of course, fixed by the inside diameter of the mould, which is usually of metal. Thus standardization of tubing outside diameters simplifies the foundry's mould inventory problem and eventually lowers tubing costs.

10. CARBURIZATION

10.1. *Carburizing Environment Effects*

In certain petrochemical processing installations, in furnaces devoted to carburizing engineering steels, and in related applications the furnace hardware is subject to a considerable carburizing potential. The engineering steels rapidly absorb carbon needed for case hardening but the heat-resisting alloys would be almost worthless in furnace parts if they did not have great resistance to carbon pick-up under the same conditions. Where the processed steels are exposed for only a few minutes, the furnace components are expected to endure the same conditions for thousands of hours.

Two aspects are especially important to the materials engineer: the rate at which carbon is absorbed and the effect of increasing carbon on the engineering properties. Alloy composition has a considerable influence on carburizing rates. The trends can be studied experimentally, but the variety of process variables may restrict the validity of simple generalizations. Temperature is important, as is the carburizing medium. The behaviour of the alloys at high carbon contents has similarity, but the various grades nevertheless retain an individuality.

10.2. *Pack Carburizing*

Pack carburizing formerly was popular, with heat-resistant alloy containers serving to hold the steel parts packed in an activated carbon powder medium. Figure 19 shows the response of five cast alloy grades in comparison with mild 1020 steel during pack carburizing at 1800°F (980°C).[4] The effect was measured by means of carbon determinations on layer cuts from cylindrical specimens. Note that resistance to absorption of carbon seems related to nickel content.

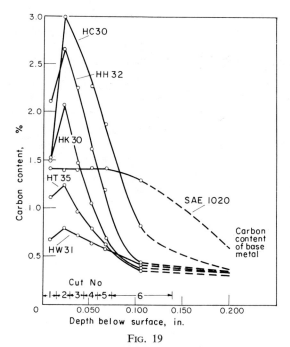

FIG. 19

Heat-resistant alloy—carbon penetration after pack carburizing at 1800°F for 100 hr in E. E. Houghton's "Pearlite Carburizing Material" Dodge Specification 5021.

Four cycles of 25 hr at 1800°F

Grade	Cr%	Ni%	Si%
SAE1020	—	—	—
HC 30	27	2	1·17
HH 32	26	12	1·18
HK 30	26	20	1·21
HT 35	16	35	1·28
HW 31	12	58	0·80

10.3. Gas Carburizing

Continuous gas carburizing has grown in favour for efficient high production operations. Sometimes the work is quenched from the carburizing temperature, imposing severe thermal cycles on the furnace hardware which may have to follow the work into a quench bath. Even if quenching is avoided, there is a normal pattern of heating and cooling, setting the stage for thermal fatigue effects. Modern gas carburizing is usually done with a carrier gas, essentially a neutral product of combustion, enriched with a few per cent of methane, natural gas, or similar hydrocarbons. The carburizing potential is further controlled by means of the water vapour content of the gas.

If the carrier gas is very rich in hydrocarbons, these will tend to crack, forming carbon (as soot) and releasing hydrogen. Such sooting is undesirable and if possible is avoided in carburizing by carefully controlling the gas composition. The aim is to have only the equilibrium amount of methane (or other hydrocarbon), with no excess available for cracking. Such gases, nevertheless, are strongly carburizing to ordinary steel parts, and eventually will carburize the Cr–Ni–Fe alloys also. Petrochemical operations, in contrast, may be based on using a large percentage of hydrocarbon, and the sooting or coking that follows can be a normal feature of the process. Eventually coke deposits may so constrict the bore of the tubing used that the coke must be burned out as a maintenance procedure. Tube overheating is possible at this stage.

10.4. *Behaviour in a Sooting Gas*

Fig. 20 shows the behaviour of five alloys: HH, HK at three silicon levels, and HT in a rich mixture that cracked readily and deposited much soot.[6]

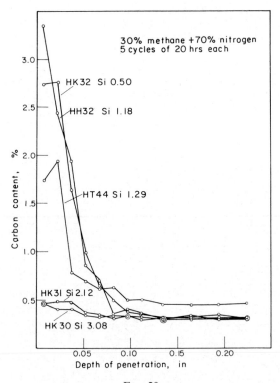

FIG. 20

Heat-resistant alloys carbon penetration after gas carburizing at 1760°F for 100 hr.

Note that silicon exerts a strong effect to inhibit carburization. It is now known that both nickel and silicon aid carburizing resistance, but their relative importance is not always clear. It seems likely that the environmental conditions also play a part in the effect of these elements.

10.5. *A.C.I. Carburizing Tests*

The Alloy Casting Institute sponsored a number of carburizing tests, including an extensive laboratory survey and several field tests.[17] Some 44 specimens exposed for 1000 hr at 1700°F (925°C) in a carrier gas with about 2 per cent methane in general showed very light carburization of the alloys, though the carbon steels were carburized throughout. Three of the alloys, HH29 with 0·30% Si, HH38 with 0·36% Si and HK36 with 0·45% Si showed relatively deep and intense carburization. The high nickel types, HN, HT, HU, HW and HX, were little effected in most cases. Some showed no visible carbon absorption. It is probably significant that two HT alloys with silicon below 1 per cent were more deeply and intensely carburized than the others. The protective effect of silicon on the HH and HK grades was noteworthy also.

These same alloys were placed in field tests, one with continuous and the other intermittent exposure. The results were much the same, but suggested that conditions (especially with the continuous exposure) were milder than in the laboratory.

10.6. *Carburization at* 980°C

Contrast these results, where with silicon above 1 per cent maximum apparent depth affected was 0·090 in., with carburization at 1800°F (980°C) from a carrier gas with 10 per cent methane. These tests were made in the American Brake Shoe Co. Research Centre, with evaluation by means of successive layer cuts (Fig. 21). All of the alloys were affected to a depth of about 0·25 in. and the lower nickel grades picked up as much as 5 per cent carbon at the surface. Nickel appears as a much more potent protector than silicon under these conditions.

10.7. *The Role of Nickel*

From this small assortment of test conditions it can be concluded that the environment has an important effect on alloy ranking. It may even be necessary to match the service conditions almost exactly to achieve a valid laboratory test for some cases. However, industry has developed opinions that are generalized; the important grades are ranked as HH, HT, HU, HW and HX in order of increasing resistance to carburization. This opinion ranking follows the nickel content. It also may be applied to thermal fatigue service, and as carburizing is frequently associated a close relation is not surprising.

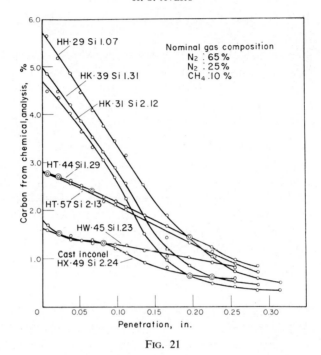

Fig. 21

Carbon penetration after gas carburizing at 1800°F for 1000 hr.

11. CONCLUSION

This paper was prepared primarily to assemble certain information that may be helpful to those who design hydrogen reformer parts or who select and specify the appropriate materials. It incidentally seeks to dispel the idea, if it actually exists, that almost nothing is known about the cast heat-resistant alloys. As a final plea, it is urged that data as precise as possible about the performance of these alloys in service, and the associated environmental conditions, be made available to the manufacturer for correlation with the laboratory data upon which designs are based. Cooperation in this area should place the engineering of high-temperature chemical manufacturing and processing equipment on a sounder basis.

REFERENCES

1. FELLOWS, COOK and AVERY, Precision in creep testing, A.I.M.E. T.P. 1443 (Metals Technology, August 1942), *Trans. A.I.M.E.* **150** (1942), pp. 358–372.
2. C. R. WILKS, Creep and Rupture Test Pyrometry, ASTM Spec. Technical Publication O. 178 (1956).
3. ASTM Recommended Practice for Conducting Creep and Time for Rupture Tension Tests of Materials—E139—58T.
4. H. S. AVERY and MATTHEWS, *Trans. A.S.M.* **38**, 957–1015 (1947).

5. AVERY, COOK and FELLOWS, *Trans. A.I.M.E.* **150**, 373–400 (1942). A.I.M.E. T.P. 1480, Metals Technology, August, 1942.
6. H. S. AVERY and C. R. WILKS, *Trans. A.S.M.* **40**, 529–584 (1948).
7. H. S. AVERY, C. R. WILKS and J. A. FELLOWS, *Trans. A.S.M.* **44**, 57–80 (1952).
8. BRASUNAS, GOW and HARDER, *Proc. A.S.T.M.* **46**, 129–160 (1946).
9. Battelle Memorial Institute, Report No. 24 of Heat Resistant Alloy Research for Alloy Casting Institute (21 Jan. 1946).
10. H. S. AVERY, Estimation of scaling resistance, *Alloy Casting Bulletin* No. 10 (May 1947).
11. J. T. GOW, *Proc. NACE* (1947), *Corrosion*, **3**, No. 6 and No. 7, July and August 1947.
12. LESLIE and FONTANA, *Trans. ASTM*, **41**, 1213–1247 (1949).
13. ROZET, CAMPBELL and THOMAS, *Welding Journal*, **52**, 481–485 (Oct. 1948).
14. CLARK and FREEMAN, *Trans. A.S.M.*, **38**, 148–169 (1947).
15. SCHOEFER and SHIELDS, A.C.I. Data Sheets, Alloy Casting Institute, 1957.
16. N. F. SIMMONS and H. C. CROSS, Report on the Elevated Temperature Properties of Stainless Steels, ASTM Spec. Tech. Pub. No. 124 (1952).
17. Behaviour of Heat Resisting Alloys under Laboratory and Field Carburizing Conditions, Battelle Memorial Institute Report No. 46 to the Alloy Casting Institute, 7 January, 1960.

THE TENSILE PROPERTIES AT ROOM AND ELEVATED TEMPERATURES OF SOME CAST AUSTENITIC STEELS

G. J. Cox

INTRODUCTION

During the past few years cast, austenitic, chromium-nickel steels have won increasing recognition as materials suitable for use under conditions of stress at elevated temperatures. This interest has, however, exposed the sparsity of reliable data on such alloys and has prompted considerable research on their rupture properties and weldability. By contrast, little interest has been taken in the room and elevated temperature tensile properties of the steels.

The tensile properties of these alloys, particularly their tensile ductility at room and elevated temperatures, are, nevertheless, of considerable importance, because in many applications they may be subjected to quite severe tensile stresses, particularly during commissioning or shutting down of plant. The work reported here was undertaken to provide background information on three types of alloys, viz: 18 per cent chromium–37 per cent nickel, 25 per cent chromium–20 per cent nickel and 20 per cent chromium–15 per cent nickel, these being chosen for a study of the effect of varying carbon content on tensile properties at room temperature and in the range 600–1000°C. Tests were made on the materials in the as-cast condition and also after ageing for 1000 hr at 900°C, since it was considered that carbide precipitation at working temperatures was likely to considerably modify the tensile properties.

In order to limit the variables as far as possible, the composition of the 25 per cent chromium–20 per cent nickel alloy was modified in accordance with results of constitutional studies already completed, to ensure that sigma would not form even at the lowest carbon content used.[1]

EXPERIMENTAL PROCEDURE

The steels were made as 100 lb high frequency, basic-induction furnace air melts, using charges consisting of high purity iron, "Mond" nickel pellet and low nitrogen ferro-chromium. Silicon and manganese were added as late furnace additions. Final deoxidation was by means of 0·05 per cent calcium silicide and the metal was poured into green-sand moulds, to produce 9-in. × 1-in. × 1-in. section keel blocks.

After removal of the feeder heads, each keel was quartered longitudinally

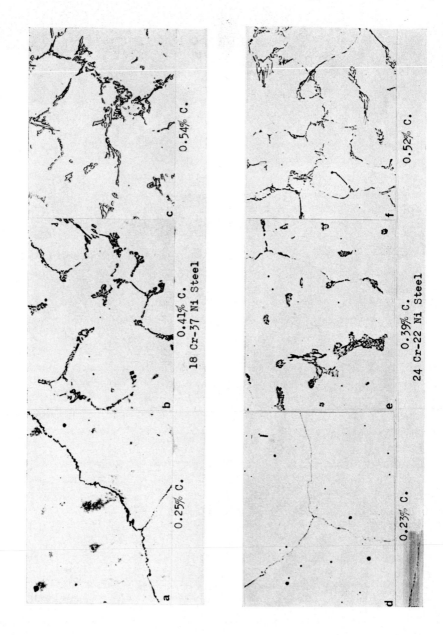

to provide tensile and impact specimen test blanks. The tensile blanks were randomized with respect to their original position in the casting and subsequently 0·252-in. diameter specimens were machined for determination, in duplicate, of as-cast properties at room temperature and at 600°, 700°, 800°, 900° and 1000°C. In the elevated temperature tests the specimens were

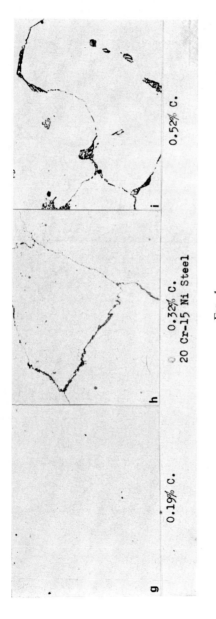

FIG. 1

Microstructures of the as-cast steels (×250). (a) 0·25% C; (b) 0·41% C, (c) 0·54% C 18 Cr–37 Ni steel; (d) 0·23% C, (e) 0·39% C, (f) 0·52% C 24 Cr–22 Ni steel; (g) 0·19% C; (h) 0·32% C, (i) 0·52% C 20 Cr–15 Ni steel.

heated for at least 1 hr at temperature before straining at a rate of 0·001-in./ in./min up to 0·5 per cent strain and then at 0·1-in./in./min to fracture.

Impact tests made at room temperature only, were carried out in duplicate on standard Charpy V-notch specimens taken from the bottom portion of the keels, with the notch machined on the side of the test-piece which had been farthest away from the feeder head. Corresponding tensile and impact tests were carried out on blanks which had been heated in air for 1000 hr at 900°C, to assess the effect of prolonged high temperature exposure on mechanical properties. Selected specimens for microscopical examination

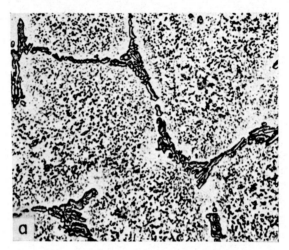

FIG. 2 (a)

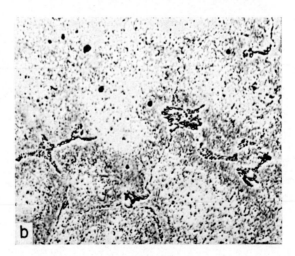

FIG. 2 (b)

were taken from the shank and fracture portions of the broken tensile bars
and these were etched in Murakami's reagent. The grain boundary or interdendritic carbide contents were determined by point counting.

It seemed possible that ageing at different temperatures could, due to the
varying amount, size and distribution of carbide precipitate formed, give
different results to those obtained by ageing at 900°C. To provide further
information on this aspect small samples of each steel were heated at 700°C
for times varying up to 300 hr, and hardness determinations were made, to
provide data for age-hardening curves. Further tensile tests were then made
at room temperature and 600°C, on material which, on the basis of the ageing
tests, would give the maximum hardness for each steel.

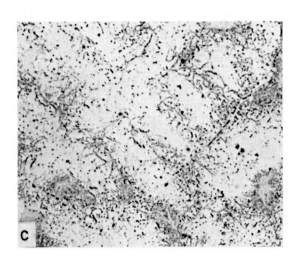

FIG. 2 (c)

FIG. 2

Microstructures after heating for 1000 hr at 900°C ($\times$250). (a) $0\cdot41\%$ C, 18 Cr–
37 Ni steel; (b) $0\cdot39\%$ C, 24 Cr–22 Ni steel; (c) $0\cdot32\%$ C, 20 Cr–15 Ni steel.

EXPERIMENTAL RESULTS

Analyses of the steels examined are given in Table 1, with details of their
microstructures in the as-cast condition and after exposure at 900°C. The
as-cast structures are illustrated in Fig. 1 (a)–(i). The structures of steels
Nos. 2, 5 and 8, after ageing, are shown in Fig. 2 (a), (b) and (c).

All the as-cast low carbon steels together with the medium carbon 20–15
steel (No. 8) were free from interdendritic, eutectic carbide, but they exhibited
varying amounts of grain boundary carbide precipitate, and the low carbon

TABLE 1

Composition and Microstructures of the Steels Examined

Steel no.	Type	Composition %					Microstructure	
		C*	Si	Mn	Cr	Ni	As-cast	After heat-treatment for 1000 hr/900°C
1	18 Cr-37 Ni	0·25	1·15	1·93	18·3	36·0	3% grain boundary C + A†	2% grain boundary C + secondary C + A
2	18 Cr-37 Ni	0·41	1·13	2·08	18·0	35·4	7·5% (interdendritic + grain boundary C) + A	6% (interdendritic + grain boundary C) + secondary C + A
3	18 Cr-37 Ni	0·54	1·16	1·98	17·9	34·5	11·5% (interdendritic + grain boundary C) + A	10% (interdendritic + grain boundary C) + secondary C + A
4	24 Cr-22 Ni	0·23	1·18	1·59	24·1	22·4	1·5% grain boundary C + A	2% grain boundary C + secondary C + A
5	24 Cr-22 Ni	0·39	1·20	1·63	24·5	22·1	7% (interdendritic + grain boundary C) + A	5% (interdendritic C + secondary C) + A
6	24 Cr-22 Ni	0·52	1·24	1·68	24·5	22·6	8% (interdendritic + grain boundary C) + A	7·5% (interdendritic + grain boundary C) + secondary C + A
7	20 Cr-15 Ni	0·19	1·10	1·65	21·2	15·1	<0·5% grain boundary C + A	<0·5% grain boundary C + secondary C + A
8	20 Cr-15 Ni	0·32	1·10	1·60	21·0	15·0	<1% grain boundary C + A	<1% grain boundary C + secondary C + A
9	20 Cr-15 Ni	0·52	1·13	1·55	20·7	14·7	6·5% (interdendritic + grain boundary C) + A	5% (interdendritic + grain boundary C) + secondary C + A

* Mean of two or more analyses.

† C—carbide; A—austenite.

Analysis of selected steels showed that the N content was about 0·015 per cent.

The ranges of sulphur and phosphorus contents in the nine steels tested were 0·009–0·016 per cent and 0·005–0·015 per cent respectively.

18–37 steel (No. 1) also contained isolated colonies of a granular carbide: Fig. 1 (a). Although the carbon contents of the steels were not precisely equivalent it seemed that for a given carbon content the 20–15 alloy was likely to contain less carbide than the 18–37 or 24–22 alloys (Table 1 and Fig. 3).

Results of X-ray examination of carbide extracts taken from steels Nos. 2, 5 and 8 in both the as-cast and the aged condition are given in Table 2. These results taken in conjunction with the corresponding microstructures

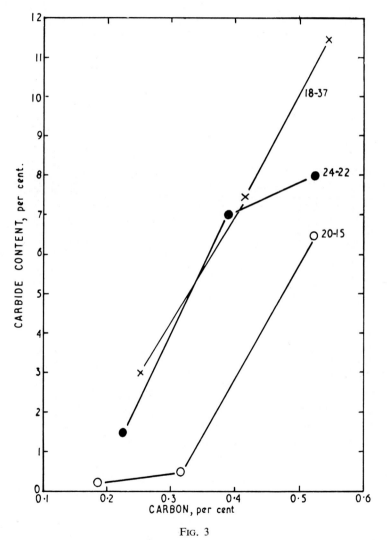

FIG. 3

Relationship between the carbon and carbide contents of the as-cast steels.

indicated that the eutectic carbide was of the M_7C_3 type and that the grain boundary carbide was of the $M_{23}C_6$ type; the latter may therefore have been mainly secondary carbide which had precipitated during slow cooling from the casting temperature. After ageing at 900°C the X-ray results show that the carbide was predominantly of the $M_{23}C_6$ type. Besides precipitation of $M_{23}C_6$ as secondary carbide it is therefore possible that the reaction $M_7C_3 \longrightarrow M_{23}C_6$ may have occurred in some areas and this supposition is supported by the microscopic examination which indicated that ageing caused a slight reduction in the volume-fraction of as-cast carbide.

TABLE 2

Results of X-ray Identification of Carbide Extracts

Steel no.	Type	Type of carbide	
		Steel as-cast	Steel aged 1000 hr at 900°C
2	18 Cr–37 Ni, 0·41 C	M_7C_3	$M_{23}C_6$ + trace M_7C_3
5	24 Cr–22 Ni, 0·39 C	M_7C_3	$M_{23}C_6$ + trace M_7C_3
8	20 Cr–15 Ni, 0·32 C	$M_{23}C_6$ + trace M_7C_3	$M_{23}C_6$

The results of room temperature tensile and impact tests and tensile tests at temperatures in the range 600–1000°C in the as-cast condition are given in Table 3. Irrespective of test temperature, increasing the carbon content over the range studied had no consistent effect upon the ultimate tensile strength or the 0·1 per cent proof stress values of the as-cast steels but at test temperatures below about 700°C high carbon significantly reduced the tensile ductility values. At higher temperatures carbon had no significant effect on ductility except that the low carbon 24–22 steel (No. 4) exhibited unexpectedly low values. Room temperature impact properties were also reduced by increasing carbon: see Fig. 4.

The results of mechanical tests on samples aged at 900°C are presented in Table 4 which show the effect of both carbon content and test temperature upon the properties. Increasing the carbon content again had little effect upon the tensile and proof strength, although there was an indication that the strength of the 20–15 alloy was raised by increasing its carbon content. Increase of carbon lowered tensile ductility at temperatures below 700°C and impact values at room temperature were also adversely affected by carbon. The low carbon 24–22 steel again gave unexpectedly poor elongation values at higher temperatures; however, they were high enough to give little concern.

Ageing in general slightly raised the tensile strength of the alloys at all test temperatures but at test temperatures below about 700°C the tensile ductility values of most of the steels was impaired and often to a very marked extent. Steels 1, 4 and 8 did not exhibit a significant ductility loss nor were the room temperature impact values of these steels impaired as a result of ageing.

TABLE 3

Mechanical Properties of the Steels, as-cast, at Room and Elevated Temperature

Steel no.	Type	Room temperature						Test temperature °C														
								600				700				800			900			1000		
		U.T.S. tsi	0.1% P.S. tsi	El. %	R.A. %	Impact ft/lb	Hardness V.P.N.	U.T.S. tsi	0.1% P.S. tsi	El. %	R.A. %	U.T.S. tsi	0.1% P.S. tsi	El. %	R.A. % ‡	U.T.S. tsi	0.1% P.S. tsi	El. %	U.T.S. tsi	0.1% P.S. tsi	El. %	U.T.S. tsi	0.1% P.S. tsi	El. %
1	18 Cr-37 Ni, 0.25 C	31.8 / 28.6	13.9 / 13.3	16.9 / 12.4	14.8 / 18.4	10.9 / 12.3	159	21.7 / 23.6	8.3 / 8.2	16.9 / 22.5	25.4 / 26.6	23.0 / 21.0	8.6 / 7.8	16.9 / 16.9	28.7 / 21.2	15.4 / 15.0	6.8 / 7.6	34.9 / 39.3	8.7 / 8.5	4.2 / 4.3	40.4 / 41.6	6.0 / 6.2	3.2 / 3.3	32.6 / 49.5
2	18 Cr-37 Ni, 0.41 C	29.0 / 29.5	12.1 / 12.0	18.0 / 16.9	11.8 / 12.6	13.0 / 9.8	156	19.5 / 22.3	8.4 / 8.4	12.4 / 18.0	31.4 / 26.0	21.5 / 20.7	8.1 / 7.8	18.0 / 18.0	31.0 / 25.0	13.0 / 14.0	7.9 / 7.3	34.9 / 38.2	9.8 / 8.5	4.9 / 4.1	42.7 / 37.1	5.7 / 5.9	2.9 / 2.5	51.7 / <0.5†
3	18 Cr-37 Ni, 0.54 C	28.2 / 28.6	12.9 / 12.3	11.2 / 11.2	19.6 / 11.8	6.5 / 6.5	160	20.6 / 20.5	8.7 / 8.7	13.5 / 11.2	17.0 / 16.2	19.1 / 19.7	8.2 / 8.6	10.1 / 11.3	19.7 / 11.8	16.3 / 14.2	6.4 / 6.4	28.1 / 28.1	9.5 / 9.7	4.7 / 4.0	33.4 / 39.4	5.9 / 6.2	2.7 / 2.6	37.2 / 39.4
4	24 Cr-22 Ni, 0.23 C	31.8 / 30.6	13.6 / 13.5	24.8 / 25.8	20.4 / 24.4	18.8 / 19.5	157	17.5 / 22.3	7.3 / 7.7	21.4 / 24.8	31.4 / 24.6	18.8 / 18.0	7.9 / 7.3	14.5 / 18.0	22.6 / 21.2	15.2 / 14.5	7.5 / 7.3	12.4 / 14.7	9.3 / 9.0	4.2 / 3.9	21.4 / 24.8	6.4 / 6.0	2.9 / 3.0	34.8 / 27.0
5	24 Cr-22 Ni, 0.39 C	30.4 / 30.0	14.1 / 13.9	19.1 / 19.1	15.4 / 16.2	10.9 / 9.4	164	21.5 / 22.5	7.8 / 8.0	15.7 / 20.2	22.6 / 24.6	21.7 / 21.4	8.5 / 8.5	16.9 / 18.0	21.2 / 24.6	15.3 / 15.5	8.1 / 8.2	34.9 / 29.2	11.1 / 10.2	4.3 / 4.1	41.6 / 40.7	6.6 / 7.3	3.1 / 3.7	47.2 / 43.9
6	24 Cr-22 Ni, 0.52 C	30.6 / 28.6	13.0 / 13.1	14.6 / 11.2	10.2 / 8.6	6.5 / 5.8	169	21.5 / 22.0	8.2 / 8.3	13.5 / 14.6	20.4 / 19.1	21.5 / 21.1	8.4 / 7.9	14.5 / 18.0	31.4 / 23.0	14.6 / 15.6	7.6 / 7.3	36.0 / 33.7	8.9 / 10.3	4.2 / 4.7	39.4 / 42.7	6.3 / 7.0	2.9 / 3.1	54.0 / 42.7
7	20 Cr-15 Ni, 0.19 C	32.2 / 32.2	12.1 / 12.0	55.0 / 55.0	49.2 / 45.0	134.0 / 120.0	140	22.4 / 22.3	6.3 / 6.0	40.5 / 46.1	48.6 / 59.1	17.3 / 18.7	6.2 / 5.8	—† / 33.8	—† / 45.6	13.1 / 13.1	6.7 / 7.0	30.4 / 37.1	9.2 / 8.9	3.5 / 3.8	54.0 / 37.1	3.9 / 4.3	1.8 / 1.9	—§ / —§
8	20 Cr-15 Ni, 0.32 C	32.4 / 32.0	14.8 / 15.0	25.8 / 21.4	13.8 / 18.1	15.2 / 25.5	159	23.4 / 24.3	7.7 / 7.7	23.6 / 21.4	29.4 / 31.9	20.3 / 20.4	8.1 / 7.7	14.5 / 16.9	21.2 / 25.7	15.4 / 14.0	7.5 / 7.7	22.5 / 23.6	8.6 / 8.0	3.9 / 4.0	31.5 / 31.5	5.5 / 5.5	2.6 / 2.6	49.5 / 51.7
9	20 Cr-15 Ni, 0.52 C	32.8 / 32.6	16.0 / 16.2	14.6 / 18.0	12.3 / 12.6	10.4 / 8.7	175	20.5 / 25.9	8.6 / 8.7	12.4 / 19.1	36.0 / 33.4	23.6 / 22.8	8.9 / 9.2	18.0 / 15.8	24.1 / 17.9	16.3 / 16.3	8.3 / 8.8	25.8 / 31.5	8.4 / 8.6	3.9 / 4.1	56.2 / 43.8	6.6 / 6.0	2.8 / 2.8	65.2 / 60.7

* Elongation values were measured on a gauge length of $4\sqrt{A}$

† Fractured outside the gauge marks.

‡ Above 700°C the R.A. figures were rendered inconsistent by the fracture type.

§ Elongation values not obtainable because of fracture characteristics.

Consideration of the above results suggested that the ductility of the alloys is mainly related to the amount of carbide initially present irrespective of whether this is of the grain-boundary or eutectic type and, at any given carbon level, the content of carbide varies appreciably according to the composition of the base metal. To demonstrate these relationships the

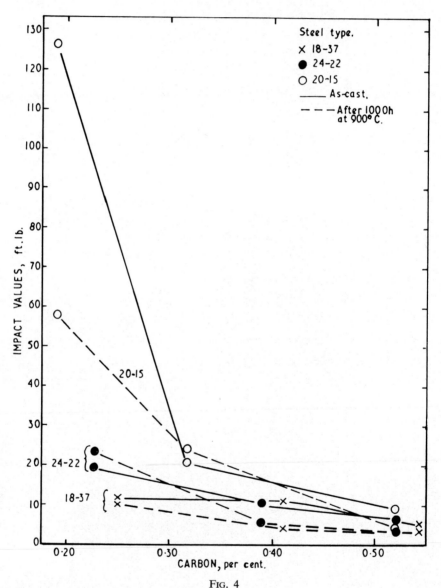

Fig. 4

Impact properties of the steels.

TABLE 4

Mechanical Properties of the Steels at Room and Elevated Temperatures after Heating for 1000 hr at 900°C

| Steel no. | Type | Room temperature | | | | | | Test temperature °C | | | | | | | | | | | | | | | | | |
| | | U.T.S. tsi | 0.1% P.S. tsi | El. % | R.A. % | Impact ft/lb | Hardness V.P.N. | 600 | | | | 700 | | | | 800 | | | 900 | | | 1000 | | |
								U.T.S. tsi	0.1% P.S. tsi	El. %	R.A. %	U.T.S. tsi	0.1% P.S. tsi	El. %	R.A. % †	U.T.S. tsi	0.1% P.S. tsi	El. %	U.T.S. tsi	0.1% P.S. tsi	El. %	U.T.S. tsi	0.1% P.S. tsi	El. %
1	18 Cr–37 Ni, 0.25 C	28.8 30.4	15.3 14.4	5.6 11.3	5.8 16.2	9.4 11.2	171	28.0 27.2	10.9 —	12.4 13.5	15.4 16.1	23.0 23.0	10.1 9.4	23.6 16.9	30.6 33.0	14.5 15.7	8.5 8.2	31.4 34.8	8.7 9.3	4.0 3.6	47.2 34.8	5.9 6.1	2.9 2.4	50.5 45.0
2	18 Cr–37 Ni, 0.41 C	30.4 31.0	15.5 14.8	5.6 5.6	7.2 7.9	5.1 3.6	184	26.4 26.9	11.3 11.2	9.0 9.0	8.8 11.0	23.5 24.0	10.3 10.0	14.6 14.6	17.0 19.8	16.4 15.9	9.4 8.9	24.7 28.1	10.1 9.6	4.3 4.1	37.1 39.4	6.0 6.7	3.1 3.1	48.4 38.2
3	18 Cr–37 Ni, 0.54 C	30.8 30.0	14.0 14.6	4.5 7.9	5.0 1.6	3.6 3.6	196	26.2 25.8	11.1 11.4	9.0 7.9	7.2 8.8	24.6 23.9	10.5 10.5	7.9 9.0	15.4 11.8	17.1 17.3	9.2 9.6	20.2 22.5	11.2 11.3	4.3 4.2	39.2 36.0	7.3 6.8	2.9 2.6	33.7 43.8
4	24 Cr–22 Ni, 0.23 C	38.6 37.9	13.7 13.4	22.5 23.6	21.8 28.0	23.2 23.2	175	27.5 26.8	8.9 8.6	24.8 15.7	34.6 23.2	23.4 22.2	8.0 7.7	16.9 21.4	32.0 39.0	15.3 15.4	7.5 7.2	23.6 24.7	10.0 10.2	3.8 3.8	28.1 25.8	7.5 6.0	3.7 3.7	27.0 43.8
5	24 Cr–22 Ni, 0.39 C	34.8 32.0	16.2 14.6	>7.9* >3.4	11.0 4.2	5.4 5.1	192	29.5 28.2	11.3 10.4	12.4 3.4	14.8 8.6	24.8 24.4	9.8 9.8	22.5 18.0	27.4 27.8	18.1 15.9	9.2 7.0	30.4 34.8	10.7 11.0	5.1 4.3	34.8 49.4	6.8 6.2	3.1 2.9	42.7 41.6
6	24 Cr–22 Ni, 0.52 C	35.2 33.3	16.8 16.5	4.5 4.8	5.0 4.0	2.9 3.3	201	29.0 28.0	12.4 12.1	10.1 6.7	7.7 9.6	25.4 25.4	11.1 10.5	16.9 14.6	27.4 14.1	17.5 18.0	6.7 7.1	27.0 12.4	12.5 11.7	4.2 4.2	36.0 51.6	7.0 7.1	3.0 3.0	46.0 32.6
7	20 Cr–15 Ni, 0.19 C	35.3 34.5	11.6 11.2	34.8 40.5	40.8 47.0	57.5 58.0	155	25.9 22.8	7.7 7.0	28.1 28.1	35.2 48.0	19.1 17.8	6.4 6.0	28.1 31.5	48.0 56.8	12.4 12.1	4.8	28.1 28.1	8.7 8.4	3.3 3.3	37.1 39.4	4.8 5.0	1.9 1.8	38.2 57.4
8	20 Cr–15 Ni, 0.32 C	38.0 38.4	14.4 13.6	18.0 24.7	16.2 40.0	25.3 24.0	181	27.4 26.9	9.6 8.6	28.1 21.4	38.4 35.2	20.7 21.2	8.0 7.7	27.0 30.4	37.8 40.2	15.0 13.9	5.9 5.5	24.7 39.4	9.7 9.2	3.8 3.6	37.1 34.8	5.9 5.9	2.6 2.4	23.6 32.6
9	20 Cr–15 Ni, 0.52 C	35.0 34.3	15.9 14.6	7.9 10.1	5.6 8.0	4.3 4.3	205	29.5 28.4	10.9 10.7	14.6 10.1	16.2 10.1	23.0 23.0	9.7 9.2	28.1 21.4	33.4 27.4	17.0 15.6	7.0 6.2	28.1 34.8	11.1 11.0	4.5 4.4	41.6 43.8	6.7 6.5	3.1 3.2	39.4 50.5

* Fractured outside gauge mark, plotted as 7.9% in Fig. 5.

† Above 700°C the R.A. figures were rendered inconsistent by the fracture type.

measured carbide contents were plotted against room temperature, percentage elongation and impact values for each of the steels in the as-cast and in the aged condition, Fig. 5. The plots indicate that the ductility of all these base compositions is closely similar, and substantiate the view that carbide content is the overriding factor determining both tensile ductility and impact resistance.

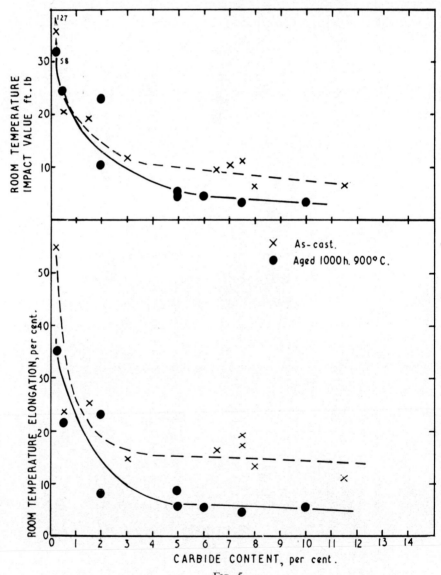

Fig. 5

Effect of carbide content on the room temperature elongation and impact values of the three types of steel.

A selection of the fractured tensile test pieces as-cast and aged were microscopically examined. In alloys containing eutectic carbide the fractures were mainly interdendritic and appeared to have followed these carbides. The fracture path in the alloys which contained only grain-boundary carbides also followed the carbide networks (Fig. 6), and it may be that the high ductility shown by these materials after ageing is associated with a slight agglomeration of these carbides. There was no evidence of multiple secondary intergranular cracking in the aged samples of any of the steels such as is reported to occur in wrought austenitic steels of low ductility.[2]

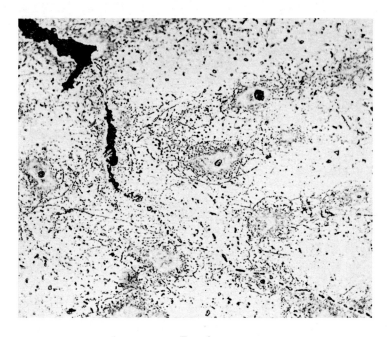

FIG. 6

Subsidiary tensile fracture in 0·32% C, 20 Cr–15 Ni steel tested at 800°C after ageing 1000 hr at 900°C (×400).

Hardness-time curves determined for each of the alloys aged at 700°C are shown in Fig. 7 (a), (b) and (c). Despite the hardness changes secondary carbide did not precipitate in any of the steels before about 100 hr heating, although in some of the steels carbide precipitate occurred after heating for only 1 hr at 900°C (i.e. microscopical examination of the tensile specimens of the as-cast steels). The results of tensile tests at room temperature and at 600°C on samples aged to peak hardness at 700°C are given in Table 5. There was no significant difference between values for these specimens and

TABLE 5

Mechanical Properties of the Steels at Room Temperature and 600°C after Various Heat Treatments at 700°C

Steel no.	Type	Heat treatment	Room temperature properties					Properties at 600°C			
			U.T.S. tsi	0·1% P.S. tsi	Elong. %	R.A. %	Hardness V.P.N.	U.T.S. tsi	0·1% P.S. tsi	Elong. %	R.A. %
1	18 Cr-37 Ni, 0·25 C	25 hr at 700°C	38·3 / 36·2	17·9 / 16·9	9·0 / 7·9	8·8 / 8·0	203	29·4 / 30·0	12·4 / 12·6	20·2 / 19·1	26·0 / 19·0
2	18 Cr-37 Ni, 0·41 C	8 hr at 700°C	36·2 / 32·2	17·6 / 17·1	9·0 / 7·9	9·6 / 7·0	206	29·3 / 29·6	12·8 / 13·6	12·4 / 13·5	8·8 / 14·8
3	18 Cr-37 Ni, 0·54 C	25 hr at 700°C	34·1 / 33·2	15·6 / 16·2	7·9 / 5·6	7·0 / 5·2	196	27·8 / 27·3	12·4 / 12·9	11·2 / 9·0	16·7 / 7·8
4	24 Cr-22 Ni, 0·23 C	8 hr at 700°C	39·3 / 38·8	18·3 / 17·4	14·6 / 14·6	11·0 / 18·4	195	29·2 / 28·6	16·6 / 12·0	18·0 / 16·9	21·8 / 16·2
5	24 Cr-22 Ni, 0·39 C	8 hr at 700°C	37·0	18·2	10·1	8·8	208	30·7 / 29·4	14·2 / 13·0	15·7 / 11·2	15·3 / 11·7
6	24 Cr-22 Ni, 0·52 C	8 hr at 700°C	36·1 / 38·2	17·7 / 19·2	7·9 / 6·7	7·1 / 8·0	218	28·4 / 29·2	13·8 / 14·3	12·4 / 10·1	11·0 / 10·2
7	20 Cr-15 Ni, 0·19 C	25 hr at 700°C	39·8 / 40·2	15·8 / 14·9	46·1 / 47·2	37·8 / 34·6	165	27·5 / 27·9	8·9 / 8·9	30·3 / 26·9	30·8 / 32·1
8	20 Cr-15 Ni, 0·32 C	25 hr at 700°C	42·5 / 43·6	17·4 / 16·9	14·6 / 16·9	13·2 / 12·6	213	28·5 / 29·1	11·2 / 11·9	15·7 / 15·7	18·5 / 17·6
9	20 Cr-15 Ni, 0·52 C	8 hr at 700°C	41·7 / 40·8	21·5 / 19·3	7·9 / —	5·6 / 7·0	232	30·4 / 31·2	13·3 / 13·7	15·7 / 14·6	15·9 / 15·4

for those samples aged at 900°C. The effects of ageing on tensile and impact properties may thus be considered as quite general. A reasonable correlation was obtained between the elongation values and hardness of the steels, Fig. 8.

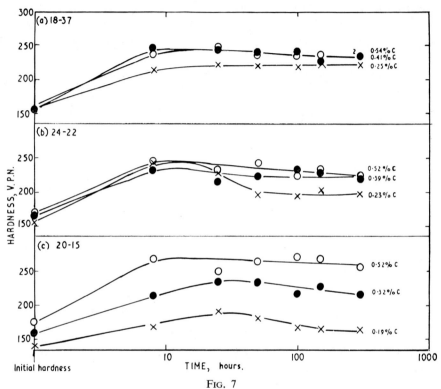

FIG. 7

Age-hardening response of the steels at 700°C.

DISCUSSION

The investigation reported has shown that for the chromium-nickel steels examined, the tensile ductility at temperatures below 700°C, and the room temperature impact resistance are strongly dependent on the carbon and hence the carbide content of the alloys. Although ageing has a general adverse effect on the ductility of the alloys containing higher carbon, it would appear that the main cause of poor elongation and impact values is the occurrence of eutectic carbide. In applications where the above properties are of prime importance, therefore, the carbon content should be limited to lower levels than are normally found in current commercially-made cast alloys of this type, e.g. 0·30–0·45 per cent.

The results of this work do not permit clear definition of the maximum carbon content that can be tolerated before serious loss of ductility occurs. It is apparent, however, that the maximum acceptable carbon content is different for each of the materials examined. As would be expected, from consideration of the solubilities of carbon in austenitic iron and in nickel at the respective eutectic temperatures,[3] the carbon level above which the ductility of 20–15 alloy is markedly impaired is higher than that for 24–22 steel, which in turn is higher than that for the 18–37 alloy. In this context

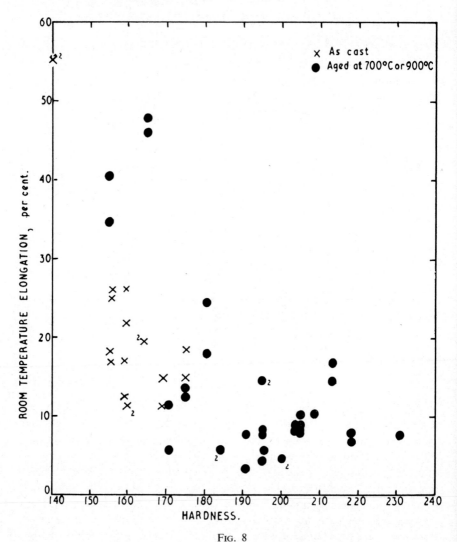

Fig. 8

Relationship between elongation and hardness values of the steels.

TABLE 6

Tensile Properties of Commercially-made Centri-cast 18 per cent Chromium–37 per cent nickel steels at Room and Elevated Temperatures

Description of steel	Composition %					Room temperature properties								Properties at 650°C, Aged 120 hr at 650°C		
						As-cast				Aged 120 hr at 650°C						
	C	Si	Mn	Cr	Ni	U.T.S. tsi	Elong. %	R.A. %	Hardness V.P.N.	U.T.S. tsi	Elong. %	R.A. %	Hardness V.P.N.	U.T.S. tsi	Elong. %	R.A. %
18 Cr–37 Ni, low C	0·12	0·82	0·71	19·0	34·2	30·8 30·4	62·0 58·5	54·0 56·8	118	37·2	36·0	38·4	190	23·8 23·4	41·6 34·8	45·0 46·8
18 Cr–37 Ni medium C	0·31	1·20	0·32	18·7	38·5	32·2 31·4	21·4 22·5	21·8 19·8	168	43·6 42·6	11·2 11·2	7·9 10·1	245	30·6 30·3	18·0 16·8	21·2 17·0

it is of interest to present some results on commercially produced centrifugally cast 18–37 alloys of low- and medium-carbon contents, Table 6. Although the ageing treatments applied are not strictly comparable with those used in the current work, it will be seen that the alloy containing 0·31 per cent carbon gave only slightly superior ductility values to the statically cast laboratory-made materials. The ductility of the low carbon commercially-produced material was, however, significantly better than any of the higher carbon statically-cast materials, which gives further indication that, providing carbon content is appropriately controlled, the three steels will show similar properties.

Obviously chromium will also have a similar effect upon the solubility of carbon in austenite but the effect will be less potent because there is less variation in chromium content than in nickel content among the alloys investigated.

It will be appreciated of course that many factors other than ductility, e.g. weldability, rupture strength, oxidation resistance, and resistance to carburization affect selection of an alloy for a specific application. It is considered, however, that the types examined are representative of the complete range of heat-resisting steels now available, and that the 20–15 alloy which is a comparatively new material represents a useful addition to this range.

CONCLUSIONS

1. The room and elevated temperature tensile strengths of 18 per cent chromium–37 per cent nickel, 24 per cent chromium–22 per cent nickel and 20 per cent chromium–15 per cent nickel cast austenitic steels in the as-cast or aged conditions are not significantly affected by variation in carbon content over the range 0·19–0·54 per cent. Tensile ductility values at test temperatures up to about 700°C, however, are markedly impaired by increasing carbon content so that some of the steels exhibit undesirably low ductility. At test temperatures above 700°C carbon exerts no significant effect upon tensile ductility. Room temperature impact values were also impaired by high carbon.

2. The tensile ductility at room and moderately elevated temperatures and room temperature impact resistance of the steels are closely related to the initial carbide content of the microstructure. Eutectic carbide has an adverse effect on ductility but the carbon content at which this phase appears in the microstructure varies for the three different base compositions examined, being lower for the 18 per cent chromium–37 per cent nickel and 24 per cent chromium–22 per cent nickel alloys than for 20 per cent chromium–15 per cent nickel steel.

3. Prior ageing generally reduces tensile ductility at temperatures below 700°C and room temperature impact values, although the low carbon alloys were not seriously affected.

ACKNOWLEDGMENT

The author is indebted to International Nickel Limited for permission to publish this paper.

REFERENCES

1. G. J. Cox and D. E. Jordan, ICI Symposium, October 1964.
2. J. Myers, *Brit. Weld. J.*, **9**, 106–14, 1962.
3. M. Hansen, *Constitution of Binary Alloys*, McGraw-Hill, 1958.

THE PROPERTIES OF CAST 25 PER CENT CHROMIUM–20 PER CENT NICKEL AUSTENITIC STEELS IN RELATION TO THEIR USE AT ELEVATED TEMPERATURES

G. J. Cox and D. E. Jordan

INTRODUCTION

Two major petrochemical processes which depend for their success on the performance of materials at high temperatures are catalytic steam reforming of hydrocarbons and steam cracking of hydrocarbons for ethylene production. In recent years centrifugally cast 25 per cent chromium–20 per cent nickel steel (A.C.I. alloy HK) has come into extensive use for high-pressure reformer catalyst tubes, and centrifugally cast tubes of the same material have been selected for a number of steam cracking installations in Europe, replacing wrought material in the interests of lower initial cost. In addition, statically-cast 25–20 is extensively used in high-temperature petrochemical furnaces, for return bends and tube supports.

With modern reformer design retention of room-temperature ductility in the catalyst tubes after service exposure at high temperatures has not been generally considered as of major importance. A few brittle failures of reformer tubes have occurred during start-up or shut-down, but these have usually involved parts made in non-standard steels of compositions notoriously prone to sigma formation. Cast 25–20 has also been used for reformer outlet headers, tube supports, ethylene furnace outlet castings and return bends, and failures of the steel in these applications have occurred more frequently and have been usually attributed to embrittlement caused by formation of sigma phase or by excessive precipitation of secondary carbides, and it is thus obvious that the use of very brittle materials must be avoided. Although many investigators have studied sigma formation in wrought steels [1–9] having very low carbon contents, little data has been published on higher-carbon cast alloys. [10–12]

In view of trends to higher reforming pressure, rupture strength has become a most important design criterion for tubes. Nevertheless, few long-term rupture results are available [13] although these have been taken to indicate that high carbon steels give markedly better stress-rupture strength than low carbon materials. Accordingly most specifications call for steels having carbon contents in the range 0·3–0·45 per cent. However, whilst high-carbon steels are not so prone to sigma formation as the lower-carbon types, they may be severely embrittled by excessive secondary carbide-precipitation.

It has been fairly widely recognized that, apart from important factors which influence the weldability of austenitic cast steels (e.g. melting procedure, deoxidation practice and grain-size[14]), the interrelated effect of carbon and silicon on the tendency to hot cracking of welds[15] in wrought material, might also be applicable to the weldability of castings. This has generally been accepted and taken into account by foundries, but recently there have been some cases of severe cracking of the heat-affected zones of centrifugally cast pipes which might have been avoided by closer observation of this compositional factor. It was, therefore, clear that this aspect merited further investigation.

The object of the work now reported was, firstly, to provide general background data, and, secondly, to find a composition range which, without the need for special alloying additions, would give a useful compromise of retention of ductility after heating, high-temperature strength, and weldability. Statically-cast test blocks were used in this investigation but it is believed that the results will be essentially applicable to the commercially important centricast forms. This paper must be regarded as only a progress report since, in the time available, it has not proved possible to complete the tests needed to cover all the aspects involved.

I. EFFECT OF COMPOSITION ON STRUCTURAL STABILITY

Table 1 shows the compositions used for study of the effects of carbon, silicon, manganese and nickel on the structural stability of steels containing nominally 25 per cent chromium. The steels were made as 100-lb high-frequency basic induction furnace air melts, using high-purity iron, "Mond" nickel pellets and low-nitrogen ferro-chromium. No deoxidation was carried out except for that provided by late furnace additions of silicon and manganese. Two carbon levels, 0·25 per cent (steels 1–12) and 0·45 per cent (steels 13–24) were studied, and at each carbon level the effect of 20, 22 and 24 per cent of nickel, 1·0 and 2·0 per cent of silicon, and 1·75 and 2·5 per cent of manganese was investigated. Two further steels, nominally 20 per cent chromium–15 per cent nickel and containing, respectively, 0·18 and 0·28 per cent carbon, were included for comparison. The melts were poured at 1550°C into green-sand moulds to give 12-in. × 7-in. × 1-in. plates.

Samples of each of the steels were aged for 4000 hr at temperatures of 700°, 750°, 800°, 850°, 900° and 950°C, for microscopical examination, and since the facilities were available a further set of specimens was left for 8000 hr at 900°C. Impact-test blanks were treated for 4000 hr at 800°C, and unnotched

TABLE 1 — Composition, Impact Values and Hardness of the Steels

Steel no.	Composition %*					Properties, as-cast					Properties after exposure for 4000 hr at 800°C			
	C	Si	Mn	Ni	Cr	Impact, ft/lb 1	2	3†	Mean	Hardness V.P.N.	Impact, ft/lb 1	2	Mean	Hardness V.P.N.
1	0·22	1·20	1·77	20·4	25·1	44·5	55·7	56·0	52·1	155	10·8	13·8	12·3	174
2	0·24	1·16	1·71	22·4	24·3	57·2	63·8	38·5	53·2	157	38·0	23·2	30·6	185
3	0·24	1·15	1·80	24·0	24·5	37·6	35·2	42·0	38·3	163	24·0	32·5	28·2	189
4	0·24	1·17	2·48	20·7	25·3	—			63·0‡	160	9·1	7·2	8·1	184
5	0·22	1·19	2·51	23·2	23·8	47·2	95·8	51·0	64·7	154	81·0	90·0	85·0	175
6	0·24	1·10	2·46	24·4	25·0	37·3	37·3	50·0	41·5	158	21·0	30·5	25·7	187
7	0·24	2·11	1·73	20·9	25·9	22·7	35·5	19·0	25·7	170	2·9	2·2	2·5	254
8	0·24	2·13	1·72	22·8	25·7	31·5	15·2	23·5	23·4	153	2·9	2·9	2·9	251
9	0·23	1·98	1·70	24·9	25·7	23·8	20·3	26·0	23·4	165	5·1	3·6	4·3	244
10	0·23	2·07	2·43	20·8	25·7	39·2	41·2	28·5	36·3	171	3·6	3·6	3·6	270
11	0·24	2·04	2·41	22·5	26·0	18·1	22·4	24·0	21·5	167	2·9	2·9	2·9	260
12	0·21	2·03	2·45	25·2	25·2	15·2	19·5	19·5	18·1	172	3·6	4·3	3·9	228
13	0·47	1·15	1·77	19·8	25·0	18·1	18·1	18·5	18·2	170	10·8	10·1	10·4	209
14	0·45	1·20	1·78	21·6	24·6	21·0	28·3	22·5	23·9	170	13·8	12·6	13·2	195
15	0·44	1·20	1·82	24·0	24·5	23·9	30·4	22·5	25·6	172	10·8	12·6	11·7	196
16	0·43	1·20	2·24	18·6	24·9	42·0	26·0	11·5	26·5	172	8·7	10·8	9·7	223
17	0·44	1·15	2·21	21·9	25·0	17·0	29·0	11·5	19·2	170	13·0	15·9	14·4	200
18	0·44	1·20	2·22	24·6	24·6	25·3	29·0	22·5	25·6	163	10·8	13·0	11·9	200
19	0·43	2·08	1·69	21·0	25·6	34·7	42·0	57·5	44·7	173	8·0	6·9	7·4	233
20	0·44	1·99	1·75	23·0	25·4	30·2	39·8	36·5	35·5	175	8·7	8·0	8·3	211
21	0·39	2·12	1·71	25·0	25·3	37·3	37·3	33·0	35·9	169	10·1	10·5	10·3	210
22	0·42	2·09	2·51	20·7	25·1	35·4	33·2	39·5	36·0	180	5·4	7·2	6·3	226
23	0·40	2·05	2·45	22·5	24·9	30·0	49·6	35·5	38·3	164	8·0	7·2	7·6	209
24	0·41	2·19	2·57	24·9	25·3	37·0	35·4	34·0	35·5	170	8·7	8·0	8·3	215
25	0·18	0·97	1·23	15·1	20·7	207·0	207·0	—	207·0	138	182·0	184·0	183·0	154
26	0·28	1·05	1·57	15·2	20·8	121·0	99·3	—	110·1	164	100·0	83·0	91·5	160

* Analysis of selected steels indicated that the S content was about 0·01%, P 0·01%, N₂ 0·02%.

† Where three tests were made specimens 1 and 2 were cut from the bottom of the plate and No. 3 from the side.

‡ This steel was used for preliminary tests: the value shown is the mean of ten tests.

impact tests were carried out on both the as-cast and aged steels. An unnotched specimen was used because preliminary tests on high-carbon steels
had indicated that the notched test specimen would not be sufficiently
discriminating. In these and all subsequent tests the position of the impact
bar and the direction of testing relative to the original casting, were standardized. The specimens for microscopical examination were first etched
electrolytically in 10 per cent oxalic acid and then by immersion in Murakami's
reagent at ambient temperature. Sigma contents were estimated by a point-
counting technique.

The as-cast microstructures consisted of excess carbide in a matrix of
austenite, the main difference among the steels being the distribution and
larger proportion of carbide present in the higher-carbon types: see Figs. 1
and 2. In the low-carbon 25 per cent chromium–20 per cent nickel alloys

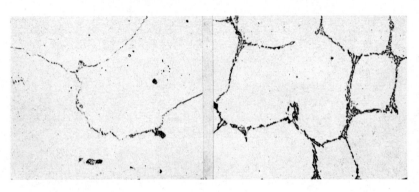

| FIG. 1 | FIG. 2 |
| Steel no. 7, as-cast ($\times 200$). | Steel no. 13, as-cast ($\times 200$). |

some of the carbide took the form of a fine granular precipitate existing as
discrete colonies whilst the remainder appeared as a grain boundary network.
In the higher carbon steels the carbides were clearly of the eutectic type and
were distributed as interdendritic networks. X-ray examination of extracts
from selected steels showed that the major proportion of the carbide present
in the low-carbon series was of the $M_{23}C_6$ type and this may have precipitated
at the grain boundaries on cooling from casting. In the high-carbon series the
carbides were of the M_7C_3 type.

The results of the impact tests are given in Table 1 and Table 2 shows the
results of the sigma counts.

In the as-cast materials a rather wide scatter of impact values was obtained
but the results indicated that raising the carbon level of the 1 per cent silicon
steels lowered the room temperature impact resistance. Raising the silicon
content of the low carbon series of steels also lowered impact toughness.

Microscopic examination showed that both of these results could be attributed to increased carbide contents. However, somewhat inexplicably these trends were reversed in the higher carbon steels and the 2 per cent silicon steels. The as-cast properties of these steels are, however, of little practical importance, since they are drastically changed by even brief exposure at elevated temperatures.

TABLE 2

Sigma Formation and Oxidation Resistance of Steels Exposed at Elevated Temperatures

Steel no.	Percentage sigma after exposure at various temperatures							Percentage weight loss after exposure at 950°C
	700°C 4000 hr	750°C 4000 hr	800°C 4000 hr	850°C 4000 hr	900°C 4000 hr	900°C 8000 hr	950°C 4000 hr	
1	1·0	2·5	3·0	1·0	1·0	1·0	N.D.	0·57
2	<1·0	1·0	1·0	N.D.	3·5	N.D.	N.D.	0·43
3	<1·0	1·0	3·0	N.D.	N.D.	N.D.	N.D.	0·49
4	4·0	7·0	7·0	3·0	5·0	4·0	N.D.	0·74
5	N.D.	<1·0	N.D.	N.D.	N.D.	N.D.	N.D.	0·45
6	1·0	2·5	4·5	N.D.	<1·0	4·0	N.D.	0·63
7	18·5	34·0	32·0	22·0	17·0	22·0	5·5	0·25
8	22·0	32·5	30·0	12·0	18·0	19·5	4·0	0·31
9	25·0	27·0	29·0	15·0	10·0	9·0	2·0	0·31
10	24·0	34·0	33·0	21·0	21·0	16·0	12·0	0·30
11	24·0	30·0	18·5	20·0	24·0	15·0	17·5	0·25
12	20·0	26·0	21·0	11·0	7·5	7·0	N.D.	0·16
13	1·0	2·0	1·5	N.D.	1·0	N.D.	N.D.	0·81
14	N.D.	N.D.	<1·0	N.D.	N.D.	N.D.	N.D.	0·69
15	N.D.	N.D.	<1·0	N.D.	N.D.	N.D.	N.D.	1·10
16	N.D.	7·0	5·0	N.D.	N.D.	<1·0	N.D.	2·30
17	3·0	9·0	N.D.	N.D.	<1·0	<1·0	N.D.	0·97
18	N.D.	8·0	<1·0	N.D.	<1·0	N.D.	N.D.	0·98
19	4·5	7·5	8·0	1·5	<1·0	2·0	N.D.	0·30
20	10·0	<1·0	3·5	3·0	N.D.	<1·0	N.D.	0·36
21	8·0	<1·0	4·0	1·5	<1·0	2·5	N.D.	0·31
22	6·0	4·5	7·0	1·5	<1·0	1·5	N.D.	0·36
23	7·5	6·0	3·0	2·0	N.D.	2·0	N.D.	0·26
24	8·0	9·0	4·5	1·0	<1·0	1·0	N.D.	0·49
25	N.D.	N.D.	N.D.	N.D.	N.D.	N.D.	N.D.	1·46
26	N.D.	N.D.	N.D.	N.D.	N.D.	N.D.	N.D.	1·55

N.D.—none detected.

After treatment in the range 700–950°C all the steels exhibited precipitation of secondary carbide, the precipitate being coarser and more extensive in the samples aged at the higher temperatures.

There was wide divergence of sigma-forming tendencies. Increase in carbon or nickel content over the ranges studied, with constant manganese and silicon reduced the amount of sigma formed although nickel did not have a strong effect. Increase in manganese content appeared mildly to promote sigma. Silicon exerted by far the most marked effect; increase in silicon from 1 to 2 per cent strongly promoted sigma-formation, in both low- and high-carbon steels, the effect being most pronounced with low carbon. Sigma phase was not detected in the 20 per cent chromium–15 per cent nickel steels. Table 1 illustrates the extremely embrittling effect resulting from excessive sigma formation; such embrittlement is more severe than that caused by the extensive carbide precipitation found in the higher-carbon steels, which were substantially free from sigma (cf steels 7–12 and 19–24). Excellent impact values were obtained from the sigma-free low-carbon steels, Nos. 5, 25 and 26, and the results from steel No. 5 which had a lower chromium content than was originally intended seemed of particular significance.

From the results of these initial tests it appeared that the temperature range most favourable for sigma-formation in the 25 per cent chromium–20 per cent nickel steels was 750–800°C. A more detailed study was, therefore, made of samples of a low-carbon steel which had shown particular susceptibility to sigma formation (No. 7) after ageing for periods up to 4000 hr at 800°C. The sigma phase in steel No. 7 was identified not only by microscopic examination, but also by standard X-ray diffraction techniques, and additionally a minor carbide, $M_{23}C_6$, was identified on electrolytically extracted residues. The composition of the sigma was determined by electron-probe microanalysis as silicon 1·5, manganese 1·2, nickel 8·3, chromium 46·7, iron 34·3 per cent.

The results of microscopical examination are illustrated in Fig. 3a–f, and the impact properties, sigma counts and hardness results appear in Fig. 4. The resultant curves, which are closely similar to those previously published,[4,7] suggest that the equilibrium sigma content at 800°C is achieved after about 2000 hr; the 8000-hr test results indicate that the same conclusion probably applies to 900°C (Table 2). After 48 hr exposure at 800°C (Fig. 3a) secondary carbides had precipitated in the grain boundaries and within the grains, but after 96 hr the grain boundary primary carbide eutectic had been partly taken into solution and had been replaced by sigma (Fig. 3b); also a few needles of sigma phase had begun to form within the grains. With further exposure the number and size of the needles increased, until a complete Widmanstätten precipitate of sigma was formed throughout the samples (Fig. 3c–3f). This apparent replacement of chromium carbide by sigma has been noted previously and various mechanisms for the process have been proposed.[16–18] For comparison, Fig. 5 shows a photomicrograph of the high-carbon, low-silicon steel, No. 13, which, after heating for 4000 hr at 800°C, did not form much sigma phase but contained extensive carbide precipitate.

The acicular precipitates of sigma were only found in the steels which contained more than approximately 5 per cent of the phase and it is apparent, therefore, that the morphology is related to the amount present.

In view of the result obtained on steel No. 5 (0·22% C, 1·2% Si, 2·5% Mn, 23% Ni, 24% Cr) the study was extended to a further series of eight steels containing 0·25% C, 0·5% Si, 0·5% Mn, and either 19 or 22 per cent nickel with varying chromium, in order to obtain more detailed information on the

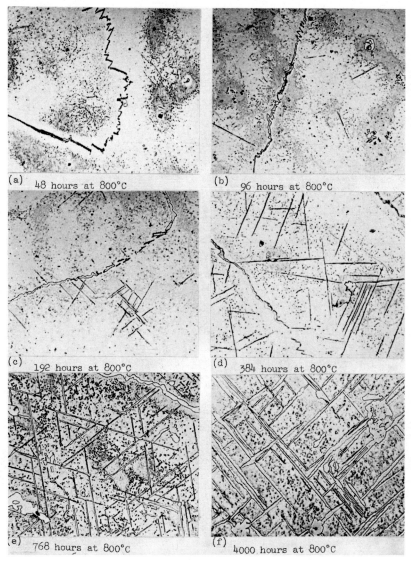

(a) 48 hours at 800°C

(b) 96 hours at 800°C

(c) 192 hours at 800°C

(d) 384 hours at 800°C

(e) 768 hours at 800°C

(f) 4000 hours at 800°C

FIG. 3
Microstructures of steel 7 after heating for various times at 800°C (× 400).

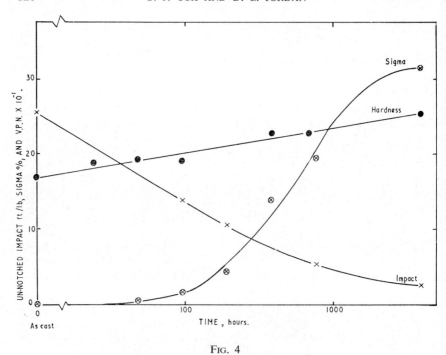

FIG. 4

Properties of steel no. 7 after heating for various times at 800°C.

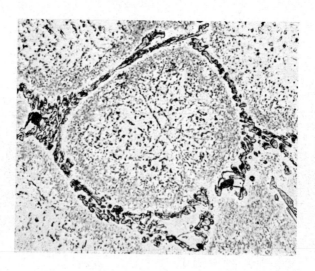

FIG. 5

Steel no. 13 after 4000 hr at 800°C (×400).

effects of nickel and chromium on susceptibility to sigma-formation. Sigma was not detected in any of these steels, after exposure for 768 hr at 800°C and good impact properties were also obtained. The findings which are incorporated in Fig. 6 suggest that, if the chromium content of HK alloy is not allowed to exceed 24 per cent, sigma formation may be avoided in steels containing 20 per cent nickel and 1 per cent maximum silicon even at low carbon levels. As a matter of interest, the austenite/austenite + sigma boundaries suggested by these results and those obtained on steels 1 to 6 are shown (in Fig. 6) in comparison with the boundaries proposed by Schafmeister and Ergang[19], Rees et al.,[20] and Talbot and Furman.[21] It must, however, be noted that the alloys studied by the investigators mentioned are not directly comparable with those used in the present work.

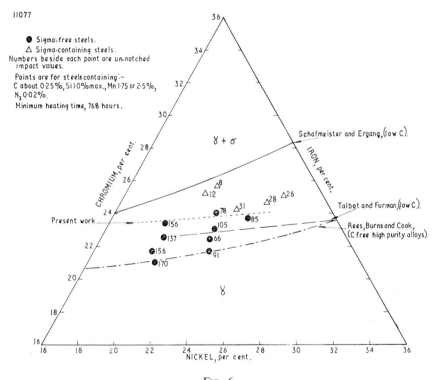

FIG. 6

Isothermal section of the Fe–Cr–Ni system at 800°C.

In order to obtain some indication of relative scaling-resistance, samples of all the steels listed in Table 1 were weighed before and after exposure at 950°C. All loose scale was removed prior to weighing. It was anticipated that the scaling tests might not be particularly discriminating, but, except in one case (steel No. 16) the results were remarkably consistent: see Table 2. These data suggest that from this aspect there is some advantage to be gained from keeping the carbon content low and the silicon content high. It also appears that at this temperature scaling-resistance of 20 per cent chromium–15 per cent nickel steels is inferior to that of 25 per cent chromium–20 per cent nickel types.

II. STEELS OF PREFERRED COMPOSITION

As a result of the work described above three 24 per cent chromium, low silicon steels containing 0·21, 0·30 and 0·38 per cent carbon hereafter designated, respectively, steels A, B and C, were made as induction-furnace, air-melted heats. High-purity iron charges were used, deoxidation was by 0·05% Ca Si, and the melts were cast at 1550°C, to produce $1\frac{1}{8}$-in. × $1\frac{3}{8}$-in. section keel-block castings for assessment of stress-rupture properties. Tensile properties in the as-cast condition were determined, and impact tests

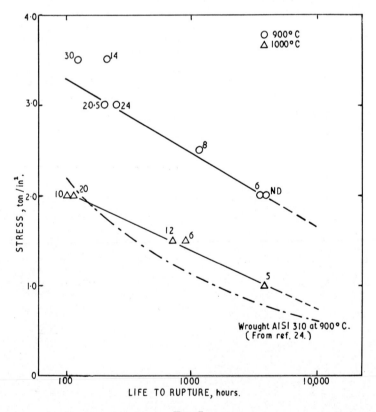

Fig. 7

Rupture properties of steel C at 900° and 1000°C.

TABLE 3

Composition, Microstructures and Mechanical Properties of Steels having the Preferred Composition

Designation	Composition %					As-cast microstructure	As-cast properties						After 4000 hr/800°C	
	C	Si	Mn	Ni	Cr		U.T.S. tsi*	0.1% P.S. tsi	El $\%$ on $\sqrt[4]{A}$	R.A. %	Unnotched impact ft/lb	Hardness V.P.N.	Unnotched impact ft/lb	Hardness V.P.N.
A	0.21	0.76	0.74	22.0	23.0	Grain boundary carbide	26.7	12.4	26.9	36.5	89.0	165	155.0	165
B	0.30	0.75	0.40	21.6	24.0	Grain boundary carbide	—	—	—	—	—	—	—	—
C**	0.38	0.72	0.70	21.2	23.6	Eutectic inter-dendritic carbide	30.5	13.3	19.6	14.4	50.3	179	15.6	203

* Duplicate tests using 0.252 in. dia. specimens.
** Also S 0.009%, P 0.006%, N_2 0.028%.

were made on steels A and C, both as-cast and after 4000 hr exposure at 800°C. The results obtained, together with the chemical composition of the steels, are given in Table 3.

The impact results for steel C, after heat-treatment, showed the anticipated loss of toughness, but the impact-resistance of steel A was increased as a result of treatment at 800°C. Microscopical examination showed that sigma had not formed in either of the steels. It was thus confirmed that, provided sigma formation is avoided, low-carbon steels will give markedly better impact properties after exposure at high temperatures than those obtainable from higher-carbon steels similarly aged.

Since previous investigators have indicated that higher-carbon steels have better rupture strength than low-carbon steels,[10–12] long-time stress-rupture tests were made on steel C at 900° and 1000°C, using specimens 0·252-in. dia., 1·25-in. parallel portion, 3-in. overall length. The stresses used were chosen to give lives up to 5000 hr. (Work on steels A and B was limited to a few short-time tests.) Since in several cases it was not found possible to extract

TABLE 4

Stress Rupture Results for Steels of Preferred Composition at 900 and 1000°C

Designation	Carbon content %	Temp. °C	Stress tsi	Properties			Hardness after rupture testing*
				Life hr	R.A. %	Elongation %	
A	0·21	900	3	(1)　231·5	6	4·7	191
B	0·30	900	3	(1)　202·5	10·2	3·5	203
				(2)　149·9	4·5	3·5	210
			2·5	(1)　324·8	11	N.D.	176
				(2)　569·7	1	N.D.	178
C	0·38	900	3·5	(1)　129·8	30	11·0	202
				(2)　218·4	14	N.D.	211
			3	(1)　257·7	24	N.D.	205
				(2)　203·5	20·5	N.D.	211
			2·5	(1) 1171·5	8	N.D.	202
			2	(1) 3539·2	6	N.D.	211
				(2) 3960·6	N.D.	N.D.	201
			1·75	†(1) 5236	1	4·5	190
C	0·38	1000	2	(1)　100·4	10	7·6	206
				(2)　116·1	20	12·9	200
			1·5	(1)　737·6	12	N.D.	194
				(2)　911	6	N.D.	202
			1	(1) 3582	5	N.D.	193
			0·75	(1) 8020			

N.D.—not determinable.

* Measured on shank portion.

† Late test result, not shown in Figs. 7 and 8.

the specimens from the machine adapter for the measurement of elongation values, estimation of ductility was supplemented by recording percentage reduction in area. Due to the mode of fracture, however, ductility measurements could not always be obtained even with that method.

The results of the stress-rupture tests for steel C are given in Fig. 7, in the form of stress/log time plots: the final R.A. value is recorded beside each point. For comparison, results for a wrought low-carbon 25–20 Cr–Ni steel (AISI 310) are included. These results suggest that in this respect the cast steel is significantly superior to the wrought steel of lower carbon content. Stress-rupture data for all the cast steels are given in Table 4 and are shown as a Larson–Miller plot in Fig. 8. At least on the basis of the limited tests made, variation in carbon over the range 0·21 to 0·38 per cent has little apparent influence on rupture strength. The results recorded in Fig. 8 further suggest that under a stress of 1·2 ton/in² steel C should give a 100,000-hr rupture life at 900°C, a conclusion which compares well with published data

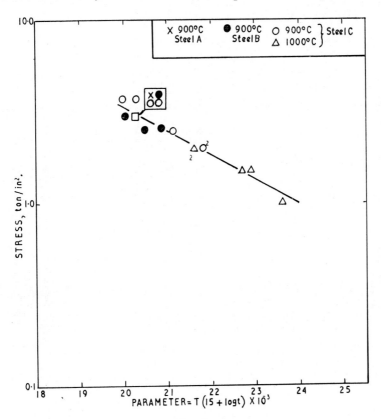

FIG. 8

Larson–Miller plot of the data for steels A, B and C.

for cast 25–20 steels. The good stress-rupture properties were not unexpected, because it is known that restriction of silicon content improves rupture life,[10–12] and there is, in addition, some evidence that reduction in chromium content is also beneficial.[11–12]

Microscopical examination of longitudinal sections of the creep-rupture test pieces, including the fracture surfaces, showed that in all the steels a large amount of secondary carbide had precipitated, and that steel C still contained primary eutectic carbides. No sigma phase was detected in any of these steels. Needles of chromium nitride were also observed, adjacent to both the main and secondary fractures, these were particularly evident in the specimens of steel C after long time testing, indicating that the steel was absorbing nitrogen from the atmosphere.

III. WELDABILITY

The basic composition of 25 per cent chromium–20 per cent nickel steels is primarily determined on the basis of heat-resistance and structural stability but, as already indicated, elements such as carbon and silicon were thought to have an important effect on the weldability of cast steels. In defining compositional limits for cast alloys it was therefore decided initially to test materials of varying carbon and silicon contents, supplemented by additional welds to determine the influence of sulphur and phosphorus.

TABLE 5

Composition of Plate Castings used for Initial Welding Tests

Composition %						
C	Si	Mn	Ni	Cr	S	P
0·06	0·73	1·05	20·9	25·2	0·008	0·006
0·06	1·73	1·09	20·6	25·0	0·009	0·006
0·07	2·62	1·01	20·5	24·4	0·007	0·006
0·15	0·67	0·95	21·3	24·8	0·010	0·006
0·15	2·50	0·94	21·2	24·2	0·009	0·006
0·21	0·71	1·05	19·8	25·0	0·008	0·006
0·21	1·64	1·05	20·0	25·4	0·011	0·006
0·21	2·63	1·10	20·2	25·2	0·012	0·005
0·36	1·63	1·13	20·5	25·2	0·007	0·003
0·38	3·05	0·98	20·5	24·8	0·007	0·003
0·45	0·70	1·02	20·6	25·2	0·005	0·002
0·47	1·45	1·04	20·3	25·0	0·004	0·002
0·44	2·20	0·92	20·2	24·7	0·004	0·003
0·53	1·61	1·05	20·6	25·1	0·009	0·004
0·54	2·61	1·05	20·4	25·2	0·009	0·005
0·63	0·63	1·05	19·8	25·8	0·013	0·006
0·67	0·61	1·00	20·2	25·0	0·010	0·005
0·68	1·54	1·05	19·8	24·7	0·013	0·006
0·70	2·46	1·45	19·4	25·9	0·013	0·004

Plates $\frac{1}{2}$ in. $\times$ 4 in. $\times$ 6 in. were cast from induction-melted heats based on high purity charges: compositions are given in Table 5. These plates were halved lengthways and were bevelled to give a single-V preparation of 70° included angle. After securing to a 3-in. thick mild-steel block, by fillet welds along the unbevelled edges, the plates were butt-welded, using "Inconel"* 182 flux-coated electrodes. Since at the time these tests were initiated the quality of matching electrodes had not been fully proven, it was considered best to employ the high-nickel electrode which was developed to meet the requirements of dissimilar-metal welding in the construction of nuclear plant. No pre-heat was used, and the plates were cooled to below 200°C between passes.

Three sections were taken from each joint, transverse to the direction of welding, at 1$\frac{1}{2}$ in., 3 in. and 4$\frac{1}{2}$ in. from the weld-start point; additional sections were cut from welds made in plates containing 0·35–0·45 per cent carbon, since the carbon content of commercial castings often falls within this range. After polishing and etching in 10 per cent oxalic acid, the weld zones were microscopically examined. The results are summarized in Fig. 9.

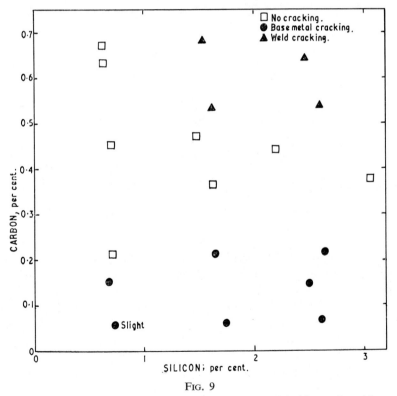

FIG. 9

Inter-relationship between carbon and silicon content and incidence of cracking.

* Trade mark.

Intergranular cracking connected to the fusion line, and sometimes propagating into the weld, was observed in plates containing up to 0·2 per cent carbon; the cracks were usually about 0·5 mm long, but in the 0·06 per cent carbon plate containing 0·73 per cent silicon a few small fissures were found, each approximately 0·1 mm long. At the 0·06 and 0·15 per cent carbon levels it was frequently observed that weld metal had penetrated into the grain-boundary region of the parent plate (Fig. 10): in other areas there appeared to have been liquation at the grain boundaries adjacent to the weld. Similar, though less strongly marked effects, occurred in the plates containing 0·21 per cent carbon.

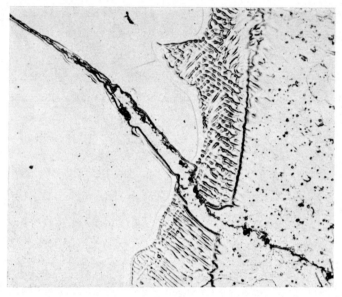

FIG. 10

Flow of weld metal into base plate containing 0·067% C and 2·62% Si (× 300).

In plates containing 0·35–0·7 per cent carbon no cracking was found in the weld heat-affected zone, but weld-metal cracking occurred in joints between plates of high carbon and high silicon content.

Supplementary tests were carried out on plates containing 0·25 and 0·44 per cent carbon and having additions of sulphur and phosphorus at the maximum levels normally encountered in commercial practice (Table 6). In these steels the compositions were adjusted to take into account the results of the sigma tests, i.e. the chromium content was controlled below 24 per cent and the silicon below 1 per cent. The whole of each joint was sectioned into ½-in. thick slices, for microscopical examination. Neither weld showed any cracking.

The results reported in the previous section indicated that $0 \cdot 25$ per cent carbon steels give good impact properties after high-temperature exposure. Provided that silicon is not high, these steels give also satisfactory weldability. If impact is not important and higher-carbon steels are used, weldability should obviously not be a problem.

TABLE 6

Composition of Plate Castings having Preferred Nickel and Chromium Contents and Increased Sulphur and Phosphorus Content

Composition %							
C	Si	Mn	Ni	Cr	S	P	Fe
0·25	0·68	0·41	21·6	23·6	0·030	0·026	Bal
0·44	0·72	0·42	21·6	23·1	0·033	0·030	Bal

Filler Materials

The majority of the flux-coated electrodes hitherto available for joining 25 per cent chromium–20 per cent nickel steels were designed for use with wrought materials, and were therefore selected to deposit low-carbon weld metals. High-nickel filler materials, for example "Inco-Weld* 'A' " electrodes, have found application in the joining of cast reformer headers, but the increasing demand for high-carbon 25 per cent chromium–20 per cent nickel tubes led inevitably to the development of electrodes depositing weld metals of matching composition. In general, the operability of such filler rods is satisfactory, although the high fluidity of some slags has necessitated some modifications in welding technique.

Stress-rupture tests were carried out on test pieces machined from weld pads, deposited on the surface of cast 25–20 steel plates by the metal-arc process, using a flux-coated electrode, and by the argon-shielded tungsten-arc

TABLE 7

Stress-Rupture Results for Weld Pads

Filler material	Composition %							Stress-rupture life at 3 tsi/900°C hr
	C	Si	Mn	Ni	Cr	S	P	
$\frac{5}{32}$-in. dia. flux-coated electrode	0·38	0·49	1·8	21·2	26·5	0·005	0·018	41·3
$\frac{1}{8}$-in. dia.	0·39	0·30	1·75	21·0	26·6	0·004	0·020	43·7
Uncoated rod	0·26	1·54	2·10	21·2	25·1	0·016	0·028	106·6, 183·1

* Trade mark.

process, using a commercially-produced uncoated filler rod. The compositions of the deposits and the results of the tests are given in Table 7. The life of the lower-carbon tungsten-arc deposit was acceptable, but that of the higher carbon deposit was clearly much inferior to those obtained from steel C (see Table 4) of similar carbon content. In order to determine whether this discrepancy was due to compositional differences or whether it was a reflection of the structural differences between base metal and weldment, further stress-rupture tests were made on weld metal deposited by the argon-shielded tungsten-arc process with filler rods cast from the same heat as a 1-in. thick plate, on which tests were also made. The results of stress-rupture tests, shown in Table 8, demonstrate that the weld structure has an unfavourable effect on rupture life. This problem is currently receiving further attention.

TABLE 8

Stress-Rupture Results for Plate Castings and Weld Pads Deposited from the Same Metal

Composition %							Stress-rupture life at 3 tsi/900°C, hr	
C	Si	Mn	Ni	Cr	S	P	Plate	Weld
0·44	0·59	0·49	21·3	24·2	0·009	0·009	216	45·9 47·5

DISCUSSION

Steels of the 25 per cent chromium–20 per cent nickel type made to the A.C.I. specification for HK alloys are likely to exhibit considerable variations in structural stability because of the wide ranges of compositions which satisfy this specification, e.g. chromium may vary from 24 to 28 per cent. These steels may also be rather more susceptible to sigma-phase formation than would be expected from the work of Mangone and Hall.[12] In this respect, the results of the present investigation are in agreement with those of Zeuner,[22] who suggested that, in order to avoid sigma-formation, at temperatures up to 950°C 20 per cent chromium–15 per cent nickel alloys should be used in preference to 25–20 steels. However, results of scaling tests suggest that at temperatures much above 900°C the 20 per cent chromium–15 per cent nickel steel may not possess oxidation-resistance adequate for some applications. It would therefore appear preferable to use 25–20 type steel, ensuring structural stability by appropriate adjustment of composition, in particular by restriction in the contents of silicon, chromium and manganese. Figure 6 shows that if sigma is to be avoided in low-carbon steels containing about 20 per cent nickel the chromium content should not exceed 24 per cent. At this chromium level scaling resistance remains unimpaired up to at least 950°C and there appears little likelihood of sigma being formed in steels containing about 20 per cent nickel provided that the silicon content is kept below about 1 per cent and manganese below 2 per cent. In general these conclusions confirm the findings of Morley and Kirkby for low-carbon wrought steels.[4]

Stress-rupture data obtained on 0·38 per cent carbon, 24 per cent chromium, 21 per cent nickel steel show that cast steels give good resistance to creep, and the few tests made on the lower-carbon materials suggest that there is not a marked change in the stress-rupture properties when carbon is reduced to 0·3 per cent and perhaps even to 0·2 per cent. This finding is somewhat at variance with initial expectations based on previous published work[10–12] on steels of this type, but it may be that the difference in rupture properties obtained as a result of varying carbon have previously been overstressed. It should be noted that in the as-cast condition interdendritic eutectic carbide appears in the micro-structure of alloys of this type somewhere between 0·30 and 0·38 per cent carbon indicating that the matrix is then saturated with respect to carbon, and that further carbon additions would serve only to increase the proportion of eutectic carbide present. Whether or not an increase in the amount of eutectic carbides in the grain boundary would improve stress-rupture life is perhaps a matter for conjecture, but because the results of impact tests have shown that after heating for prolonged periods a significant difference in toughness exists between steels containing 0·2 or 0·38 per cent carbon, further work on this aspect is obviously necessary. In this context the fact that both low- and high-carbon, low-silicon steels may be satisfactorily welded, but the stress-rupture properties of the higher-carbon welds are inferior may also be significant.

It is suggested therefore, that in applications where the retention of toughness or ductility is important some advantage might be gained by controlling carbon within the range 0·25 to 0·35 per cent. This range is lower than that currently shown in the A.C.I. HK specification (0·35 to 0·75% C) but experiments carried out on similar alloys have indicated that such reduction in carbon should not drastically impair casting properties.[23] If retention of toughness is not very important then steels having higher carbon contents might be used because it may be that these steels will have the best possible stress rupture properties. Further, it is suggested that higher chromium contents (i.e. Cr ⩽25 per cent) are permissible in such high carbon alloys firstly because carbon tends to prevent sigma-phase formation, and secondly because the toughness of higher carbon steels is in any case reduced by the secondary carbide precipitation which occurs on ageing so that the presence of small amounts of sigma may not have a critical effect on toughness.

CONCLUSIONS

(i) To prevent sigma-formation in cast austenitic steels of the 25 per cent chromium–20 per cent nickel type, the silicon content should not exceed

1 per cent and chromium should not be greater than 24 per cent, even in the presence of carbon up to 0·45 per cent and nickel up to 24 per cent.

(ii) In the absence of sigma-phase, steels of lower carbon (0·25 per cent) content give very high room-temperature impact values, even after prolonged exposure at 800°C. Such steels are much superior to higher-carbon steels (0·45% C) which suffer carbide embrittlement, although these latter steels are still better than alloys which contain large amounts of sigma phase.

(iii) Cast steels of the 25 per cent chromium–20 per cent nickel type with silicon and chromium contents adjusted to avoid sigma phase give good stress-rupture properties at 900° and 1000°C. The limited stress rupture data obtained suggest that variation in carbon over the range studied (0·21–0·38 per cent) does not exert a marked influence on the rupture strength of the steel.

(iv) Base-metal cracking was not encountered in weld joints made in castings containing more than 0·2 per cent carbon: below that carbon level susceptibility to cracking increased with increasing silicon. At high carbon levels (0·4 per cent) the stress-rupture life of matching weld metals was inferior to that of the casting, but the life of a weld metal containing 0·26 per cent carbon was more nearly comparable.

(v) It is suggested that, from the point of view of retention of toughness, stress-rupture properties, and weldability, the optimum composition for steels of the HK type is C 0·25–0·35 per cent, Si 1 per cent max., Mn 1 per cent max., Cr 24 per cent max., nickel 19 per cent min. However, it may be advantageous to use higher carbon steels in applications where retention of toughness is not considered important and, because carbon tends to prevent sigma-phase formation, a chromium content above 24 per cent could be used in these steels.

ACKNOWLEDGMENTS

The authors are indebted to International Nickel Limited for permission to publish this paper. The assistance of their colleague, Mr. J. A. Towers, who supervised the stress-rupture testing, is also acknowledged.

REFERENCES

1. P. PAYSON and C. H. SAVAGE, Trans. A.S.M., **39**, 404–439, 1947; disc., 439–452.
2. G. J. GUARNIERI, J. MILLER and F. J. VAINTER, Trans. A.S.M., **42**, 981–1000, 1950; disc., 1000–1007.
3. G. N. EMMANUEL, The nature, occurrence and effects of sigma phase, A.S.T.M. Special Tech. Publ., 82–99, 1951; disc., 100–127.
4. J. I. MORLEY and H. W. KIRKBY, Jnl. Iron and Steel Inst., **172**, 129–142, 1952; disc., ibid, **175**, 407–408, 1953.
5. G. V. SMITH and E. J. DULIS, A.S.T.M. Special Tech. Publ., No. 128, 225–235, 1953; disc., 236.

6. R. C. FRERICHS and C. L. CLARK, *Trans. A.S.M.*, **46**, 1285–1296, 1954; disc., 1296–1297.
7. A. J. LENA and W. E. CURRY, *Trans. A.S.M.*, **47**, 193–202, 1955; disc., 203–210.
8. R. A. LULA, A. J. LENA and H. M. JOHNSON, *Trans. A.S.M.E.*, **79**, 921–926, 1957.
9. K. RICHARD and G. PETRICH, *Chemie-Intenieur-Technik*, **35**, 29–36, 1963.
10. H. S. AVERY and C. R. WILKS, *Trans. A.S.M.*, **40**, 529–577, 1948; disc., 577–584.
11. J. H. JACKSON, The nature, occurrence and effects of sigma phase, *A.S.T.M. Special Tech. Publ.*, 100–109, 1951; disc., 120–127.
12. R. J. MANGONE and A. M. HALL, *Alloy Casting Bull.*, No. 17, 10 pp., Oct. 1961.
13. J. F. MASON, J. J. MORAN and G. L. SWALES, Sixth World Petroleum Congr., Preprint VII–21, 10 pp., 1963.
14. K. ROESCH and K. H. SCHMITZ, *Giesserei Tech. Wiss. Beihefte*, **13**, 43–55, 1961.
15. J. C. BORLAND and R. N. YOUNGER, *Brit. Welding Jnl.*, **7**, 22–59, 1960.
16. R. E. LISMER, L. PRYCE and K. W. ANDREWS, *Jnl Iron and Steel Inst.*, **171**, 49–58, 1952.
17. F. B. PICKERING, Precipitation processes in steels, *Iron and Steel Inst. Special Rept.*, No. 64, 118–124, 1959.
18. H. W. KIRKBY and R. J. TRUMAN, Precipitation processes in steels, *Iron and Steel Inst. Special Rept.*, No. 64, 242–258, 1959.
19. P. SCHAFMEISTER and R. ERGANG, *Arch. Eisenhuttenwesen*, **12**, 459–464, 1939.
20. W. P. REES, B. D. BURNS and A. J. COOK, *Jnl. Iron and Steel Inst.*, **162**, 325–336, 1949; disc., *ibid*, **166**, 220–212, 1950.
21. A. M. TALBOT and D. E. FURMAN, *Trans. A.S.M.*, **45**, 429–440, 1953; disc., 441–442.
22. H. ZEUNER, Heat-resistant 20/15 nickel–chromium cast steel for petrochemical plant, Communication from Bergische Stahl-Industrie, 1962.
23. G. J. COX, *Brit. Foundryman*, **56**, 1–8, 1963.
24. T. M. KREBS, *Petroleum Refiner*, **41**, 135–140, Aug. 1962.

INTRODUCTION TO THE USE OF CAST ALLOY MATERIAL FOR HYDROCARBON PROCESSING IN THE U.S.A.

R. B. COOPER

THIS paper will cover the use of cast heat-resistant alloy in the high temperature petrochemical and hydrocarbon processing industries, where high temperature is arbitrarily defined as 650°C to about 1250°C. This will be based on Electro-Alloys experience in the U.S.A., with centrifugally cast tubes.

REFORMER PROCESSES

Since 1957, Electro-Alloys has produced or is currently producing 46 original equipment reformer tube jobs. Seven of these have been for synthesis gas plants, 21 for ammonia plants, and 18 for miscellaneous hydrogen plants. There are no towns-gas plants since this use of the reformer furnace is unknown in the U.S.A. To give an indication of the size of reformer tube job which Electro-Alloys has produced, the largest to date was for a 50 million s.c.f.d. hydrogen plant. Currently in production are the tubes for a 1000 t.p.d. ammonia plant.

Most reformer furnaces in the U.S. are similar to the ones in the U.K., that is, vertical catalyst tubes, usually suspended independently in the fire box and independently connected by pigtails to a common header system, which, depending on the furnace builder concerned, may be produced from centrifugally cast or wrought tubes.

Some furnace builders, however, are using banks of reformer tubes, rigidly connected to cast header tubes. A number of these banks are then connected to a general header and transfer piping system. This type of arrangement is working well in the field.

There are two clear advantages to using cast tubes in reformer service rather than any available wrought materials. The first is the higher elevated temperature strength properties obtainable in the high carbon cast alloys. The second advantage is economic. Cast tubes can be produced and fabricated at a lower cost than wrought or extruded tubes.

Regarding the various processes in which reformer furnaces are involved in the U.S.A. by far the most important is in the ammonia industry. At this time

143

the ammonia based fertilizer industry in the States is undergoing a vast expansion. In 1960, the production capacity of ammonia in the U.S.A. was about 5 million short tons per year, and approximately 70–75 per cent of the required synthesis hydrogen was obtained from reformer furnaces, the remainder from chlorine cells, by-product sources and partial oxidation plants. It is estimated that by the end of 1965, the production capacity of ammonia in America will have increased to 11 million short tons per year. All of this expansion will be accomplished using reformer furnaces with centrifugally cast catalyst tubes.

The earliest commercial ammonia plants where hydrogen was generated in steam methane reformers were installed during World War II, for the production of ammonia-based explosives rather than fertilizers. These were relatively low pressure plants, 30 p.s.i. maximum, and the first catalyst tubes were rolled and welded Type 310 stainless steel. Some of these tubes are still in operation, one plant still possessing the original spare tubes which have never been used. However, in some cases, these early tubes have failed, mainly due to failure in the longitudinal weld seams. Such tubes have been economically replaced with cast tubes in Thermalloy "47" (26+ Cr/20% Ni alloy) of the same inside diameter.

The earliest use of cast tubes in ammonia reformers was in 1952. These tubes now have some 12 years' service on them. Design conditions for these tubes were 90 p.s.i. at 925°C operating temperature. Earlier this year Electro-Alloys had the opportunity to examine one of these tubes after 12 years service. No failure was involved, the user was carrying out a routine check on the furnace. There was no significant indication of oxidation or decarburization on either the inside or outside surfaces, and no signs of structural damage to the metal in the tube wall. The tube appeared to be in good condition, with several years of successful service yet to be obtained.

In the past few years there has been a very noticeable trend in the ammonia industry to go to higher and higher pressures in the primary reformer furnace. It is common to find reformer tubes being designed for pressures in excess of 300 p.s.i. In fact, discussions have been held with one of the leading catalyst manufacturers in the U.S.A. on the possibility of supplying a pilot reformer tube for service at 850 p.s.i. and 826°C. The aim behind this increase in pressure is, of course, to reduce overall plant costs by reducing compressor horse power requirements.

The major part of the ammonia capacity expansion presently under way in the U.S.A. is in the form of very large plants of 600 short tons per day capacity or larger. A number of very small plants to produce 60–120 tons per day are also under construction. These use shop assembled units which can be erected rapidly at the job site. Such plants may use rigid banks of short tubes connected into a common header. These are proving very satisfactory in service.

As far as we know all the ammonia plants being built or considered at present in America use reformer tubes produced in HK-40 alloy. This is an excellent alloy from the standpoint of reliability. Its properties are well defined, and well known, and there has been generally very good experience with it.

The second class of reformer furnace tubes to be considered are for use in synthesis gas operations, such as methanol or for the oxo alcohol process.

Synthesis gas contains hydrogen and carbon monoxide, and the chemical reaction to produce the required gas analysis is aided by high temperature and low pressure. Temperatures were rarely higher than 950°C. Generally, the cast tubes have given good service, and have adequately replaced the wrought alloy tubes when these have failed. Some furnaces using cast tubes have had failures, however, these appear to be functions of the furnace operation rather than the tube material. Since this reaction is aided by higher temperature, at least one of the American furnace builders has gone to considerably higher operating temperatures than mentioned above. As temperatures increase, the strength of the HK-40 decreases and tube walls may become excessively heavy when designed in this material. The oxidation resistance of the alloy is sufficient, but there is a possibility of surface decarburization and intergranular oxidation which will weaken the tubes.

The first of these high temperature synthesis gas units was built in 1961 in Texas for oxo alcohol synthesis gas production, and was designed to operate at 1200°C or higher and 50 p.s.i. The original tubes were supplied in a cast so-called "super" alloy. After a short time on stream, the user reduced the operating temperature to about 1150°C, due partly to failure of these tubes. In early 1963, eight tubes went into service cast in our Supertherm. Supertherm is a patented 25% Cr/35% Ni alloy, strengthened and stabilized with cobalt and tungsten.

This was the first time this alloy had been used in reformer tube service. Service experience to date has been very good with no failures, although the original tubes had a service life of only about 18 months. More recently a considerable quantity of random lengths of Supertherm tubing was supplied to repair a series of failures in the competitive alloy tubes. The material was field welded by the user without difficulty.

The second high temperature unit with which Electro-Alloys has been associated has just gone on stream in Italy. This was designed for 1150°C, 50 p.s.i., methanol synthesis gas service. The tubes produced for the Italian unit were in Thermalloy "63" (25% Cr/35% Ni) alloy, which is the base material from which Supertherm was developed. This alloy has excellent strength, considerably stronger than HK-40 at this temperature and very good oxidation resistance. Considerable interest is being shown in the U.S.A. on the use of alloys other than the HK grade for such uses.

The other main use of the reformer furnace in the U.S.A. is for the production of hydrogen. This is second in importance to ammonia production, due to a new family of oil-refining processes, which have recently been developed. Other reformers supplying hydrogen vary widely in size. The biggest of them produce hydrogen for use as a missile or rocket fuel as liquid hydrogen. These plants are designed to produce up to 60 tons per day of hydrogen. The smaller hydrogen units with 2, 4 or 8 reformer tubes in the furnace, are used to generate hydrogen for hardening fats and oils and providing protective atmospheres in the steel industry.

REFORMER TUBE DESIGN

It is necessary to stress that my company is not a reformer tube designer. This is the furnace builder's responsibility. However, through the years, and through test programmes, a large volume of information has been collected on the high temperature properties of the cast heat resistant alloys. It is common practice in American to use either the A.P.I. formula, or one of the A.S.M.E. formulae. There is little difference in the results obtained in calculating a tube wall with either formula. It is probably safe to say that all tube walls are calculated with many safety factors, and tend to be over-designed.

It is standard to make a $\frac{3}{32}$ in. per wall allowance for unsoundness in cast reformer tubes in the U.S.A., the soundness being checked with the use of macro-etched rings. It must be stressed that this $\frac{3}{32}$ in. is not a continuous band of unsoundness all around the inside surface of the tube, nor is it continuous down the length of the tube. It is a random occurrence, and probably 85 per cent of the unsoundness in our tube is less than $\frac{1}{16}$ in. deep. Thus, the $\frac{3}{32}$ in. allowance may be regarded as a safety factor, similar to the safety factors contained in the formula employed to calculate wall thickness. The same comment can be made about the corrosion allowance that is sometimes added to the cast wall. Experience shows that corrosion is not a serious problem in a well-designed reformer furnace using a clean fuel.

Regarding design stress criteria available for designing tubes, in the past it was common to use a fraction of the limiting creep stress (LCS) as the design stress, where LCS is defined as the stress to produce a minimum creep rate of 1 per cent in 10,000 hr or to be more accurate, a minimum creep rate of 0·0001 per cent per hr. This is dangerous, and a far safer design may be accomplished using the stress to produce rupture in a given length of time such as 100,000 hr. The danger in using creep stresses for design can be easily understood since creep rates do not take into account the actual time to rupture of the material under stress at high temperature. Figure 1 shows a plot of applied stress versus temperature for HK-40 (Thermalloy 47) for 50 per cent LCS, and the stress to produce rupture in 100,000 hr. The values are very similar over the temperature range for normal reformer tube opera-

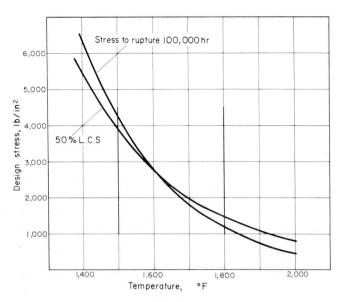

FIG. 1

Variation of design stress with temperature for Thermalloy "47".

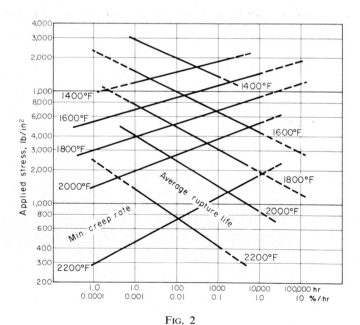

FIG. 2

Variation of average life and minimum creep rate of T47 (HK-40 Type) with temperature and applied stress.

tions. The two plots intersect at about 1600°F (870°C). Comparison of this chart with Fig. 2 will show that at higher temperatures, use of design stresses based on LCS will result in a significantly shorter life than 100,000 hr. For example, at 1800°F (980°C) the stress to produce rupture in 100,000 hr is about 1200 p.s.i. for this alloy. The 50 per cent LCS is 1500 p.s.i. at the same temperature. Reference to Fig. 2 shows that the latter stress will produce rupture in 30,000 hr. In using creep stresses as design criteria, without reference to stress rupture information, dangerously short lives may be obtained.

Figure 2 is a standard plot of applied stress versus minimum creep rate, and on the same graph, applied stress versus average time to rupture, both for various temperatures. Until recently, the longest time results available were for tests of a few thousand hours' duration. Tests up to 15,000 hr are now completed, and the results confirm earlier shorter time test results, allowing extrapolation to 100,000 hr life with an excellent degree of confidence.

The only other point that should be made regarding cast reformer tube walls is that at Electro-Alloys, an arbitrary limit of 1 in. thick cast tube wall has been set. There are two reasons for this. First is that there is a feeling that thermal stresses will become critical in walls heavier than 1 in. and will seriously shorten the life of the tube. Secondly, there is a chance that the unsoundness allowance may have to be increased for tubes heavier than 1 in. So far, no orders have been placed in the U.S.A. for reformer tubes with a cast wall heavier than $\frac{3}{4}$ in. thick. However, if tube wall calculations show that the tube wall is likely to be too heavy, two possible remedies are available. The first is to use a stronger alloy, for example, Thermalloy "63" rather than Thermalloy "47". The second, and probably for lower temperature work the more logical one, is to use a higher design stress, that is, instead of using a stress to produce rupture in 100,000 hr, use a stress to produce rupture in 60,000 or 70,000 hr. This will shorten tube life, but will avoid thermal stress or quality problems.

FAILURES

There have been a few failures in cast reformer tubes in the U.S.A. Most of these have occurred due to incorrect furnace operation. Some of them have occurred in cast tubes produced in the early fifties. The basic reason for failure in these latter cases was probably a lack of understanding of the requirements of reformer tubes, and less sophisticated production techniques than are now available. For instance, in an ammonia plant, on-stream in 1954, the tube welds started to fail. On inspection, the reason was found to be that there was a complete lack of penetration in the root pass of the assembly welds which was, in places, $\frac{1}{8}$ in. deep.

The second failure in early cast reformer tubes occurred in centrifugally cast tubes produced in sand or ceramic moulds. In this case the shrinkage was in the form of microfissures in the tube wall visible under the microscope. Over some 5 years' service these fissures had propagated as cracks through the weld metal, causing the welds to fail. Possibly, this was a case where tubes should have been scrapped and replaced with new tubes. Instead, the tubes were rewelded and returned to service. The cause of the failures was not removed and eventually failures could well re-occur.

Another failure recently occurred when a reformer furnace was operated without any steam for 12 hr, just methane passing through the tubes. This caused complete disintegration of the catalyst. This, coupled with heavy carbon deposition, completely fused within the tube. An attempt was made to remove this fused product with a diamond tipped oil well drill, but the only result was to break the seriously carburized and overheated tubes. Replacement of all tubes was required.

One interesting case was experienced with the early reformer tubes produced by us. These were produced in 1957 and were put into service in a synthesis gas furnace in a detergent plant, producing hydrogen and carbon monoxide for some process involving the production of a synthetic detergent. These tubes were originally designed for 980°C, 150 lb pressure. After a short time on stream at these conditions, the operating temperature was raised to increase production. The customer was advised that this would seriously shorten the life of the tubes. The user decided that increased production would offset any life reduction, and boosted the operating temperature to around 1100°C, leaving the pressure at 150 p.s.i. One of the tubes failed at about 35,000 hr, and all tubes were replaced. Several of the tubes were made available for examination. The immediate cause of failure in the one tube was probably a local overheating problem, since the failure had occurred in a very short length of tube where considerable bulging prior to failure was evident. In this area the metal had expanded to such an extent that an etch ring taken from one of the original cast tubes on the order could be fitted inside the bulged ring. In actual fact, linear elongation of about 22 per cent had taken place in the bulged area. The metal section contained many very small stress rupture cracks, one of which had finally gone all the way through the metal section causing failure. There was similar evidence of deterioration in some of the assembly welds. Severe oxidation had occurred on the outside of the tube at the bottom, or hot, end. No sigma phase was detectable anywhere, even in the cooler areas of the tubes, which were in the temperature range for sigma formation in the unbalanced alloys.

HEADERS AND TRANSFER LINES

Besides catalyst tubes, there are two areas where cast heat resistant alloy can be used to good effect in reformer furnace construction. These are for outlet headers and transfer piping.

We have produced two manifold assemblies, both of which have been in service for about 2 years, besides several currently in production. The tubes of these assemblies were centrifugally cast, the connections being statically cast to Class II radiography standards, repair welding also being allowed to the same standard. The material used was HK-40. Service to date has been most satisfactory. The choice of alloy in both cases was that of the furnace builder. An equal, or even better choice, and certainly a more economical one would have been Thermalloy "30" (20% Cr/10% Ni, HF grade).

In connection with one of these headers, a transfer line about 200 ft long was produced in HK-40, and this has also seen some 2 years' satisfactory service. This line was produced as a number of sub-assemblies, consisting of tube lengths and 90° elbows for field erection. Again, the elbows were cast to Class II standards, with repairs allowed.

A large number of cast header assemblies are in service, or in production in the U.S.A. There have been few, if any, problems experienced with them in recent years. Alloy selection is generally either the HK or HT materials, but a number of HF assemblies are performing well, at a considerable cost saving. The HF assemblies are all of circular shape, produced from bent centrifugally cast tubing.

In no case are the tubes used in American manifolds or transfer lines bored. The need for this does not exist. The same applies, incidentally, to cast reformer tubes. Again, this is not economically feasible, and the lack of boring has not proved harmful in any way.

The most important factor in the use of cast tubes in these applications is good basic design engineering. The restraint placed on the assemblies should be reduced as far as possible. Expansion should be calculated and allowed for. Given good engineering, then the high quality cast tube assemblies today will perform very well in these applications, providing the most economic service available.

MISCELLANEOUS

Besides the clearly defined uses of cast materials described above, which are of relatively long standing, a number of other applications may be of interest. The first is in steam superheaters for styrene monomer plants. These heater tubes operate in the area of 850°C and 100–150 p.s.i. Traditionally, Type 304 stainless steel has been used, and has in general given good service. However, due to its low resistance to creep deformation, tubes in this alloy have warped and deformed badly, giving serious firing and maintenance problems. Use of cast Thermalloy '30' (20% Cr/10% Ni, HF Grade) in this application has removed these problems at a considerable economic saving. There is also the use of cast tubes in refinery heaters for certain high temperature cases. This use of cast tubes is in its early stages, but can be expected to expand.

Two further uses of centrifugally cast heat resistant alloys in hydrocarbon processing are worthy of note. In heaters for the pyrolysis of hydrocarbons for ethylene production, cast tubes in Thermalloy "47" (HK-40 Grade) are giving excellent service and are being adopted for many plants currently under construction. Also in heaters used in the production of Carbon bisulphide, this alloy is also becoming the Standard material for cracking coils.

CONCLUSION

An attempt has been made to outline some of the current applications of cast heat-resisting alloys in the field of hydrocarbon processing. There can be no doubt that, as the petrochemical industry continues to increase operating conditions of both temperature and pressure, the cast materials will be more and more widely used. Improvements in the metallurgy of these alloys and in the techniques available to produce them economically in recent years have widened their scope of application. Continuing work to further improve them will enable even more economic applications of these materials to be made in the future.

It is necessary that the user and producer of these alloys work together closely. A mutual understanding of each other's problems is a prime requisite in their successful application in today's petrochemistry. Above all else, the user should select a competent, experienced producer, whom he can trust implicitly with regard to alloy selection and production.

NOTES ON THE PROPERTIES AND WELDING OF CENTRIFUGALLY CAST 25 PER CENT CHROMIUM 20 PER CENT NICKEL ALLOY STEEL TUBE

J. F. B. JACKSON, D. SLATER and D. W. O. DAWSON

SYNOPSIS

The results of a series of tests to establish the stress to rupture properties at a temperature of 900°C and for periods of time ranging from 50 up to 5000 hr, are reported. It is shown that within the scope of the tests conducted there is no clear correlation between the contents of lead and tin as trace elements, the application of vacuum or air melting, or the form of macrostructure, with any variation in the elevated temperature properties determined. There is, however, slight evidence to suggest that a particular form of microstructure may be advantageous.

Comparison is made of the ambient temperature tensile properties, microstructure and hardness distribution in tube joints produced by orthodox manual welding and by an automatic tungsten-inert gas continuous process, which produces narrow welds but wider heat-affected zones. Comparison is made of the microstructures of welded joints, both manual and automatic with microstructures produced during the course of elevated temperature creep testing. Observations are made on the metallurgy of welded joints between 25 per cent chromium 20 per cent nickel and low carbon steel.

INTRODUCTION

THE work reported in this paper is part of a long-term programme directly concerned with reformer tube manufacture and it relates to production techniques, both in casting and in welding, that are peculiar to the organization with which the authors are associated.

The process by which the tube under examination has been centrifugally cast, involves the use of steel moulds which are water-cooled during the casting operation, these moulds having no sand or slurry lining. In addition, it is an essential feature of the casting process employed that for tubes in excess of 8 ft in length, liquid steel is poured simultaneously from both ends of the mould. This pouring technique avoids the need for excessively high casting temperatures insofar as the liquid steel is not normally required to flow over distances greater than 9 ft within the rotating mould cavity, while at the same time maximum uniformity and symmetry in the development of the casting in tubular form is favoured. The centrifugal casting technique in question does not differ otherwise in principle, as far as is known, from those techniques applied by other organizations in this manufacturing field.

F

153

The welding process employed is essentially automatic and continuous, involving initially an autogenous root weld followed by the deposition of a filler wire of matched 25 per cent chromium 20 per cent nickel composition, produced from a vacuum melted base. It is, however, not within the scope of this paper to deal with details either of the centrifugal casting process or the automatic welding technique to which reference has been made.

Data from a number of separate investigations coming within the overall research project in this field have been selected for the purpose of this paper. This has been done in the hope that a useful contribution can be made to the general pool of information that both users and producers of centrifugally cast reformer tubes have already recognized[1] as being so important in the future and so relatively lacking at this present time.

After giving details of the experimental materials employed and procedure followed in the course of the work undertaken to date, the test data and findings are presented under the following headings:

    I. Stress to rupture properties.

   II. Factors influencing stress to rupture properties, including:
        (a) Low melting point trace elements.
        (b) Vacuum and air melting.
        (c) Macro- and microstructure.

  III. Changes resulting from prolonged high temperature exposure:
        (a) Hardness.
        (b) Microstructure.

  IV. Metallurgy and properties of welded joints at ambient temperatures:
        (a) Joints in 25 per cent chromium 20 per cent nickel tube.
        (b) Joints in 25 per cent chromium 20 per cent nickel tube and low carbon steel.

EXPERIMENTAL MATERIALS AND PROCEDURE

Detailed information relating to the production of centrifugally cast tube and of tube welds which are the subject of this report, and relating to the conditions and procedure on which all tests were conducted, are recorded as follows:

(i) Centrifugally Cast Tube

Six tubes cast centrifugally from six different furnace melts were employed for the provision of test material. The as-cast dimensions of the tubes were

15 ft in length with an outside diameter of approximately 5¾ in. and a wall thickness in the range $\frac{9}{16}$ to ¾ in.

(ii) *Steelmaking*

The six melts from which the tubes were cast were based on raw material charges consisting of scrap and virgin metal additions, all being melted in air in basic lined high frequency induction furnaces. One melt (Ref. JGW/2) was subject to vacuum treatment for a period of 15 min at 1600°C and at a pressure equivalent of 1 mm Hg, before pouring in air.

In all cases the intended nominal composition conformed with A.S.T.M. Specification A297-HK and A351-CK-45, as follows:

Chromium	25	per cent
Nickel	20	per cent
Carbon	0·4	per cent
Silicon	1·0	per cent
Manganese	1·3	per cent
Sulphur	0·02	per cent
Phosphorus	0·02	per cent

(iii) *Chemical Analysis*

Elements other than lead and tin, were all determined by orthodox methods. Lead and tin were, however, determined by optical spectrograph (quartz DC excitation), using reference standards, the composition of which had been established independently by the National Physical Laboratory. The results are recorded in Table 1.

(iv) *Tensile Properties at Ambient Temperatures*

Tensile test pieces were machined from the wall sections of the tubes, longitudinally in relation to the axis of the tubes and at distances varying along their length. The test pieces were machined in accordance with British Standard 18, and, in order that they should be as representative as possible of the sound walls of the tube, the largest possible diameter test piece was selected, consistent of course with avoidance of the porosity zone associated with the internal periphery. The results of these tests are given in Table 2, which also includes the results of tensile tests on statically cast test blocks from 3 of the 6 furnace melts.

(v) *Mechanical Properties at Elevated Temperatures*

Test pieces of 0·357 ($\pm$0·0005) in. diameter, with a parallel length of 3·125 ($\pm$0·005) in. and a shoulder radius of 0·5 in. were taken from each of the centrifugally cast tubes, from positions adjacent to those from which the ambient temperature tensile test pieces were removed. As in the case of the

TABLE 1

Chemical Composition of Melts

Melt No.	Composition %										
	C	Si	Mn	Ni	Cr	Mo	S	P	N	Pb	Sn
EWG	0·40	0·93	1·41	19·1	25·7	0·25	0·02	0·02	0·09	0·001	0·007
JGW/1*	0·35	1·16	1·44	19·5	24·7	0·22	0·01	0·02	0·06	0·023	0·027
JGW/2*	0·38	0·82	1·34	19·4	24·8	0·05	0·02	0·02	0·06	0·002	0·029
MGY/2	0·37	0·73	1·31	20·8	25·7	0·34	0·03	0·03	0·08	0·001	0·011
LRN/1	0·35	1·15	1·32	21·9	25·0	0·28	0·01	0·02	0·06	0·004	0·010
LKH/2	0·40	1·34	1·30	21·8	26·2	0·22	0·02	0·02	0·05	0·019	0·010

* Melts JGW/1 and JGW/2 were produced from the same melting base charge, i.e. they originated from a split melt—JGW/2 being poured after vacuum treating JGW/1 (1 mm Hg for 15 min). With the exception of JGW/2 all metal was air-melted in H.F. furnaces.

latter, dye-penetrant surface flaw detection was applied to the test pieces to ensure freedom from surface-connected defects, prior to testing.

For the purpose of determining the stress to rupture and minimum creep rate properties (secondary creep), $\frac{3}{4}$ ton Denison T-47C testing machines were employed in line with the conditions of British Standard 3500 Part 1, the temperature of testing (900°C) being held at $\pm 6°$ and the load being held at ± 1 per cent. The stress applied varied from 4000 to 9600 lb/in.² and the time to rupture ranged from 50 to 5000 hr.

Efforts to measure elongation at room temperature after fracture, employing a fine divider and light pock marking, were largely nugatory insofar as fracture, in the majority of cases, occurred outside the $4\sqrt{So}$ or $5\cdot65\sqrt{So}$ gauge length. In cases where fracture occurred within the gauge length, elongation values of between $3\frac{1}{2}$ per cent and 10 per cent were recorded.

TABLE 2

Ambient Temperature Tensile Properties of Cast 25 per cent Chromium 20 per cent Nickel Steel

Identity of melt and test piece*	Origin of test piece†	Properties			
		U.T.S. t.s.i.	0·2% proof-stress t.s.i.	Elong. % $5\cdot65\sqrt{So}$	Red. in area %
EWG/1.B17	Tube wall 17 in. from end B	31·8	19·6	10	12
EWG/1	Static casting	35·0	19·1	15	15
JWG/1.B12	Tube wall 12 in. from end B	35·5	15·6	20	20
JGW/1	Static casting	32·0	16·0	15	15
JGW/2.B13	Tube wall 13 in. from end B	34·8	16·5	20	22
JGW/2	Static casting	33·2	18·5	16	20
MGY/2.B77	Tube wall 77 in. from end B	35·4	15·9	11	17
LRN/1.A2	Tube wall 2 in. from end A	30·1	15·8	17	20
LKH/2.A7‡	Tube wall 7 in. from end A	34·4	—	22	25

* Tensile test pieces were machined to 0·399 in. diameter in accordance with B.S.18.

† Test pieces were machined longitudinally from the wall section of the centrifugally cast tube—their centres being displaced slightly towards the outside periphery.

Also where indicated, test pieces were machined from 1 in. diameter × 7 in. long wedge fed static cast bars, poured from the same melt as the corresponding centrifugally cast tube.

‡ A tensometer test piece (0·178 in. diameter) was used in this case as the original 0·399 in. diameter bar contained defects.

(vi) *Hardness Testing*

For the purpose of determining the effect of prolonged exposure to high temperature upon hardness, the fractured stress to rupture specimens referred to in (v) were employed and Vickers diamond hardness determinations made at ambient temperature, using a 30 kg load.

(vii) *Macrostructure*

Ring sections were taken from each tube for macrostructure examination, the location of these rings being adjacent to each of the 7 in. long cylinders from which the tensile and stress to rupture test bars were also machined. In addition a number of 7 in. long sections, longitudinal in relation to the axis of the tube and adjacent to the tensile test bars, were taken to determine consistency of structure along the tube length.

Macrosections were etched cold for a period of 10 min in an aqueous nitric-hydrochloric acid reagent containing cupric chloride and then examined at a magnification of 8.

(viii) *Microstructures*

The locations from which microsections were prepared were also adjacent to the tensile and stress to rupture specimens for direct correlation purposes and were electrolytically etched in 10 per cent oxalic acid.

For further comparison microsections were prepared from the shoulder sections of four fractured stress to rupture specimens (Ref. JGW/2-B13/F, JGW/2-B13/G, LRN/1-A2/P and EWG/1-B17/P), these representing material which had been exposed at 900°C for periods of 52, 230, 490 and 4487 hr, respectively. Microexamination was performed at magnifications between 100 and 1200 to enable particular attention to be paid to the form and distribution of the carbide phases.

(ix) *Preparation of Weld Tensile Test Samples*

In a programme designed to assess the handling characteristics of manual arc welding electrodes from four different manufacturers, welds were made in a single piece of 25 per cent chromium 20 per cent nickel alloy centrifugally cast tube, of $7\frac{1}{2}$ in. outside diameter and 0·5 in. sound wall thickness. The tube composition is shown in Table 8A. Deposit pads were made from each of the four electrode samples and the results of chemical analysis are also shown in Table 8A. Three further welds were prepared by automatic inert gas-shielded tungsten arc (t.i.g.) welding using a different, but similarly sized, tube sample. Again, the tube and filler wire were analysed and results are shown in Table 8A.

The test welds were radiographed and, apart from occasional small slag inclusions in the manual metallic arc welds, no defects of any consequence were revealed. Duplicate 0·399 in. diameter transverse tensile test pieces were prepared from each manual weld and six transverse tensile test pieces were prepared from each of the three automatic welds. Tensile test results are shown in Table 8B.

(x) *Microexamination of* 25 *per cent Chromium* 20 *per cent Nickel Welds*

A typical microsection showing the weld metal and heat-affected zone taken from one of the manually welded samples is shown in Fig. 10. These particular $\frac{1}{2}$ in. wall samples welded by the automatic process were not sectioned for microexamination but, instead, a further test weld was made in thicker tube of 4 in. bore and $\frac{3}{4}$ in. sound wall thickness. A macrosection of this weld is shown in Fig. 11 and Fig. 12 shows the macrostructure of a manual t.i.g. weld also made in $\frac{3}{4}$ in. thick tube. Figures 13 to 16 illustrate microstructural features of weld metal, parent metal and heat-affected zone, and relate to the automatic weld shown in Fig. 11.

(xi) *Hardness of* 25 *per cent Chromium* 20 *per cent Nickel Welds*

Vickers hardness impressions at 30 kg were made on a mounted and polished cross-section taken from one of the automatically welded $\frac{3}{4}$ in. thick test samples. Following this, microhardness determinations at 200 g using a Vickers microhardness tester were made for comparison purposes. All the results are expressed in Table 9.

(xii) *Investigation of Welded Joints of* 25 *per cent Chromium* 20 *per cent Nickel and Low Carbon Steel*

As part of a wider research into the metallurgical aspects of various production techniques for welding low carbon steel to high carbon 25 per cent chromium 20 per cent nickel steel, microhardness and microanalytical surveys were performed on the following:

1. Weld beads produced on mild steel plate, using 10 s.w.g. electrodes run at 95 amps D.C., electrode positive and of the following types:
   (a) 25 per cent chromium 20 per cent nickel 0·1 per cent carbon.
   (b) 25 per cent chromium 20 per cent nickel 0·4 per cent carbon.
   (c) "Nicrex MC55" (18 per cent chromium 10 per cent nickel $4\frac{1}{2}$ per cent molybdenum).

2. Joints made between low carbon steel and high carbon 25 per cent chromium 20 per cent nickel centrifugally cast tube, using a single 60° vee preparation with a $\frac{1}{16}$ in. thick root face. The joint was close butted and was welded by the manual t.i.g. process exactly as would be the case in conventional production techniques for root running. Two fillers were used:
   (a) 25 per cent chromium 20 per cent nickel 0·4 per cent carbon.
   (b) Inconel 92.

3. An automatic weld between a low carbon steel flange, and a 0·5 in. sould wall high carbon 25 per cent chromium 20 per cent nickel centrifugally cast tube, made with an autogenous root run followed by t.i.g. filling passes,

using high carbon 25 per cent chromium 20 per cent nickel filler wire. This was also sectioned and examined.

Examination was made in the as-welded state and at a later stage micro-examination only was carried out after the samples had been heat treated for 1 hr at 850°C and allowed to furnace cool.

DISCUSSION OF DATA

I. *Stress to Rupture Properties*

(i) Table 3 records the results of 21 tests carried out under this research project to date and it will be noted that the most extended period is approximately 5000 hr. This series of tests is continuing and in due course further data will become available.

No attempt has been made to extrapolate or to predict long-term

TABLE 3

Elevated Temperature Mechanical Properties of Cast 25 per cent Chromium 20 per cent Nickel Steel at 900°C

Identity of melt and test piece*	Origin of test piece†	Stress applied p.s.i.	Time to rupture hr	Minimum‡ creep rate % per hr
JGW/1.B12. A	Tube wall 12 in. from end B	9600	67	0·016
JGW/1.B12. B	Tube wall 12 in. from end B	9600	50	0·011
JGW/2.B13. E	Tube wall 13 in. from end B	9600	80	0·006
JGW/2.B13. F	Tube wall 13 in. from end B	9600	52	0·012
MGY/2.B77. I	Tube wall 17 in. from end B	9600	90	0·008
LRN/1.A2. M	Tube wall 2 in. from end A	9600	86	0·006
JGW/1.B12. C	Tube wall 12 in. from end B	7400	333	0·0002
JGW/1.B12. D	Tube wall 12 in. from end B	7400	300	0·0013
JGW/2.B13. G	Tube wall 13 in. from end B	7400	230	0·002
JGW/2.B13. H	Tube wall 13 in. from end B	7400	182	0·0008
MGY/2.B77. K	Tube wall 77 in. from end B	7400	232	0·002
LRN/1.A2. O	Tube wall 2 in. from end A	7400	556	0·0009
LRN/1.A2. P	Tube wall 2 in. from end A	7400	490	0·0008
LKH/2.A7. S	Tube wall 7 in. from end A	7400	289	0·0006
EKH/2.A7. U	Tube wall 7 in. from end A	7400	264	0·001
EWG/1.B17. M	Tube wall 77 in. from end B	5800	649	0·00048
EWG/1.B17. 3	Static casting	5800	1113	0·00019
EWG/1.B17. 4	Static casting	5800	1760	0·00016
EWG/1.B17. L	Tube wall 17 in. from end B	5000	1426	0 00009
EWG/1.B17. N	Tube wall 17 in. from end B	4000	3053	0·00008
EWG/1.B17. P	Tube wall 17 in. from end B	4000	4487	0·00003

* 0·357 in. diameter test pieces were used.

† Test pieces were machined similarly and were adjacent to those used for ambient temperature tensile tests—see Table 2.

‡ Over secondary creep range.

behaviour in the 10,000 or 100,000 hr range, it being considered preferable at this stage to concentrate upon considering trends noticeable in the 200 to 5000 hr period.

(ii) Figure 1 shows the times to rupture of each of the 21 tests, plotted logarithmically against applied stress at 900°C and the mean of these 21 tests, together with data extracted from three other sources,[1, 2, 3] plotted similarly for comparison purposes.

It will be seen that the overall scatter on the time scale corresponds to a factor of 3 on life taken over the series of tests as a whole. This difference in life is, however, reduced to a factor of approximately 1·3 when considered in relation to duplicate tests from a single tube rather than over a batch of tubes as a whole. Certain comparable data[1] relates to centrifugally cast tube in 37 per cent nickel 18 per cent chromium alloy where a scatter of 10 was reported. It is appreciated, however, that the relatively small scatter associated with the test results reported in this paper may in itself be associated with the small number (six) of tubes tested and that with greater variations of, for example carbon, the scatter in life may well become greater.

(iii) Figure 1 indicates that the cast tubes under examination are comparable with cast material of different origin produced by different casting techniques, the mean time to rupture results being straddled by those from the three external sources.

(iv) No significant correlation is apparent between tensile properties at

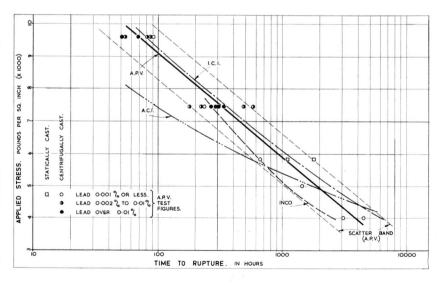

FIG. 1

Cast 25/20 per cent chromium–nickel steel comparison of various rupture data with A.P.V. test figures at 900°C. (A.P.V.—Sept. 1964).

ambient temperatures and the time to rupture properties at elevated temperatures.

(v) A significant proportion (14 out of 21) of elevated temperature test pieces failed outside the gauge length in locations that could not be said to be associated either with the pock marking or with the test piece shoulder. This location of fracture is the subject of further investigation.

II. *Factors Influencing Stress to Rupture Properties*

(a) *Low melting-point trace elements*

(i) Within the range of time and of stress applied, there is no evidence

TABLE 4

Effect of Lead and Tin on Stress-Rupture Properties of Cast 25 per cent
Chromium 20 per cent Nickel Steel at 900°C

A. *Effect of Lead*

Sn level %	Pb %	Identity of melt and test piece		Time to rupture, hr	Minimum creep rate, % per hr
0·01	0·001	MGY/2.B77.	K	232	0·002
	0·004	LRN/1.A2.	O	556	0·0009
	0·004	LRN/1.A2.	P	490	0·0008
	0·019	LKH/2.A7.	S	289	0·0006
	0·019	LKH/2.A7.	U	264	0·001
0·03	0·002	JGW/2.B13.	G	230	0·002
	0·002	JGW/2.B13.	H	182	0·0008
	0·023	JGW/1.B12.	C	333	0·0002
	0·023	JGW/1.B12.	D	300	0·0013

B. *Effect of Tin*

Pb level %	Sn %	Identity of melt and test piece		Time to rupture, hr	Minimum creep rate, % per hr
0·001– 0·002	0·011	MGY/2.B77.	K	232	0·002
	0·029	JGW/2.B13.	G	230	0·002
	0·029	JGW/2.B13.	H	182	0·008
0·02	0·010	LKH/2.A7.	S	289	0·0006
	0·010	LKH/2.A7.	U	264	0·001
	0·027	JGW/1.B12.	C	333	0·0002
	0·027	JGW/1.B12.	D	300	0·0013

Notes: (a) The above data is extracted from Table 3.
   (b) These data refer only to those specimens stressed at 7400 p.s.i.

that either tin or lead has an adverse effect on the stress to rupture properties of 25 per cent chromium 20 per cent nickel alloy in centrifugally cast form (see Fig. 1 and Table 4). If indeed these elements do have a real effect, then it is concluded either that the data available is inadequate or the significance of the effect of these elements is swamped by other unknown factors of greater significance.

(ii) While it has been shown[4] that trace quantities of lead can have an adverse influence on the high temperature properties of nickel-base alloys containing up to 20 per cent cobalt and up to 20 per cent chromium, there is no evidence available at this stage from the tests to which these notes refer to justify or support the conclusion that trace quantities of lead have the same effect on 25 per cent chromium 20 per cent nickel alloy.

TABLE 5

Effect of Time at 900°C on Ambient Temperature Hardness of 25 per cent Chromium 20 per cent Nickel Centrifugally Cast Steel Tube

Tube Identity	Sample No.	Condition*	Hardness † V.P.N.
EWG. B9–17	B9	As-cast	188
	M	649 hr at 900°C. A.C.	251
	L	1426 hr at 900°C. A.C.	255
	N	3053 hr at 900°C. A.C.	268
	P	4487 hr at 900°C. A.C.	251
JGW/1.B12	B12	As-cast	181
	B	50 hr at 900°C. A.C.	224
	A	67 hr at 900°C. A.C.	239
	D	300 hr at 900°C. A.C.	223
	C	333 hr at 900°C. A.C.	223
JGW/2.B13	B13	As-cast	179
	F	52 hr at 900°C. A.C.	245
	E	80 hr at 900°C. A.C.	240
	H	182 hr at 900°C. A.C.	249
	G	230 hr at 900°C. A.C.	243
MGY/2.B77	B77	As-cast	198
	I	90 hr at 900°C. A.C.	260
	K	232 hr at 900°C. A.C.	235
LRN/1.A2	A2	As-cast	189
	P	490 hr at 900°C. A.C.	226
	O	556 hr at 900°C. A.C.	218

* Hardness determinations carried out on fractured stress-rupture test pieces after treatment as indicated.
† 30 kg load $\frac{2}{3}$ in. objective—scatter approx: ± 7 V.P.N.

(iii) The imposition of very low limits ($0 \cdot 01$ per cent and below) of lead as a specification requirement appears to be as questionable at this stage on metallurgical grounds as it undoubtedly is undesirable on economic. The case for a similar imposition upon the limit of tin seems to be even more questionable, especially insofar as its influence on the nickel-base alloys referred to does not even appear to have been established.

(b) Vacuum and air melting

(iv) There is no evidence that vacuum treatment of the liquid steel before casting improves stress to rupture properties. Such treatment substantially reduces lead content, without significantly influencing either nitrogen or tin contents.

(c) Macro- and microstructure

(v) There is some evidence (Fig. 1) that the stress to rupture properties of statically cast material are superior to those of centrifugally cast tube of the same composition, a difference which may well be a function of grain size and grain form.

(vi) Detailed examination of the six centrifugally cast tubes showed a wide variety and size of crystal structure, varying from completely columnar growth from the periphery to the bore in some cases, to others which demonstrated a chill crystal zone on the periphery, followed by a central columnar zone and finally by an equiaxial. Typical macrostructures are described in detail in Table 6.

(vii) Consideration of the macrostructure of each tube, in relation to corresponding stress to rupture properties, provides no grounds for suggesting that any particular crystal form has a significant influence upon elevated temperature test data. There is no support for any contention that a completely columnar grained structure shows marked improvement in stress to rupture properties.

(viii) It was noted that considerable variation in macrostructure was found from tube to tube. Within the 7 in. long sections removed from each tube for the provision of test material, however, no evident variation in macrostructure was detected.

(ix) Detailed examination of microstructures showed a marked variation radially through the wall of any given tube, particularly in relation to the form and distribution of the carbide phases in the austenitic matrix. However, there appeared to be a consistent pattern of change in structure across the tube section, from tube to tube.

Typical microstructures are shown in Figs. 2 to 9 and are described in Table 7.

(x) There is no evidence to show any significant correlation between macro- and microstructure throughout the tubes examined.

TABLE 6

Macro-examination of Sections Cut from Centrifugally Cast Tube

Identity of Macro	Site	Section	Results of examination
JGW/1. B12	12 in. from end B	Ring cross-section ($\frac{3}{4}$ in. as-cast wall)	Fine columnar grains extending $\frac{1}{16}$ in. from outside periphery (O.D.), followed by medium columnar grains to $\frac{3}{8}$ in. from O.D., then medium equiaxed grains to bore (I.D.). Extent of I.D. porosity $\frac{3}{32}$ in.
JGW/1. B12–B19	12 to 19 in. from end B	Longitudinal section ($\frac{3}{4}$ in. as-cast wall)	Similar to JGW/1. B12 above.
JGW/2. B13	13 in. from end B	Ring cross-section ($\frac{3}{4}$ in. as-cast wall)	Small columnar grains extending $\frac{1}{8}$ in. from O.D., followed by small equiaxed grains to $\frac{3}{8}$ in. from O.D., then medium columnar grains to bore. Extent of I.D. porosity $\frac{1}{32}$ in.
MGY/2. B77	77 in. from end B	Ring cross-section ($\frac{9}{16}$ in. as-cast wall)	Chill crystals extending $\frac{3}{32}$ in. from O.D., followed by small columnar grains to $\frac{1}{32}$ in. from O.D. then small/medium equiaxed grains to bore. Extent of I.D. porosity $\frac{3}{32}$ in.
MGY/2. B85	85 in. from end B	Ring cross-section ($\frac{9}{16}$ in. as-cast wall)	Similar to MGY/2. B77 above.
LRN/1. A2	2 in. from end A	Ring cross-section ($\frac{9}{16}$ in. as-cast wall)	Small/medium columnar grains extending $\frac{5}{16}$ in. from O.D., followed by small/medium equiaxed grains to bore. Extent of I.D. porosity $\frac{5}{32}$ in.
LKH/2. A7	7 in. from end A	Ring cross-section ($\frac{9}{32}$ in. as-cast wall)	Medium/large columnar grains extending from O.D. to I.D. However near I.D. there are some small/medium equiaxed grains. Extent of I.D. porosity $\frac{1}{8}$ in.

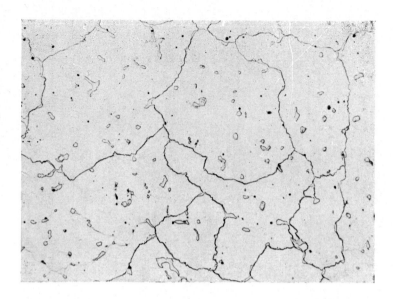

Fig. 2

JGW/2 B13. Near outside periphery. Mag. ×110.

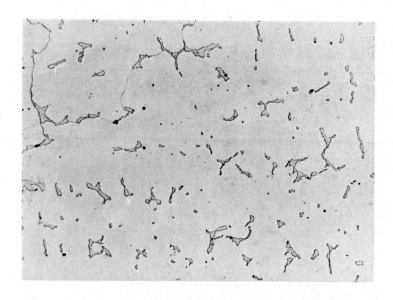

Fig. 3

JGW/2 B13. Centre. Mag. ×110.

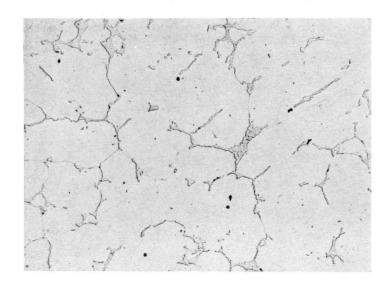

FIG. 4

JGW/2 B13. Near bore. Mag. ×110.

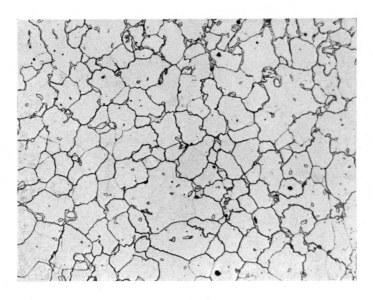

FIG. 5

MGY/2 B77. Near outside periphery. Mag. ×110.

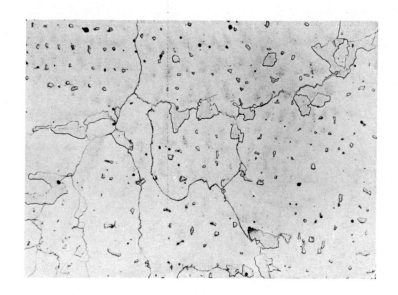

FIG. 6

MGY/2 B77. Centre. Mag. ×110.

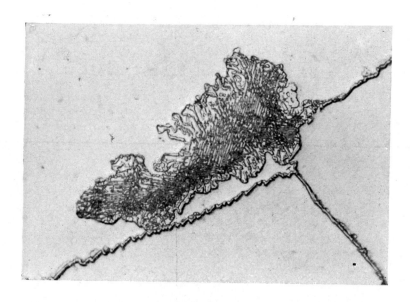

FIG. 7

MGY/2 B77. Centre. Mag. ×1200.

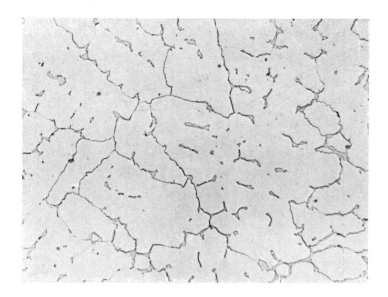

FIG. 8

LRN/1 A2. Centre. Mag. ×110.

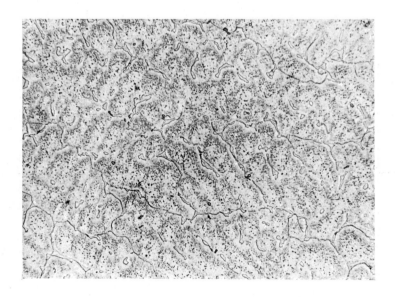

FIG. 9

LRN/1 A2 P. Centre. Mag. ×110.

TABLE 7—Micro-examination of Sections Cut from Centrifugally Cast Tube

Identity of micro.	Fig. No.	Location across-wall section	Results of examination
JGW/2. B13	2	Near outside periphery	Austenitic matrix with pronounced grain boundary type (i)* carbides and some scattered interdendritic carbides eutectic type (iv)*. This corresponds to the small equiaxed grains in the macro-section.
JGW/2. B13	3	Centre	Austenitic matrix with pronounced type (iv) carbides and some type (i). This corresponds to the medium columnar zone in the macro section.
JGW/2. B13	4	Near bore	Austenitic matrix with coarse almost continuous network of type (iv) carbides.
MGY/2. B77	5	Near outside periphery	Austenitic matrix with fine grain outlined by continuous type (i) carbides. There is also a small amount of lamellar type (ii)* carbides associated with grain boundaries. A few scattered type (iv) carbides are present. This corresponds to the chill crystal zone in the macro-section.
MGY/2. B77	6	Centre	Austenitic matrix with substantial quantity of massive lamellar type (ii) carbides associated with continuous type (i) carbides. Scattered type (iv) carbides also present. This corresponds to the small columnar grain zone in the macro-section.
MGY/2. B77	7	Centre	As Fig. 6 showing types (i) and (ii) carbides in detail (magnification × 1200).
LRN/1. A2	8	Centre	Austenitic matrix with pronounced grain boundary type (i) carbides with some eutectic type (iv) carbides scattered in matrix and associated with grain boundaries. This is similar to JGW/2. B13 except that the continuous type (i) carbides extend well into the centre section. This corresponds to the small/medium columnar grain zone in the macro-section.
LRN/1. A2.P	9	Centre	Similar to Fig. 8 but showing granular secondary carbides precipitated in an interdendritic pattern in the matrix around the primary carbides. (Result of treatment at 900°C for 490 hr slow cool.)

* For convenience of identification four distinct forms of primary carbides quite frequently found in cast 25 per cent chromium 20 per cent nickel steel containing 0·4 per cent carbon, are defined as follows:

Type (i) Thin, but continuous grain boundary films.

Type (ii) Lamellar masses, closely resembling pearlite located on or near grain boundaries.

Type (iii) Isolated interdendritic islands, complex in nature, frequently nucleated round small sulphide or non-metallic inclusions. These islands may be surrounded by rings of fine globular carbides. It should be noted, that while type (iii) carbides have been found in the statically cast alloy—they have not as yet been identified in centrifugally cast tubes.

Type (iv) Coarse eutectic type, frequently forming a semi-continuous interdendritic network and in some cases replacing the thin grain boundary films (type (ii)).

(xi) Three of four distinct types of carbide phase were identified in these centrifugally cast tube sections and occurred in various combinations. The four types which may be found in both static and centrifugally cast 25 per cent chromium 20 per cent nickel steel are listed below. Type (iii) is usually associated with non-metallic inclusions and is seldom, if ever, found in centrifugally cast materials.

Type (i) Thin continuous grain boundary films.

Type (ii) Lamellar masses closely resembling pearlite, located on or near grain boundaries.

Type (iii) Isolated interdendritic islands.

Type (iv) Coarse eutectic type, frequently forming semi-continuous inter-dendritic network.

(xii) In the majority of cases the microstructure adjacent to the periphery conforms to a Type (i), with some scattered interdendritic eutectic Type (iv), whereas the zone near the bore tends to be predominantly Type (iv). The centre regions normally contain Type (iv) carbides with a little continuous grain boundary carbides of Type (i).

(xiii) While there is insufficient data available at this juncture to determine which form or forms of microstructure give rise to the best stress to rupture properties, there is some evidence to suggest, however, that that which contains pronounced grain boundary Type (i) carbides, together with some eutectic Type (iv) scattered in the matrix and also associated with the grain boundaries, is to be preferred. There may be particular advantage where such a structure extends from the periphery to well over the middle sections of the tube wall, as shown in Fig. 8.

It is considered that this evidence (see also Tables 3 and 7—Ref. LRN/1A2), slender as it is, should be pursued further in view of its obvious potential importance.

III. *Changes Resulting from Prolonged High Temperature Exposure*

(a) *Hardness*

(i) The data recorded in Table 5 indicate quite clearly that exposure within the period of 50 hr produces an increase in hardness of between 30 and 60 VPN, this with some variation between melts, being maintained up to 5000 hr of exposure. Corresponding data[1] in respect of 37 per cent nickel 18 per cent chromium alloy, over shorter periods of time, show similar behaviour.

(b) *Microstructure*

(ii) The hardening effect is considered to be associated with the precipitation of supersaturated carbides in the matrix, which is confirmed by micro-examination of the specimens after exposure (see Fig. 9 and Table 7—Ref.

LRN/1.A2.P). The related hardening effect in welded joints is referred to subsequently.

IV. *Metallurgy and Properties of Welded Joints at Ambient Temperatures*
    (a) *Joints in 25 per cent chromium 20 per cent nickel tube.*
    (i) *Weld Tensile Tests on Manual and Automatic Welds*

The results given in Table 8B indicate little significant difference between the properties of the manual and automatic welds tested, with the single exception of ductility as measured in the standard way by percentage elongation. In every case fracture of the test pieces occurred away from the weld and heat-affected zone. In the case of the automatic welds, fracture was outside the gauge length on four occasions out of eighteen. This led to an indication of low elongation figures and yet, despite this, the mean elongation percentage remained high. As failure occurred away from the weld zone, these particular tests are rather a measurement of parent metal than of weld metal strength. The test results, however, appear to indicate that the composite joint, and by inference the weld metal, is markedly more ductile where the automatic t.i.g. welding process is used.

This inference is not necessarily valid. Two possible explanations exist:

1. Different tubes were used for the manual and automatic welding tests, and these may have had different ductility.

2. Observations of the microstructure suggest that the weld metal and heat-affected zone hardness may be increased as a result of carbide precipitation, and this suggestion is substantiated by hardness measurements.

It may be inferred from these observations that the weld metal and heat-affected zone ductility is reduced by this carbide precipitation. The type of carbide precipitation is similar in the manual and automatic welds examined and therefore a second explanation for apparently increased ductility in the case of the automatic welds may be found in the relative weld zone widths.

Due to the overall higher rate of heat input, short welding time and heat build-up in the weld zone, the heat-affected zones produced in automatic t.i.g. welding are wider than those produced in manual arc welding. The weld width in automatic welding is, however, substantially less than that produced by conventional manual techniques (Figs. 11 and 12), and hence the overall size of the stiff weld and heat-affected zone tend to be smaller. It follows therefore that transverse tensile test pieces of a given size and gauge length, will contain more ductile material between the gauge marks where narrow automatic welds are being tested. High elongation figures may be expected but it should not be concluded on the basis of this measurement alone, that the weld zones are inherently more ductile.

Although transverse elongation measurements are of doubtful significance in weld testing, it is to be regretted that such measurements often occur as specific manufacturing requirements.

TABLE 8

Transverse Tensile Tests on 25 per cent Chromium 20 per cent Nickel Welds at Ambient Temperature

A. *Materials Composition*

Material	Composition %							
	C	Si	Mn	Ni	Cr	S	P	N
Tube for manual welding	0·40	1·34	1·33	21·1	25·1	0·020	0·025	0·034
Manual electrodes (deposit pads)								
Manufacturer A	0·42	0·25	2·42	20·8	26·3	0·008	0·017	0·016
Manufacturer B	0·35	0·41	1·74	21·5	26·2	0·018	0·021	0·088
Manufacturer C	0·41	0·26	3·72	19·2	25·6	0·018	0·025	0·088
Manufacturer D	0·41	0·13	2·42	20·4	25·8	0·011	0·024	0·060
Tube for automatic welding	0·40	1·26	1·03	19·6	23·3	0·015	0·007	
Wire for automatic welding	0·40	1·13	1·26	21·5	24·9	0·012		

B. *Tensile Test Results*

Welding process	Number of replicates	0·1% proof t.s.i.	0·2% proof t.s.i.	0·5% proof t.s.i.	Elongation % on 2 in. gauge length	Reduction in area %	U.T.S. t.s.i.	Fracture position
				Mean results				
Manual	8	19·4	21·6	24·0	6·5	12	34·7	Parent metal in every case
Automatic	18	18·1	20·0	22·2	12	23	33·0	Parent metal in every case
				Range of results				
Manual	8	18·4–20·5	20·0–22·8	22·4–25·2	4–8	10–20	32·8–35·6	Parent metal in every case
Automatic	18	16·4–19·2	17·7–21·4	19·9–23·5	6 (O.G.)–16	15–30	27·9–35·7	Parent metal in every case

Despite marked differences in thermal condition during welding, it may be concluded from this series of tests that, whatever the reasons for apparent differences in joint ductility, the ambient temperature tensile properties obtained by automatic welding are not worse than those produced by conventional manual welding.

(ii) *Weld and parent metal composition.* Perhaps the most significant feature of the figures presented in Table 8A is the relatively high silicon level in the wire used for automatic t.i.g. welding. The desirability from a welding standpoint of maintaining a high carbon/silicon ratio and of restricting the silicon level is of course widely known and general acceptance of this, as a means of reducing the tendency of weld metals to microfissure, is reflected in the very low mean silicon content of the four manual electrodes tested. In one case silicon was as low as 0·13 per cent while the maximum was no more than 0·41 per cent.

It is also well known that microfissuring can be avoided if the manganese level is raised. One manufacturer's electrodes deposited metal containing 3·72 per cent manganese, whereas it will be noted that the matching wire for automatic welding contained only 1·26 per cent. In no case has microfissuring been seen on examination of automatic welds in tubes varying between $\frac{5}{16}$ in. and $\frac{3}{4}$ in. sound wall thickness when employing filler wire of the composition shown.

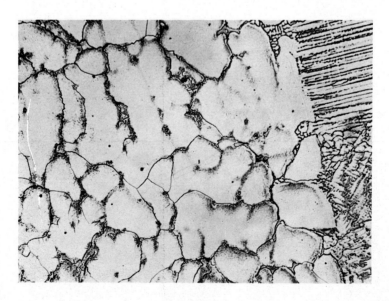

Fig. 10

Manual metallic arc weld. Weld metal and heat affected zone Mag. × 100.

A number of weld bead tests have been carried out on tubes of varying composition, the results of which are not reported here. A tungsten arc was run across the tube surface under constant conditions of current, voltage and traverse speed, and the resulting fused bead was examined for crack type and frequency by fluorescent penetrant techniques. Although some tube compositions revealed startling cracking tendencies in this test, in no case was difficulty encountered in welding by the automatic t.i.g. process.

The automatic technique was developed specifically with crack-sensitive materials in mind. All welding situations conducive to the production of microfissuring were carefully eliminated from the technique and the measure of success achieved in this direction is perhaps emphasized by the relatively high-silicon low-manganese composition of the matching filler wire which has in practice proved quite satisfactory. The use of such relatively high silicon levels in the weld metal may conceivably be beneficial from the point of view of scaling resistance and it may well be that limitation of manganese level is of some benefit in maintaining creep properties comparable with those

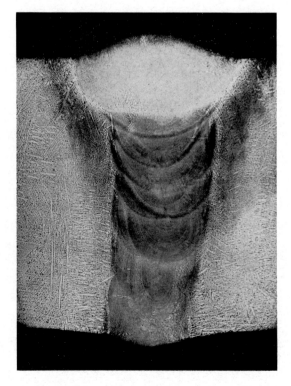

Fig. 11

Automatic t.i.g. weld. 0·75 in. section thickness. Mag. ×4.

of the parent material. So far as the authors are aware, this factor has not received detailed attention as yet.

(iii) *Microexamination of* 25 *per cent chromium* 20 *per cent nickel weld sections.* Figures 13 and 14 show the structure of the parent tube to be similar to that of the capping weld run, particularly with respect to the absence of intragranular carbide precipitation. This structural similarity is evident despite differences in grain size resulting from higher freezing rates in the weld metal and is in itself, of course, hardly remarkable and would be expected where attempt has been made to match closely the structural properties of the tube by automatic deposition of bare wire of matching composition.

Figures 15 and 16, also taken from a section of ¾ in. thick automatic weld, show pronounced fine intragranular carbide precipitation in the heat-affected zone and similarly in the re-heated weld runs. It will be noted from Fig. 16 that the weld metal exhibits a marked coring tendency, resulting presumably from its high freezing rate.

Figure 10 shows the weld and heat-affected zone structures of a manual metallic arc weld. Here the carbide precipitation can be seen to be similar

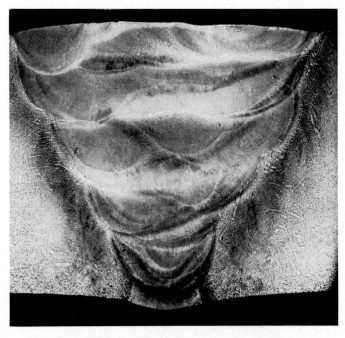

FIG. 12

Manual t.i.g. weld. 0·75 in. section thickness. Mag. ×4.

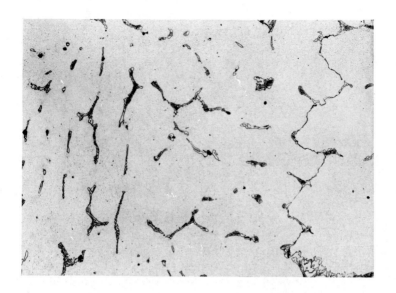

FIG. 13

Automatic t.i.g. weld. Parent metal microstructure. Mag. ×200.

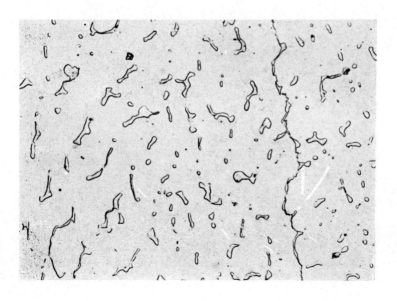

FIG. 14

Automatic t.i.g. weld. Capping run microstructure. Mag. ×700.

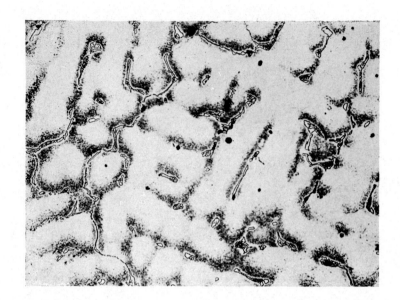

FIG. 15

Automatic t.i.g. weld. Parent metal heat affected zone. Mag. ×200.

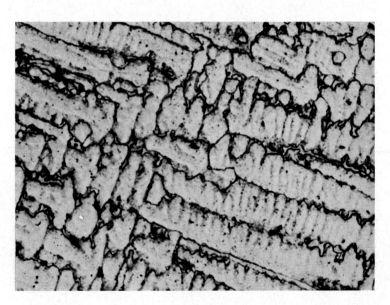

FIG. 16

Automatic t.i.g. weld. Reheated weld run. Mag. ×350.

in form to that which occurred in automatic welding, but appreciably less in quantity. This again is to be expected as the overall rate of heat input in manual welding is much lower than that in the continuous automatic process, where, owing to the relatively low thermal conductivity of 25 per cent chromium 20 per cent nickel alloy steel, heat build-up occurs and the heat-affected zones remain longer in the carbide precipitation temperature range.

Reference to Fig. 9 shows that the carbide precipitation produced in the presence of applied stress at 900°C is similar in form to that produced in the heat-affected and re-heated parts of the weld zone, although different in distribution. The significance of this is not understood, but the effect in terms of hardness is similar. Edeleanu[1] suggests by inference that the hardness of 37 per cent nickel 18 per cent chromium high-carbon alloy decreases after prolonged exposure at 700°C and, if this results from a strain-ageing mechanism, then it is possible that similar effects may also be noticed, in conditions yet to be investigated, in the high-carbon 25 per cent chromium 20 per cent nickel alloy.

The object of using matching fillers in welding is of course to avoid the production of a metallurgical notch. It may of course be that as precipitation occurs in the weld zones in the as-welded state, two forms of metallurgical notch are unavoidable. At the time of installation the weld-assembled tubes have relatively stiff weld zones. After some period of time in operation, however, the weld and tube material may have equal stiffness due to carbide precipitating in the parent material. After a longer time, the weld zones may then over-age and soften before the parent material thus generating an inverse notch.

The authors have no data suggesting that the high-carbon 25 per cent chromium 20 per cent nickel alloy behaves as the 37 per cent nickel 18 per cent chromium alloy from the point of view of over-ageing. Whether this mechanism obtains in practice and indeed if these effects are of any importance, can only be gauged in the light of service behaviour. Detailed metallurgical analysis of service failures is obviously urgently necessary.

(iv) *Weld geometry.* It is possible that the residual stress pattern around a narrow parallel-sided weld may be more uniform and less likely to contribute to premature failure than the complex stress pattern existing around a conventional "V" or "U" type single side manual weld. Figure 11 illustrates what may well be a very desirable shape for joints in thick sections. This particular section was taken from an automatic t.i.g. weld in 25 per cent chromium 20 per cent nickel centrifugally cast tube of ¾ in. sound wall thickness and it will be observed that the weld is virtually parallel-sided over 80 per cent of its thickness. It is merely the capping and possibly more ductile run that is wider.

Wider grooves are required in manual welding in order to permit torch and filler rod manipulation and the consequent greater weld width is well illustrated by Fig. 12. It will be evident that the narrow weld form is only practicable by machine-welding techniques and therefore such techniques, with their obvious economic advantage in terms of welding consumables and technical advantage in terms of reproducibility, demanded serious consideration, if only for these reasons.

The weld penetration bead shape can not only be predicted by the adoption of machine-welding, but can also be uniform provided that attention is paid to every process variable. This uniformity may be of some importance in considering either the passage of internals into the tube assemblies or the generation of turbulent gas conditions, with consequent risk of high temperature corrosion or erosion.

As with manual welding, the inward protrusion of the weld penetration bead is made up of two parts; first that produced by the weld penetration itself, which can usually be contained within $\frac{1}{16}$ in., and, second, that produced by local contraction of the heated parent metal adjacent to the weld. This contraction usually adds another $\frac{1}{32}$ in. to the inward protrusion.

(v) *Effects of residual bore shrinkage.* In a series of experiments to determine the effect of residual bore microshrinkage on the automatic t.i.g. welding process, a number of tubes were machined to varying depths in the bore,

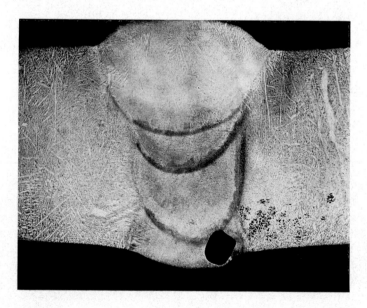

Fig. 17

Automatic t.i.g. weld. Cavities in weld metal associated with residual bore microshrinkage. Mag. × 4.

TABLE 9

Hardness Survey

25 per cent Chromium 20 per cent Nickel Automatic t.i.g. Weld in 0·75 in. Sound Wall Tube

A. *Traverse through capping run*

Zone	Heat affected zone	Capping run	Heat affected zone
Distance (in.)	0 0·2		0·6 0·8
Microhardness at 200 g load (VPN)	266 296 302 300 296	296 296 300 322 292 302 320	280 298 318 286 298

B. *Traverse through re-heated weld run*

Zone	Heat affected zone	Re-heated (penultimate) weld run	Heat affected zone
Distance (in.)	0 0·25		0·55 8·0
Hardness at 30 kg load (VPN)	223 253 269 254	246	260 248 216

C. *Traverse through root*

Zone	Heat affected zone	Root run	Heat affected zone
Distance (in.)	0 0·25		0·5 0·8
Microhardness at 200 g load (VPN)	296 320 290 322 314	356 330 350 350 314 350 302	336 260 254 254 254

checked by dye-penetrant examination and the indications noted before welding. On completion of the series of test welds, radiographs were taken and it was found that welding defects occurred only in those cases where the dye-penetrant indications had run into metal which was subsequently incorporated into the weld root.

Figure 17 illustrates one zone where residual microshrinkage is associated with gaseous cavities in the weld metal. It is presumed that these cavities result from the formation of vapour when cutting fluids, which are trapped in bore surface connected microshrinkage, come under the influence of the welding arc. These cavities are invariably gross, readily detected by radiography, and may exist either in spherical form or as pipes where the cavity persists in more than one weld run.

(vi) *Hardness of 25 per cent chromium 20 per cent nickel welds.* The results presented in Table 9 show a hardening of about 50 points VPN resulting from the precipitation of carbide by the operation of welding.

These indications, from hardness testing at 30 kg load, are confirmed by the microhardness traverse at 200 g load. The high load traverse was made in the heat-affected zone and in re-heated weld metal. This held good also for one microhardness survey which was made near the weld root; the other microhardness survey was made through the capping run where much less hardening was observed. The microhardness figures themselves are between 50 and 100 points higher than comparable figures obtained at 30 kg load and in the parent material considerable scatter is evident.

The carbide particles and microstructure generally are coarser in the parent material than in the weld metal and therefore it is likely that the hard carbide particles reflect their presence in terms of microhardness scatter. It has been observed, when taking microhardness measurements on single phase homogeneous material, that, as the load is decreased in the range 200 to 5 g, so the apparent hardness of the material tested increases. At these very light loads of course the impression depth is only a few microns and it is possible that surface work hardening on specimen polishing may be a significant factor.

(b) *Joints in 25 per cent Chromium 20 per cent Nickel Tube and Low Carbon Steel*

(i) A typical microhardness survey across the fusion boundary between high carbon 25 per cent chromium 20 per cent nickel weld metal and carbon steel plate is shown in Fig. 18.

The microhardness impressions are spaced by approximately 10 μ. The section was polished and etched in $\frac{1}{2}$ per cent Nital, so that structural features of material containing more than about 2 per cent chromium are not revealed.

Table 10 shows the results of X-ray fluorescence micro-probe analysis in

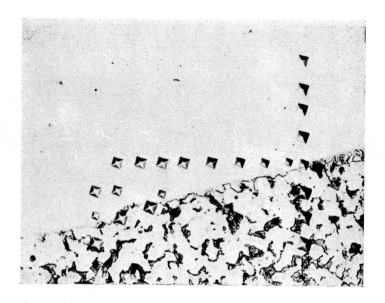

FIG. 18

High carbon 25/20 weld metal on mild steel 5 g. Microhardness impressions
spaced by approximately 10 μ. Mag. $\times 700$.

conjunction with the microhardness readings for an 18 per cent chromium
10 per cent nickel $4\frac{1}{2}$ per cent molybdenum metallic arc bead on carbon
steel plate.

These results show that in the as-welded state a hard zone, approximately
8 μ thick, exists on the high alloy side of, and 2 μ away from, the boundary
revealed by $\frac{1}{2}$ per cent Nital. Analysis shows this zone to be composed of
material containing between 11·9 per cent and 6·6 per cent chromium,
2·4 per cent and 1·5 per cent molybdenum and 6·2 per cent and 3·0 per cent
nickel. Such steels are of course air hardening[5, 6] and the thermal cycles
in welding are such that the hardness and analytical results are consistent.

This correlation of hardness with micro-probe analysis was evident in a
number of other cases examined and Table 11 summarizes these findings.
It is particularly interesting to note that, in the case of high-carbon and low-
carbon 25 per cent chromium 20 per cent nickel beads on carbon steel plate
in the as-welded condition, hardening has occurred to a similar extent, the
carbon level of the weld metal being of no apparent significance.

The boundary hardening tendency when manually t.i.g. welding with
either high carbon 25 per cent chromium 20 per cent nickel or Inconel 92
filler wire is interesting. Micro-probe analysis shows the hard zone to contain
about 12 per cent nickel and 7 per cent chromium which agrees with

TABLE 10

Composition and Hardness of Fusion Boundary between 18 per cent Chromium 10 per cent Nickel 4½ per cent Molybdenum Weld Metal and Mild Steel Plate

| | Distance from fusion boundary μ | Micro-hardness (VPN at 5 g) | Micro-probe analysis | | |
			Composition %		
			Cr	Mo	Ni
HIGH ALLOY WELD	80	371	16·6	4·0	10·8
	60	353	16·7	3·8	11·0
	40	336	17·0	3·7	9·8
	30	336	16·5	3·7	9·5
	20	321	14·4	3·1	9·1
	12	411	13·0	2·9	8·3
	9	514	11·9	2·4	6·2
	8	544	11·0	2·2	5·4
	6	544	9·7	2·0	4·5
	5	544	8·3	1·7	3·9
	4	514	6·6	1·5	3·0
	3	434	4·9	1·5	2·3
	2	371	3·0	1·3	1·2
	1	336	2·0	1·3	0·8
	0	293	1·4	0·8	0·6
MILD STEEL	−1	280	1·2	0·8	0·5
	−4	280	1·0	0·5	0·5
	−7	211	0·7	0·5	0
	−15	204	0·3	0	0
	−30	196	0	0	0

Schaeffler's[5] prediction for the formation of martensite. For this composition to arise it is clear that very considerable dilution of the filler metal, by pick-up from the carbon steel, must have occurred. This is not unreasonable, and is characteristic of composition heterogeneity encountered when manually t.i.g. welding dissimilar materials.

An automatic weld between high-carbon 25 per cent chromium 20 per cent nickel centrifugally cast tube and a carbon steel flange was microhardness tested in the as-welded state and it may be noted from Table 11 that relatively high hardness levels were discovered in a similar narrow zone adjacent to the fusion boundary. The precise significance of this hard thin film, which on the basis of micro-probe analysis seems little influenced by carbon content in the as-welded state is as yet not fully understood. Despite its presence, reasonably satisfactory bend test ductility was demonstrated.

A number of the bead samples were heat-treated at 850°C for 1 hr and furnace cooled. On microexamination it was apparent that decarburization of the carbon steel, at the fusion boundary, had occurred in every case.

TABLE 11

Microhardness and Composition of the Fusion Boundary between High Alloy Weld Metal and Mild Steel

Distance into weld metal from ½% Nital etched boundary (μ)	Manual metallic arc beads						Manual t.i.g. deposits						Automatic t.i.g. welds					
	25/20 Low (0·1%) carbon			25/20 High (0·4%) carbon			25/20 High (0·4%) carbon			Inconel 92			Autogenous 25/20–M/S root			25/20 High (0·4%) carbon		
	Microhardness VPN at 5 g	*Composition % Cr	Ni	Microhardness VPN at 5 g	*Composition % Cr	Ni	Microhardness VPN at 5 g	*Composition % Cr	Ni	Microhardness VPN at 5 g	*Composition % Cr	Ni	Microhardness VPN at 5 g	*Composition % Cr	Ni	Microhardness VPN at 5 g	*Composition % Cr	Ni
= −5																176	0	0
= −2																		
= −1											3·0	4·5					5·0	3·5
0	336	3·5	1·5	353	3·5	2·0	336			258	4·4	6·0	353					
1	321	4·0	2·0	514	4·5	2·5	371			411	5·0	6·5	757					
2	514	5·0	3·0	411	6·0	3·5	484			544	5·5	7·5	757					
3	484	6·0	4·0	390	8·0	5·0	514			514	6·0	8·0	706					
4	484	7·0	4·5	390	11·0	7·0	390			514	6·5	9·0	580					
5	411	8·0	5·5	336	14·5	10·0	293			514	7·0	10·0	544			544	10·0	7·0
6		9·5	6·5	293	16·0	11·5	258				7·6	11·0						
7	293	10·5	7·0		17·5	13·0	258			484	8·4	12·0	514					
8	258										9·0	13·5						
9											9·6	14·5						
10	258									269	10·2	15·5						
12										247	11·4	17·5	438					
14				280							12·0	18·5	434					
16							237			237	12·7	19·0				258	12·5	10·0
18	269			280							13·0	19·5						
20											13·5	20·0						

* Accurate correlation between microhardness and composition is at present being established. The composition figures presented are interpolations from other data and are thought to be accurate to within about ±1 μ in terms of distance from the Nital etched boundary.

G

There was some variation in the depth of the decarburized zone and measurements are presented in Table 12. The decarburization adjacent to the fusion boundary between the 18 per cent chromium 10 per cent nickel $4\frac{1}{2}$ per cent molybdenum bead and mild steel plate is shown in Fig. 19, and this is typical of other examples given in Table 12.

TABLE 12

Depth of Decarburization in Mild Steel Adjacent to Fusion Boundary
(Heat treated for 1 hr at 850°C and furnace cooled)

Weld deposit type	Welding process	Depth of decarburization (in.)
25/20 0·1% carbon	Metallic arc	0·015
25/20 0·4% carbon	Metallic arc	0·012
18/10/4½ molybdenum	Metallic arc	0·016
Inconel 92	Manual t.i.g.	0·006
25/20 0·4% carbon	Automatic t.i.g.	0·012
Autogenous root fusion. 25/20 0·4% carbon 50% diluted with mild steel	Automatic t.i.g.	0·005

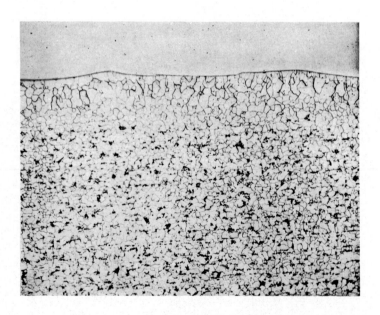

FIG. 19

$18/10/4\frac{1}{2}$ molybdenum metallic arc weld bead on mild steel. Decarburization of mild steel after treatment at 850°C for 1 hr. Mag. × 32.

Microsections taken from the high- and low-carbon 25 per cent chromium 20 per cent nickel deposits showed very similar decarburization and grain growth in the carbon steel and according to Carpenter *et al.*[7] and Emerson and Hutchinson[8] this decarburization results from carbon migration towards the austenitic weld metal. At first sight it would seem that migration towards weld metal containing 0·4 per cent carbon ought to be slower than migration towards weld metal containing 0·1 per cent carbon, yet this does not appear to occur in practice.

From the limited investigation so far made, conclusions are drawn as follows:

1. If high carbon 25 per cent chromium 20 per cent nickel weld metal is deposited on low carbon steel, carbon does not migrate or diffuse into the carbon steel, and hardening does not occur on the carbon steel side of the fusion boundary.

2. Within the limits of this investigation a very narrow hard zone a few microns thick has been found to develop on the high alloy side of the fusion boundary. The formation of this zone is independent of welding method or weld metal composition.

3. The composition of this hard zone has been confirmed by micro-probe analysis to fall within the limits suggested by Schaeffler[5] for the formation of martensite.

4. The role of carbon in affecting the behaviour of this martensitic zone is at present uncertain. On the basis of hardness measurements carbon appears to have little influence in the as-welded state.

5. Decarburization of the carbon steel adjacent to the fusion boundary following heat-treatment at 850°C, is common to all the weld metals and techniques investigated, and cannot be prevented by the use of any one in preference to another.

It must be emphasized that this work is far from complete and that further information is continuing to be brought to light. It is hoped that in due course publication will be of interest.

REFERENCES

1. C. EDELEANU and B. ESTRUCH, *Iron and Steel Institute Special Report* 86, p. 220.
2. J. F. MASON JR., J. J. MORAN and G. L. SWALES, Section VII, paper 21—World Petroleum Congress 1963.
3. R. J. MANGONE and A. M. HALL, *Alloy Casting Bulletin*, No. 17, October 1961.
4. D. R. WOOD and R. M. COOK, *Metallurgia*, **67**, March 1963.
5. *Metals Handbook*, Eighth Edition 1961, vol. 1, p. 436.
6. C. L. CLARK, *High Temperature Alloys*, Pitman 1953, p. 270.
7. O. R. CARPENTER, N. C. JESSEN, J. L. OBERG and R. D. WYLIE, *Some Considerations in the Joining of Dissimilar Metals for High Temperature High Pressure Service*.
8. R. W. EMERSON and W. R. HUTCHINSON, *Welding Research*, Supplement March 1952, pp. 126-s to 141-s.

INTRODUCTION TO THE METALLURGY OF CAST HEAT-RESISTING ALLOYS

A. R. WARD

TWO cast heat-resisting alloys have dominated the picture concerning materials used for reformer tubing and headers involved in the growth of the steam hydrocarbon reforming process in Britain. Cast 25 per cent chromium, 20 per cent nickel type HK alloy is being used for reformer tubing. Cast 18 per cent chromium, 37 per cent nickel type HU is being employed for headers and also for the earliest ICI process reformer tubes.

The types HK and HU materials are only two of the comprehensive series of Alloy Castings Institute iron–chromium–nickel alloys. The entire range of A.C.I. grades is shown in Table 1. They contain various amounts of

TABLE 1

A.C.I. type	HC	HE	HF	HH	HI	HL
Thermalloy type	T28	T38	T30	T40	T43	T48
% Chromium	26–30	26–30	18–23	24–28	26–30	28–32
% Nickel	4·0 max.	9–12	8–12	11–14	14–18	18–22
Structure (F = Ferritic)	F	A	A	A	A	A
(A = Austenitic)						
Elongation % as cast						
A.S.T.M. Specification						
A297 minimum	—	9	25	10	10	10
Typical value	—	21	34	20	18	15
% Thermal expansion 27–870°C	1·14	—	1·58	1·56	—	—

A.C.I. type	HK	HN	HT	HU	—	HW	H
Thermalloy type	T47	T45	T50	T58	T63	T72	T85
% Chromium	24–28	19–23	13–17	17–21	24–28	10–14	16–2
% Nickel	18–23	23–27	33–37	37–41	34–38	58–62	65–6
Structure (F = Ferritic)	A	A	A	A	A	A	A
(A = Austenitic)							
Elongation % as cast:							
A.S.T.M. Specification							
A297 minimum	10	8	4	4	—	—	—
Typical value	18	19	12	12	—	—	—
% Thermal expansion 27–870°C	1·49	—	1·42	—	1·49	1·32	—

chromium and nickel between about 12 and 30 per cent and 3 and 65 per cent respectively.

Thermalloy is a collective term embracing the alloys produced by Lloyds (Burton) Ltd., and the Electro Alloys Division of the American Brake Shoe Company Limited, for use in the temperature range 600–1200°C. Most Thermalloy materials are essentially equivalent to the A.C.I. types, relying on derived optimum compositions within the A.C.I. specifications. In turn, the A.C.I. alloys conform to A.S.T.M. specification A297 : 1961. Several Thermalloy grades have been developed for specific types of application. These include reformer tube alloys for use above 1000°C.

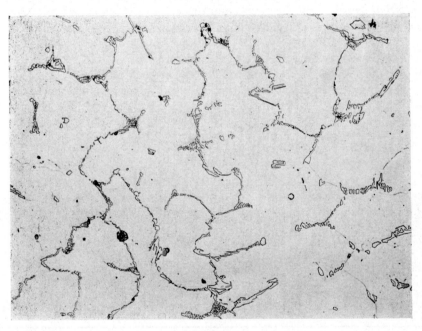

Fig. 1
18% Cr, 37% Ni type HU (×208).

The microstructure of the nickel predominant alloys (types HN, HT, HU, Thermalloy 63, HW and HX) in the "as cast" condition consists of an austenite matrix with networks of primary carbides of iron and chromium. Figure 1 is a photomicrograph of 18 per cent chromium, 37 per cent nickel type HU. Figure 2 shows that the microstructure of 25 per cent chromium, 20 per cent nickel type HK in the "as cast" condition is similar to that of 18 per cent chromium, 37 per cent nickel alloy, though more carbide network is generally present in type HU. Also apparent are small amounts of a lamellar carbide phase, which may occur in cast 25 per cent chromium,

20 per cent nickel alloy. There is no evidence to suggest that this phase has any weakening influence. It is unlikely that it has such a potent strengthening effect, however, as that caused by further carbide phases that occur in service.

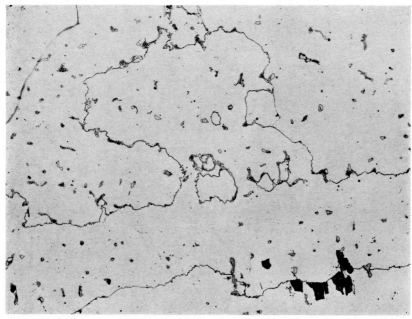

FIG. 2
25% Cr, 20% Ni type HK (×208).

The primary carbide networks of the "as cast" structure cannot be readily modified by economical solution heat treatment. Heat treatment to achieve metallurgical changes is seldom carried out, either in the case of single castings, or fabricated assemblies.

Figure 3 shows the microstructure of 18 per cent chromium, 37 per cent nickel alloy after service exposure at 700° to 750°C. Precipitation of fine iron–chromium carbides has taken place within the grains. This "pepper-pot" type precipitation takes place in all of the Thermalloy materials contributing to their strengthening mechanism above 600°C. The strengthening effect of intragranular carbide precipitation is most prominent between 600° and 1050°C. Very gradual growth in precipitate size is associated with advancement towards the onset of increase in creep rate in stage III creep. In service, the rate of change in the size of strengthening carbides may be accelerated by accidental overheating, of course. Examination of material that has not fulfilled the life expectancy, particularly when operation has been at 950–1050°C, quite often shows evidence of overheating, emphasizing the importance of good operational temperature control to achieve optimum alloy life.

FERRITE IN HEAT-RESISTING ALLOYS

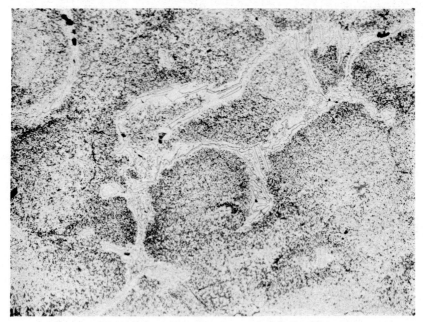

FIG. 3.   18% Cr, 37% Ni alloy after service at 750°C (×315).

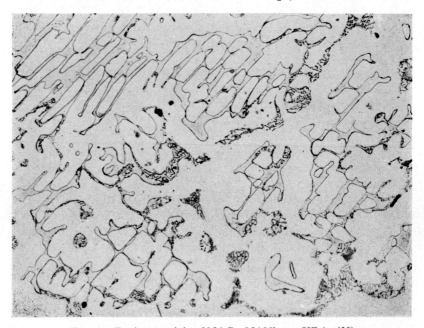

FIG. 4.   Ferrite containing 29% Cr, 9% Ni type HE (×430).

In Fig. 4, the microstructure of 29 per cent chromium, 9 per cent nickel type HE is shown. This alloy has ferrite in the "as cast" structure, in addition to austenite and primary carbide networks. Ferrite, firstly, has a weakening effect at elevated temperatures. Secondly, it promotes the formation of sigma phase between 600° and 900°C. This intermetallic compound of iron–chromium can form rapidly from ferrite at 850°C. Incidentally, it may form in heat-resisting alloys that are high in chromium and marginally austenitic, but at significantly reduced rates. Sigma phase is brittle and causes loss of hot strength, ductility and toughness. Thirdly, ferrite increases thermal conductivity. Fourthly, ferrite reduces the thermal expansion coefficient in comparison with the fully austenitic alloy of similar composition.

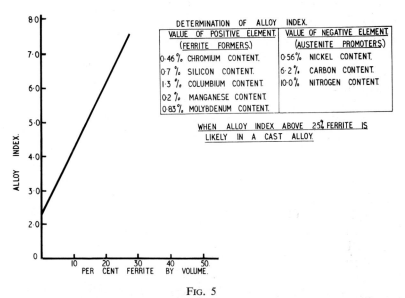

Fig. 5

Influence of alloying elements on stability of austenite, and presence of ferrite in cast-iron–chromium nickel heat-resisting alloys.

In Fig. 5, a graphical means of assessing the tendency of a certain cast alloy to contain ferrite is shown. The alloy index is obtained by deducting the sum of the austenite promoters from the sum of the ferrite formers. Ferrite is likely to occur when the index value exceeds $+2 \cdot 5$ per cent.

Chromium, silicon, columbium and molybdenum promote ferrite. So does tungsten, which is not shown. In opposition, carbon, nitrogen, and nickel stabilize the austenite phase.

The relative potency of the various elements is shown numerically. Carbon and nitrogen are eleven and eighteen times as potent as nickel respectively in stabilizing the austenite, in the case of the alloy concerned.

The chromium predominant alloys are more subject to the needs of careful alloy balancing due to chromium promoting ferrite occurrence. 25 per cent chromium, 12 per cent nickel Thermalloy 40 (HH) is a borderline grade requiring good compositional control to avoid ferrite. Apart from using the potent influence of carbon in this respect, a critical amount of nitrogen is also employed. 20 per cent chromium, 10 per cent nickel Thermalloy 30 (HF) is also critical concerning alloy balance. The carbon and nickel to chromium and silicon ratio of 25 per cent chromium, 20 per cent nickel Thermalloy 47 (HK) ensures austenitic stability with quite an appreciable margin.

EFFECT OF COMMON ELEMENTS ON VARIOUS ALLOYS

With such a wide range of cast alloy compositions very significant differences in properties result. The roles of the major elements illustrate this point.

Iron is an economic base.

Nickel, firstly, contributes to high-temperature strength, promoting austenite. Secondly, nickel assists in reducing hot gas corrosion rates in oxidizing conditions. Increasing nickel content increases the stability of surface oxides when they are frequently cooled from operating temperatures and subsequently reheated.[1] Thirdly, nickel improves carburization resistance. Fourthly, the nickel predominant grades have slightly better hot ductility above, say, 600–650°C than the chromium predominant alloys. Fifthly, the nickel predominant grades have a lower thermal expansion co-efficient than the ferrite-free chromium predominant alloys. The reduced expansion co-efficients, in terms of percentage expansion up to 870°C, caused by increased nickel and reduced chromium are shown in Table 1.

Of the beneficial property influences of nickel, the good hot ductility, lower thermal expansion coefficient and carburization resistance of the nickel-predominant alloys are important factors affecting their popularity in industrial applications involving thermal cycling. Incidentally, other properties have important effects on thermal fatigue life, particularly high-temperature strength, which limits deformation at the highest temperature of the thermal cycle when the alloy is weakest.[2]

On the debit side concerning nickel; increased high-temperature corrosion rates occur in alloys containing, say, 12 per cent nickel, or more, in reducing gas atmospheres containing, say, 100–200 grains of hydrogen sulphide in 100 cubic feet, at approximately 900°C, particularly in cyclic operations. The formation of low melting point nickel sulphides is responsible.

When high sulphur fuels are burnt with excess air, so that sulphur dioxide occurs, alloys containing at least, say, 20 per cent nickel may be used with advantage. The precise nickel contents that may be employed in high sulphur atmospheres are affected by the operating temperatures concerned. Each application has to be carefully considered in relation to corrosion rate data.[3]

Chromium, firstly, has a very pronounced influence in controlling high-temperature oxidation rates. Secondly, chromium contributes to high-temperature strength.

Regarding silicon. Silicon is varied between 0·75 and 2·0 per cent in the Thermalloy grades. It has several less well defined effects, which vary in potency dependent on the alloy base. Firstly, silicon is used as a deoxidant and generally improves foundry characteristics. Secondly, silicon enhances oxidation resistance. Thirdly, silicon improves the carburization resistance of the lower nickel grades, such as the 25 per cent chromium, 20 per cent nickel HK alloy. Fourthly, silicon improves the corrosion resistance of cast heat-resisting alloys in high sulphur reducing atmospheres, measured in terms of depth of surface metal affected by corrosion. Silicon does tend to cause loss of hot strength as it approaches 2·0 per cent and is adjusted accordingly where appropriate.

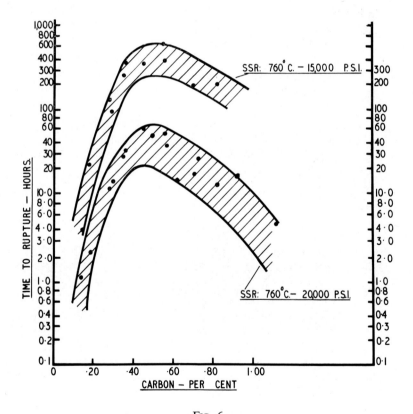

FIG. 6

Effect of carbon on short-term rupture properties of 16% Cr, 35% Ni heat-resistant alloy at 760°C.

Carbon is last but by no means least of the common effective elements. Its austenite stabilizing influence has already been referred to. The strengthening influence of carbon above 600–650°C is a particular feature of the Thermalloy materials. The amounts of carbon necessary to provide optimum hot strength for each individual grade have been carefully derived. For example, 0·35/0·45 per cent carbon in the case of 25 per cent Cr, 20 per cent Ni Thermalloy 47.

The relation between the carbon content of a 16 per cent chromium, 35 per cent nickel alloy and high-temperature strength is shown in Fig. 6. The short-term stress to rupture life of alloys of different carbon contents has been derived at two stress levels. The peaks of the curves represent the best carbon range for optimum alloy hot strength. In addition, it is apparent that at this optimum carbon level, minimum strength variations occur from one end of the 0·10 per cent carbon range to the other. At lower carbon contents, say below 0·20 per cent, the slope of the graph suggests that greater scatter in hot strength is likely within a similar 0·10 per cent carbon specification. Additionally, the lower carbon alloy is weaker, of course.

Incidentally, the higher hot strength conferred by carbon contents above 0·25 per cent is the very feature which precludes economical forming operations. Thus a 0·40 per cent carbon, 25 per cent chromium, 20 per cent nickel alloy is not amenable to forming by the conventional wrought processes, used, say, for making tubes.

The production of material of optimum carbon content is the main metallurgical difference between cast and wrought materials of equivalent alloy content. It is a good example of the general flexibility of composition inherent in the casting process.

ALLOY SELECTION

The first requirement in selecting the most suitable alloy for a particular application is knowledge of the essential properties of the available cast compositions. The material features may then be related to the service operating conditions, such as maximum operating temperatures, applied stresses, thermal cycling and the effects of gaseous environments.

If high-temperature strength alone were the only basis for alloy selection, the common alloys would be employed in certain ranges of temperature. Such an arrangement may rely more on the chromium-predominant alloys to achieve the best cost per operating hour performance in view of the relative cost of nickel. For comparison purposes, the stress to cause rupture in 1000 hr of certain common alloys, over the temperature range 650° to 1200°C, is shown in Fig. 7. (The preferred temperature range for each alloy is shown as a bold line.)

To date, one European reformer furnace is employing Thermalloy 63 tubes. At 1000° to 1050°C the 10,000 hr stress to rupture property is similar to 25 per cent chromium, 20 per cent nickel type HK. The higher alloy grade has lower hot gas corrosion and surface carburization and decarburization rates in this temperature range, which partly accounts for its selection.

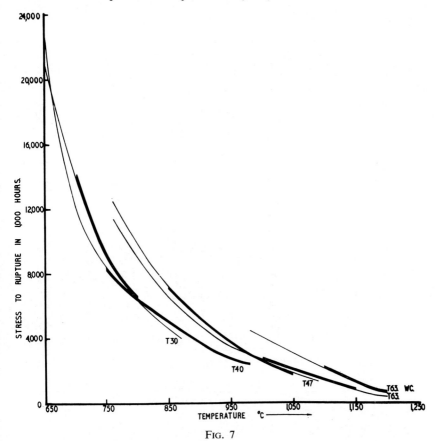

Fig. 7

Strength variation of various grades with increase in temperature.

Between 1050° and 1100°C, Thermalloy 63 is stronger than HK, but its use above 1100°C is only contemplated when stresses are modest. The potent strengthening of intragranular carbide precipitates is not so influential at such temperatures. Thus, from 1100° to 1200°C, further strengthening is provided by the use of cobalt and tungsten additions to a 25 per cent chromium, 35 per cent nickel base. This alloy, known as Supertherm, has been produced for one reformer tube plant to date, in the U.S.A. It is performing successfully in certain other industrial applications.

When castings are exposed to oxidizing gases at a fairly continuous temperature, and are subject to stress, the above hot strength classification is a good guide. If strength requirements are less important in this gaseous environment, choice of alloy follows reference to hot gas corrosion rate data at the temperature concerned. Generally, weaker lower alloy materials may be used, such as ferrite containing, 28 per cent chromium, 3 per cent nickel type HC.

When service conditions are carburizing, the more expensive nickel-predominant alloys, such as 18 per cent chromium, 37 per cent nickel, are necessary. Otherwise the hot strength of type HU is slightly inferior to 25 per cent chromium, 20 per cent nickel HK between 800° and 900°C. It is noteworthy that the main use of type HU has been in industrial applications where strength has rarely been the main property requirement such as parts for carburizing and oil quenching service.

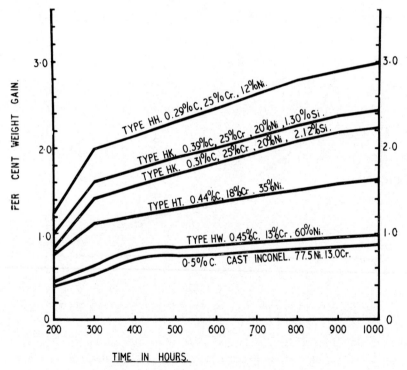

FIG. 8

Effect of nickel content on gas carburization rates.
Gas: 65% N_2, 25% H_2, 10% CH_4. Temperature: 980°C.

In Fig. 8, the carburization rates of certain common alloys are shown in terms of weight gain in a carburizing gas. The improved carburization resistance of the nickel-predominant grades is apparent. Also shown is the improved carburization resistance of the 2·1 per cent silicon, 25 per cent chromium, 20 per cent nickel alloy, compared with the 1·3 per cent silicon equivalent.

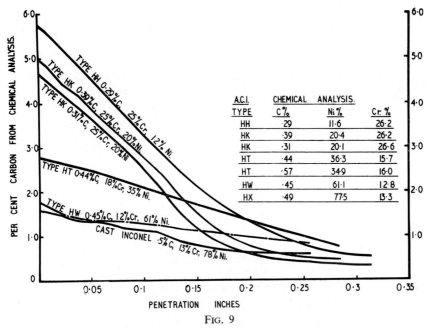

FIG. 9

Carbon penetration after gas carburizing at 980°C for 1000 hrs.
Nominal gas comp.: 65% N_2, 25% H_2, 10% CH_4.

The effects of gas carburization are shown in a different manner in Fig. 9, which depicts carbon layer analysis beneath the metal surface exposed to the carburizing gas. After carburization, high carbon concentrations are apparent at the surfaces of the low nickel 25 per cent chromium, 12 per cent nickel and 25 per cent chromium, 20 per cent nickel alloys. Appreciably lower surface carbon levels have occurred in the higher nickel alloys. Due partly to the lower surface concentrations of carbon, the nickel-predominant alloys have better retention of surface ductility and strength in carburizing conditions.[4]

When an application involves a high carburizing potential, the 12 per cent chromium, 60 per cent nickel HW alloy is favoured. Otherwise the higher nickel material is weaker than the cheaper 18 per cent chromium, 37 per cent nickel alloy.

18 per cent chromium, 37 per cent nickel alloy is also popular when operations involve cyclic heating. This is affected by the improved surface oxide stability of the higher nickel alloys in cyclic heating conditions and

good general thermal fatigue characteristics. Carburization is often associated with cyclic heating. Carburization resistance has affected the popularity rating of nickel-predominant alloys for thermal fatigue service generally.

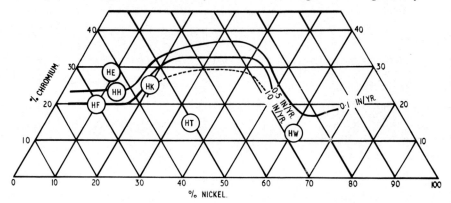

METAL LOSS AT 1,000°C. IN REDUCING FLUE-GAS ATMOSPHERE
CONTAINING   300 GRAINS OF SULPHUR/ 100 CU.FT.

Fig. 10

Metal loss at 1000°C in reducing fine-gas atmosphere containing 300 grains of sulphur/100 ft³.

In Fig. 10, the most common A.C.I. alloys are plotted on part of an iron–chromium–nickel ternary graph. Lines representing corrosion rates of 0.1, 0.5 and 1 in. per year in terms of actual surface metal loss in a reducing gas containing 300 grains of sulphur per 100 ft³ at 980°C are also shown, relating to alloy compositions.[3] The low corrosion rate of the high 29 per cent chromium, low 9 per cent nickel type HE alloy is apparent. The Thermalloy 38 equivalent contains weakening ferrite and, therefore, it is mainly used in applications not having appreciable requirements of hot strength.

Iron–chromium–nickel alloys are sometimes subject to deep internal oxidation at surfaces exposed to certain gaseous environments. This is known as "green-rot" due to the dark green colouration of the oxide path revealed on fracturing the embrittled material. The type of attack concerned may be found in alloys which have been carburized, oxidation penetrating by way of the chromium depleted matrix adjacent to the chromium carbide precipitates. It is apparent that at the operating temperatures concerned, chromium diffusion is sufficiently rapid to theoretically inhibit the attack. In severe cases it is, therefore, likely that almost simultaneous oxidation and carburization from reducing atmospheres must take place. The attack of carbide precipitates at the grain boundaries and within the grains may take place without actual carburization, depletion of chromium locally being most important.

Silicon and columbium have been found to reduce "green rot", at levels of approximately 2·0 per cent.[5] Internal oxidation is less likely to occur in iron base chromium nickel alloys of the Thermalloy type, than nickel base nickel–chromium materials.

Cast heat-resisting alloys are also employed in carburizing and neutral salt service, besides use as containers for liquid metals, such as lead baths. Alloy selection for these applications is dependent on the individual features of each application.

Certain less common A.C.I. alloys such as types HI (27% Cr, 15% Ni), HL (30% Cr, 20% Ni) and HN (21% Cr, 25% Ni), complete a comprehensive range of available cast materials. Choice of the most suitable alloy is often very difficult, representing a compromise between several service requirements related to potential alloy life and cost.

Concerning alloy selection, it is helpful if the user provides details of all relevant operating conditions when submitting enquiries. This can help the foundry to avoid delays in providing a quotation when guidance concerning alloy selection is required. Alternatively, the user's choice of alloy may be checked. At the same time, knowledge of service requirements help the founder to have some appreciation of designs, related to foundry techniques and fabrication. If possible, details provided should include likely operating temperatures of alloy material when they differ from furnace recorder temperatures, based on previous experience. For example, the fired radiant tube elements used in heating a controlled atmosphere furnace often exceed the furnace temperature by 150°C, in certain parts of the tube assembly.

DUCTILITY OF CAST HEAT-RESISTING ALLOYS

The minimum A.S.T.M. specification A297 tensile elongation requirements of the common alloys in the "as cast" condition, together with typical levels of ductility achieved are shown in Table 1. The "as cast" 18 per cent chromium, 37 per cent nickel type HU alloy has a room temperature ductility of 8–15 per cent in the tensile test. The 20 per cent chromium, 10 per cent nickel alloy has a typical elongation of 33·0 per cent.

In service at elevated temperatures, fine iron–chromium carbides precipitate within the grains, contributing to the strengthening mechanism of the Thermalloy materials. Following these changes the ductility at room tempera-ture decreases. The decrease in ductility is most pronounced after service at 600–750°C, associated with the fineness of carbide precipitates. Levels such as 4–5 per cent occur in the case of cast 18 per cent chromium, 37 per cent nickel and 25 per cent chromium, 20 per cent nickel alloys. As precipitate size increases with time, room temperature ductility tends to improve.

The relatively low cold ductility picture prevails below 600°C, but hot ductility is not likewise affected. A comparison of hot and cold ductility is shown in Table 2. 25 per cent chromium, 20 per cent nickel alloy has a room-temperature tensile ductility of 4·0 per cent after high temperature ageing. In the same state, hot tensile elongation at 760° and 870°C was much higher at 17·5 per cent and 19·5 per cent respectively.

TABLE 2

Comparison of Hot and Cold Ductility
Alloy 25% Cr, 20% Ni (0·40%)

Test temperature °C	Yield strength		U.T.S. psi	Elongation %	Reduction of area %	Condition treatment °C cooling
	0·1% proof psi	0·2% proof psi				
20°	42,120	45,120	79,000	16·0	16·0	As cast
20°	52,000	57,240	87,200	4·0	4·0	760° 24 hr Furnace cool
760°	28,400	31,000	47,800	17·5	28·0	760°C 48 hr Furnace cool
870°	19,000	20,900	27,900	19·5	39·0	870° 48 hr Furnace cool

Constant Strain Rates

Part of the picture involving the variation of the proof strength, ultimate tensile strength and ductility of cast 15 per cent Cr, 35 per cent Ni type HT with temperature and associated metallurgical condition is shown in Table 3. The latter feature has been further assessed by determining room temperature hardness as a guide to the amount and fineness of intragranular carbide precipitates.

The levels of hardness suggest that carbide precipitation in short-term ageing is negligible at 540°C. Tests of material that have not been heated above 540°C show a decrease in strength and increase in ductility as the temperature increases to 540°C.

At room temperature, material that has been aged for short periods at 760° and 870°C is stronger, but less ductile than the "as cast" alloy, due to carbide precipitation. The progressive weakening and increase in ductility of the material, aged at 760° and 870°C, as temperatures increase to these levels is shown.

It is apparent that material that has been aged at 870°C is weaker and more ductile at 650°C than the alloy after ageing for the same time at 650°C. Although less carbide is likely to have formed at the lower temperature it is in a finer form.

TABLE 3

Elevated Temperature Tensile Properties*

0·48% C, 16% Cr, 35% Ni Heat-Resistant Alloy—A.C.I. Type HT

Test temperature		Prior heat treatment °F — hr — cool	Yield strength—psi offset			U.T.S. psi	Elong. in 2 in. %	Red. area %	Hardness BHN†
°F	°C		0·01%	0·1%	0·2%				
70	21	As cast	22,800	32,400	35,880	70,300	11·0	11·5	156
70		1400 — 24 — FC	22,560	35,880	40,560	82,100	7·5	8·9	187
70		1600 — 48 — FC	27,600	38,400	42,960	87,200	6·0	9·3	196
800	430	800 — 48 — FC	21,000	26,100	27,780	59,200	13·5	16·3	159
800		1600 — 48 — FC	24,900	33,540	36,950	78,800	9·0	11·9	207
1000	540	1000 — 48 — FC	21,000	24,720	26,400	55,500	11·5	10·4	163
1200	650	1200 — 48 — FC	21,240	33,480	38,160	60,400	8·5	13·4	217
1200		1600 — 48 — FC	21,840	28,320	31,200	61,300	14·0	19·2	202
1400	760	1400 — 48 — FC	18,960	27,720	30,780	41,200	19·0	26·8	196
1600	870	1600 — 48 — FC	9780	15,120	16,560	21,600	24·0	30·2	192
1800	980	1800 — 48 — FC	6900	8700	9250	11,000	39·0	58·3	174

Notes: * Properties on 1-in. rounds, headed over central section.

† Hardness at room temperature after test.

Test specimens held 1 hr at temperature before loading. Testing speed was 0·1 in./min strain rate to fracture.

Increase in temperature between 650° and 980°C shows an increase in ductility in the "hot ductility" range. It is likely that the 8·5 per cent elongation at 650°C, after ageing at this temperature, is lower at room temperature, representing the least ductile form of the alloy.

This partially embrittled condition often concerns design engineers, particularly when operating stresses are increased by the thermal stresses associated with temperature gradients on heating. Thermal stress damage is expected if combined stresses exceed material yield points. The high yield point of the type HT material after ageing at 650°C shown is, therefore, noteworthy.

It is well known that the cast A.C.I. type heat-resisting alloys that have been in service are not particularly ductile when cold. Improvements in residual ductility after high-temperature service are often considered in relation to weaker, lower carbon alloy modifications. As illustrated by Avery, Cook and Fellows,[6] the low residual ductility encountered is often affected by service overstressing, causing early structural damage to the alloy (associated with tertiary creep). Modified compositions may improve short-term ductility, but reduce ultimate service ductility by reducing strength and promoting earlier structural damage.

In using cast heat-resisting alloys of the Thermalloy type, designers take precautions to avoid unnecessary limitations to expansion and also to avoid hindered contraction of a system during cooling. Reasonable freedom of movement minimizes thermal stresses associated with differential temperatures. If stresses do not exceed material yield points, thermal stress damage is avoided. Therefore, low cold ductility need not be a drawback and designers are then able to reap the full benefit from the hot strength of the alloys at the operating temperatures concerned, at which ample hot ductility is available. That is, when fairly high strain rates occur, as in the case of short-term overloads.

If excessive thermal stresses cannot be avoided in design, however, then modified compositions providing weaker, more ductile cast alloys can be readily produced with appropriate metal section changes.

WELDING CHARACTERISTICS

The policy of both Lloyds (Burton) Ltd., and the Electro Alloys Division of the American Brake Shoe Company Ltd., is to weld the Thermalloys with electrodes producing deposits of identical chemical composition. This is primarily to achieve similar metallurgical properties of welds. Exceptions are when customers specify otherwise. On such occasions, great care is necessary to avoid producing deposits differing from the parent material in properties to such an extent as to promote either deposit fissuring, or parent material cracking problems adjacent to the welds.

On initial cursory consideration of the welding characteristics of cast resisting alloys, it is common to suspect that at, say, 0·4 per cent carbon an alloy will prove more difficult to weld than a 0·15 per cent carbon equivalent. This thinking often follows experience with ferritic steels. On examination of actual experience, it is well known that ferrite-free austenitic steel weld deposits having carbon contents below, say, 0·20 per cent are prone to contain fine microfissures. Experience has shown that deposits of equivalent alloy content, but with higher carbon levels, for example, 0·40 per cent, have a very low susceptibility to fissure formation, in contrast. It is considered that the narrower temperature range of solidification of the higher carbon deposits and their greater strength at hot cracking temperatures are factors affecting the low tendency to fissure.

In this picture, certain rules have to be obeyed. In the case of 18 per cent chromium, 37 per cent nickel weld deposits, the carbon to silicon ratio is important concerning fissuring likelihood, as illustrated in Fig. 11. This fairly well-known plot based on work by Rozet, Campbell and Thomas Jnr,[7] indicates that at 0·4 per cent carbon and 1·50 per cent silicon, a sound deposit should result. Experience at Lloyds (Burton) Ltd., has not entirely confirmed this indication, and hence lower silicon contents are employed in 18 per cent chromium, 37 per cent nickel weld deposits.

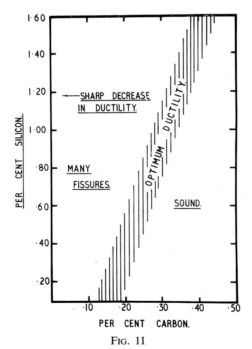

FIG. 11

Effect of carbon and silicon on 18% Cr, 37% Ni weld deposit fissuring.

It is felt that the cast heat-resisting alloys of the Thermalloy type are one of the highlights of alloy steel metallurgical developments. It is justifiable to use these alloys based on (a) high-temperature strength, (b) surface stability resisting the effects of various gaseous environments, (c) the metal-lurgical flexibility of the casting process, and (d) good welding characteristics, after all, it is this feature that assists in increasing the range of sizes and shapes that may be produced.

REFERENCES

1. H. L. EISESTEIN and E. N. SKINNER, *A.S.T.M. Spec. Tech. Publ.* No. 165, 1954, 162–172, disc. 172.
2. H. S. AVERY, *Metal Progress*, August 1959.
3. J. H. JACKSON, C. J. SLUNDER, O. E. HARDER and J. T. GOW, *Trans. A.S.M.E.*, August 1953, 1021–1034.
4. H. S. AVERY and N. A. MATTHEWS, *A.S.M. Trans.*, Vol. 38, 1947.
5. H. R. COPSON and F. S. LANG, *Corrosion*, Vol. 15, April 1959, 44–48.
6. H. S. AVERY, E. COOK and J. A. FELLOWS, *Tech. Publication* No. 1480, American Institute of Mining and Metallurgical Engineers, Metals Technology, August 1942.
7. D. ROZET, H. C. CAMPBELL and R. D. THOMAS JR., *The Welding Journal Research Supplement*, October 1948.

FORMS OF SUPPLY OF
CENTRIFUGALLY CAST REFORMER TUBING

Z. Z. J. KOSARSKI and J. CUMBERLAND

SINCE the centrifugal casting process supplanted the use of wrought tubing for the manufacture of reformer tubes some 6 years or so ago, there has been a certain amount of controversy as to which is the best condition in which to use cast tubing. The competitive methods of production by hot working or plate rolling gave a sound tube of relatively uniform section and smooth surface which was readily accepted by the chemical engineer as suitable for direct employment in his reformer furnace. When castings entered into this established field the characteristically slightly rough "as-cast" surfaces given by the centrifugal process were treated with suspicion and many early reformer tubes cast in this country and on the Continent were machined all over, or at least on one of the surfaces. As experience was gained and the centrifugal casting established a useful reputation for itself, costs reared their head, the pendulum swung in the opposite direction and, following American practice, the use of un-machined reformer tubes came into vogue. Eventually the engineers' innate suspicion of potential notch effects returned and this, together with a realization of the many advantages to be gained by working with minimum wall section, led to a reassessment of the value of fully machined tubes for some applications, with the result that currently tubing is supplied in four different ways:

1. As-cast.
2. Machined outside diameter, bore as-cast.
3. As-cast outside diameter, bore machined.
4. Machined all over.

The first condition gives the cheapest tube, although the saving in cost is not as great as might initially be thought, since the effect of eliminating machining operations tends to be offset by the increase in weight of alloy steel per unit length resulting from the greater section thickness required to give the designed minimum sound wall in the as-cast tube. Against this small saving in price one has to consider the difficulty of effective inspection and the possible risk of surface imperfections growing with time and leading to a premature failure. Fully machined tubes, whilst being the most expensive, can easily be inspected to a very high standard and thus would be expected to give the highest level of reliability in service. For this reason, machined tubes

207

are generally specified for header tube manufacture where failure would result in a complete shutdown of the plant. In the case of reformer tubes where techniques exist for sealing-off defective units, there is a tendency to avoid extras in order to reduce the initial cost of the installation, but the choice of machined tubes for header applications leaves little doubt as to which form of supply is considered to be the more reliable. In addition to the greater reliability of fully machined reformer tubes several important advantages result from the use of the thinnest wall section that will meet strength requirements. Improved heat transfer minimizes the thermal gradient across the tube wall and allows a somewhat lower furnace temperature, thus reducing the mean temperature of the tube and increasing the effective strength of the material. Susceptibility to thermal shock effects is less with minimum tube section and is an important consideration for Gas Board reformers where weekend variations in the demand for towns' gas can lead to deliberate changes of operating temperature in order to balance production against demand. Working with greater than necessary tube section thickness (an unmachined reformer tube may be $\frac{1}{8}$ to $\frac{1}{4}$ in. thicker than an equivalent fully machined reformer tube designed for the same application) requires higher furnace temperature, thereby lowering the effective strength of the material; increases the level of thermally induced stresses with temperature fluctuation; and presumably results in a marginal increase of fuel consumption.

Whilst we would not presume to advise the designer whether to use a fully machined or an entirely as-cast tube, in our opinion, the use of reformer tubes machined on one surface only, whether internal or external, is the least desirable alternative. With present machining techniques, it is difficult to ensure concentricity and uniform section thickness at economical speeds of machining when only one of the surfaces is machined, whilst the difference in price between such a tube and one machined all over is very small indeed. We feel that this somewhat marginal saving is hardly justified when all the known factors mentioned above are taken into account and when one considers the possibility that the one remaining cast surface might conceivably contain some weakening discontinuities.

Relative prices per unit length for a typical reformer tube in the widely used 25% Cr/20% Ni alloy steel based on a $\frac{1}{2}$ in. minimum sound wall in the four alternative forms of supply are of the following order:

	Tube condition	Relative price
1	As-cast	100
2	Machined outside diameter, bore as-cast	105
3	As-cast outside diameter, bore machined	108
4	Machined all over	110

In the case of tubes supplied with as-cast external surfaces, two types of surface finish are currently being produced—a relatively smooth one which will clean up to sound metal with the removal of a $\frac{1}{32}$ in. cut and a somewhat rougher one which requires a $\frac{1}{16}$ in. cut. There appears to be some difference of opinion between the users regarding the merits of the two types of finish; some users prefer the smooth finish because of the ease of inspection and the slightly reduced wall section, while others prefer the rougher finish because they believe the increased surface area improves heat transfer. Whilst we produce both types of finish, we would favour the rougher finish for the following reasons:

1. The greater surface area of the rougher coating increases the effective chilling action of the metal mould by aiding heat transfer during solidification thus resulting in a more consistent quality of metal at the bore.

2. Tube castings made by the process which results in a rougher finish are less prone to exhibit surface defects of the gas or pinhole types. This is attributed to the increased facility for the drying out of moisture during the multiple application of refractory slurry which is used to give this type of finish.

3. In spite of a slight difference found in the thickness of tubes cast by the two different processes when measured to the tops of the undulations (the rougher being the thicker), the weight of the tube remains the same whilst the heat transfer improves slightly due to the greater area of the rougher surface finish.

SPECIFICATIONS

Currently most tube purchasers set their own standards of acceptance and consequently there are many specifications in existence which vary in emphasis and coverage whilst overlapping on the more important points. Many of these specifications derive originally from A.S.T.M. 362-52T with modifications arranged between the supplier and user as experience increased. Most tube specifications agree on the following major points:

(a) Chemical composition check on each melt of steel.

(b) Tensile test taken on bars cut from tubes representing a fraction (usually one in five, or one in ten) of the total number of melts.

(c) Dimensional checks of external and internal diameter and length, with limitation of permissible ovality, eccentricity and bow.

(d) Visual examination of external and internal cast surfaces to some agreed standard of freedom from blemishes and excessive roughness.

(e) Hydraulic testing of individual tubes and hydraulic and air pressure test of the final welded assembly.

(f) Dye penetrant check on weld preparations and machined surfaces.

In the opinion of this Company, the above six points will give adequate inspection coverage to ensure reliability in service at an overall economic price. The chemical analysis will ensure heat to heat uniformity. Periodical tensile tests cut from tubes will establish the general order of strength and ductility obtained in the centrifugally cast product and can also be regarded as an index of raw material and melt quality. The internal pressure test will locate defects which are continuous across the section of the tube and can, under suitable circumstances, give an assessment of strength, while dye penetrant examination of external machined surfaces and weld preparation detail confers a most searching inspection of the sound wall requirements, and in the case of tubes having "as-cast" bores, the depth of internal porosity and fissures.

As suppliers of tubes we cannot make any recommendations regarding hydraulic testing since pressures will depend on design considerations, but we would suggest the following limits as representing good practice for a specification covering reformer tubes in the widely used 0·4 per cent carbon, 25 per cent chromium, 20 per cent nickel heat resisting alloy steel.

1. *Composition*

Carbon	0·35–0·45
Silicon	0·80–1·40
Sulphur	0·04–max.
Phosphorus	0·04–max.
Manganese	0·50–1·50
Nickel	18·0 –22·0
Chromium	24·0 –28·0
Molybdenum	0·50–max.
Lead	0·005–max.

2. *Mechanical Properties*
   Tensile test bar cut from tubes representing one heat in ten.
   U.T.S.: 30 t.s.i. min.
   Elongation: 10 per cent min.

3. *Dimensional Tolerances on As-cast Tubes*
   Cast diameter—External: minus nothing, plus $\frac{1}{16}$ in.
                   Internal: plus nothing, minus $\frac{1}{8}$ in. (up to 6 in. N.B.)
                             plus nothing, minus $\frac{3}{16}$ in. (above 6 in. N.B.)
   Eccentricity: $\frac{1}{16}$ in. max.
   Ovality: $\frac{1}{16}$ in. max.
   Bow: $\frac{1}{16}$ in. max. over 7 ft.

4. Visual examination of internal and external cast surfaces to some mutually acceptable standards using comparison samples.

5. Dye penetrant check of weld preparations, full coverage of external machined surfaces, with examination of machined bores to a distance of 4 in. from each end face.

Other inspection requirements which are sometimes made include:

1. Flattening test on rings cut from one or both ends of each tube casting. This gives a measure of the ductility of the metal and may also reveal laminated or unsound material.
2. Radiographic examination of tube section adjacent to the weld preparation ends.
3. Etch test carried out on rings or sections cut from tubes. This may reveal uniformity of macro-structure and freedom from laminations, cracks, porosity, or other defects.
4. Tensile from each melt.
5. Air pressure testing of individual tubes.

In our experience the above additional tests which are specified in some instances increase cost and cause delays to a degree disproportionate to their effectiveness and value as inspection procedure for reformer tubing. The flattening test is erratic and gives results which vary with the manner and rate of loading and smoothness of machined finish and corner radii. The degree of inconsistency increases with the increase of carbon content and for carbon levels of over $0 \cdot 35$ per cent, this test does not give useful information. Radiographic examination is generally unnecessary with tubing made by the centrifugal casting process using metal moulds and we rather fail to see the reason for specifying it, particularly since it is mainly called for on fully machined tubes. Dye penetrant examination is far more sensitive and considerably cheaper. Admittedly, dye penetrant could not be used at the ends of "as-cast" tubes, but in 5 years of carrying out X-ray examination of tubes when specified, only one film has been found having indication of other than acceptable soundness. The defect in question was, in any case, not typical for the end of the tube and could have been present anywhere along its length. Etch tests do reveal grain structure and can be used to assess product uniformity in this respect. However, since there is little agreement on the significance, if any, of the shape, size and distribution of the grains on the performance of the reformers, we feel that there is nothing of real value to be gained by calling for macro-etch tests at the present moment. Etching will reveal defects or discontinuities, but is probably less sensitive and less valuable for this purpose than the dye penetrant examination normally carried out on the adjacent weld preparations. Whilst we have already agreed that periodical tensile tests are well justified, we consider it superfluous to check mechanical properties on each heat since, in the case of un-heat-treated austenitic steel tubes, chemical analysis, together with occasional tensile checks, provides ample guarantee of the consistency of the product. Air pressure testing of individual reformer tubes is hardly justified on economic grounds, since in our experience only a fraction of 1 per cent of tubes ever fails to withstand the air pressure test on the completed assembly and the cost of welding of a replacement tube, in the unlikely event of such a necessity ever arising, would be far less than the cost of pressure testing of all the tubes. In view of the high cost of welding sockolets, we agree that such a precaution might be justified in the case of Header tubes, even though none of the Header tubes we have tested to date have failed on air pressure.

The cost of each individual test may appear to be insignificant, but the total cost of all five tests, which we consider to be superfluous, may increase the cost of tubes by anything up to 10 per cent. It may well be that with the ever-increasing tendency for higher pressures and operating temperatures all possible means of testing are justified regardless of cost, but if this should be the case let us not overlook the basic inspection facility provided by the fully machined tube.

Finally, a few words about the method used to define tube sections on inquiries and orders. A practice has arisen with many users of applying standard surface allowances to minimum design sections when specifying sizes for un-machined tubes. Typical practice is to allow $\frac{1}{32}$ in. thickness at the outside and $\frac{3}{32}$ in. at the bore, almost irrespective of considerations of tube diameter and radial thickness. Since such factors, together with the actual casting process used, do influence the degree of soundness at the external and internal surfaces, we would suggest that both the drawing and the inquiry should state the minimum wall thickness required by the designer, leaving it to the tube manufacturer to make his recommendations regarding suitable casting allowances.

Although the primary purpose of this paper is to describe briefly forms of supply of centrifugally spun tubes, we feel it appropriate to conclude by mentioning that, for a number of years, the centrifugal casting process has been used for the manufacture of ancillary components such as weld neck and blind flanges, reducers, taper pieces, etc. This type of component often is produced in refractory moulds, but the results obtained do indicate that the quality of such castings is comparable to that achieved on reformer tubes manufactured in metal dies.

DEVELOPMENT OF IMPROVED WROUGHT ALLOYS
FOR REFORMER TUBES

J. Heslop, D. J. Hopkins and C. H. White

INTRODUCTION

Centricast HK steel has superseded wrought Incoloy alloy 800 for reformer tubing. This has arisen largely for economic reasons and because of the availability of longer lengths of centricast tube than hitherto. Nevertheless, many engineers are still of the opinion that a wrought tube has advantages over a cast tube and provided that the economics could be remedied would prefer to use a wrought alloy. The main advantages of wrought tubing are:

(i) The structure, and hence the properties, of the wrought product are more consistent, being free from defects such as porosity and segregation to which castings are prone. As a result of such uniformity the stress-rupture properties of all the tubing from each heat of the alloy could be reliably assessed by means of a short-time test on material from a small extruded "pilot" ingot or from a sample of extruded tube. In the case of centricast material even a test from each cast tube would not be as good a guarantee of properties because of segregation, varying grain structure and porosity.

(ii) The wrought tube is fine grained and much more ductile than centricast tube. It should also be less susceptible to intergranular corrosion than a relatively coarse grained cast tube.

(iii) There should be fewer welding problems with a wrought alloy tube which should also usually be available in longer lengths than a tube in centricast steel. With a wrought alloy stronger than Incoloy 800 even longer tube lengths should be available because a thinner wall would probably be required.

The future trend in reformer plant will be to higher temperatures and pressures and this will mean either the use of stronger alloys or the use of thicker walled tubing. To obtain efficient heat transfer it would be thought that the tube wall should be kept to a minimum and provided a strong enough and corrosion-resistant enough alloy could be developed, one could visualize tubes being used with wall thicknesses only practicable in a wrought product.

With these thoughts in mind, particularly the possible future trends, work has been commenced to examine the possibility of developing a very much

213

stronger wrought alloy of the Incoloy 800 type, having a strength/cost ratio more in line with HK steel. Thinking in terms of an alloy for use at temperatures of about 1000°C and bearing in mind that 100,000 hr properties are of prime importance, it was decided that only solid solution hardened alloys would be of interest. Such alloys are characterized by relatively shallow stress-rupture life curves compared with precipitation hardened alloys and thus in general are likely to have higher 100,000 hr stress carrying capacity than such alloys, although of course the reverse is true at shorter times.

There are other difficulties with precipitation hardened alloys, such as welding, which also preclude them from consideration.

PRELIMINARY STUDY OF ALLOYING ADDITIONS

The number of possible alloying elements to the nickel–chromium–iron system is small and of course, to be of advantage the increased strength would have to outweigh their cost. The alloying elements so far considered are (i) tungsten, (ii) molybdenum, (iii) niobium, (iv) cobalt, (v) carbon, (vi) aluminium, (vii) silicon, (viii) manganese.

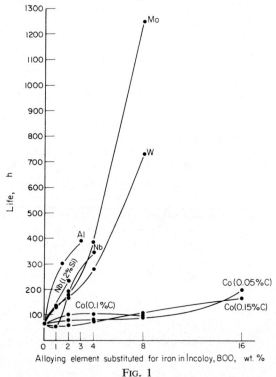

FIG. 1

The effect of alloying additions on stress rupture life at 19,000 lbf/in², 700°C.

Ten pound laboratory ingots made to the basic composition 22 per cent chromium, 32 per cent nickel, balance iron, with varying amounts of the additions (i) to (vii) above substituted for iron were forged to ¾ in. bar.

Blanks were cut and annealed for 1 hr, 1150°C prior to testing each composition as follows:

(a) Stress-rupture tests at 700°, 900° and 1000°C with stresses aimed to give lives of approximately 100, 300 and 1000 hr.

(b) Tensile tests at room temperature, 700°, 900° and 1000°C.

(c) Impact tests both in the as-annealed condition and after exposure at 800C for 1000 hr.

Curves showing the effects of increasing amounts of the various alloying additions on rupture life at a given stress for each temperature are given in Figs. 1–3. Tensile test results are given in Table 1, and impact results in Fig. 4 and Table 5.

Tungsten additions gave the best improvement in stress-rupture properties, followed by molybdenum and niobium. Silicon is known to impair welda-

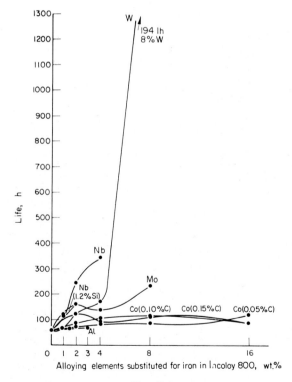

FIG. 2

The effects of alloying additions on stress rupture life at 5000 lbf/in², 900°C.

TABLE 1

Results of Hounsfield Tensometer Tensile Tests at Room Temperature, 700°, 900° and 1000°C

Lab. mark	Alloying addition	Room temp.			700°C			900°C			1000°C		
		Y.S. tonf/in²	T.S. tonf/in²	El. %	Y.S. tonf/in²	T.S. tonf/in²	El. %	Y.S. tonf/in²	T.S. tonf/in²	El. %	Y.S. tonf/in²	T.S. tonf/in²	El. %
dp/r	Incoloy 800	13·5	37	44	8·5	22·5	43	5·2	7·6	51	2·67	3·75	44
ds/t	1% Mo	13	38	44	8·0	22·0	38	5·67	8·75	48	3·89	5·02	46
dr/w	2% Mo	16	40	39	—	—	—	—	—	—	3·32	4·01	43
dx/y	4% Mo	17	41·5	44	12·0	28·0	40	8·5	11·0	46	4·69	5·91	38
dz/ea	8% Mo	19	45	39	9·5	25·5	36	11·25	14·0	38	5·58	7·58	33
eb/c	1% W	14·5	38	37	9·0	22·0	43	6·75	9·0	58	2·67	3·79	37
ed/e	2% W	14	38·5	44	8·5	23·5	38	4·25	5·87	48	4·01	5·25	40
eh/j	4% W	16	40	42	10·0	25·5	40	4·75	6·25	53	3·57	4·48	38
ek/l	8% W	—	—	—	10·0	27·5	36	5·75	7·37	55	5·25	7·14	32
em/o	2% Co, 0·05% C	13·5	38	43	8·0	21·0	40	4·0	5·5	46	3·79	5·02	42
ep/r	4% Co, 0·05% C	15	37	31	8·0	21·5	37	—	—	—	4·35	5·36	31
es/t	8% Co, 0·05% C	15·5	39·5	44	—	22·7	—	6·0	8·25	41	3·46	5·02	40
ev/w	16% Co, 0·05% C	15	41	48	8·5	24·5	33	7·25	8·87	44	3·68	5·13	36
ex/y	2% Co, 0·10% C	14	40	40	10·0	22·0	31	6·5	8·5	51	3·68	5·13	43
ez/ha	4% Co, 0·10% C	13·5	37·5	40	9·5	23·5	39	7·5	9·5	27	3·57	5·02	42
hb/c	8% Co, 0·10% C	15	42	43	10·0	25·0	37	6·5	8·5	46	4·25	5·47	43
hd/e	16 Co, 0·10% C	17	44·5	44	11·5	27·0	35	7·0	9·1	55	4·01	5·91	52

hh/j	2% Co, 0·15% C	16·5	42	39	10·0	22·0	41	5·25	7·25	58	4·62	5·13	62
hk/l	4% Co, 0·15% C	17	43·5	37	10·0	23·5	38	6·25	8·4	53	3·35	5·02	50
hm/o	8% Co, 0·15% C	17·5	44	38	11·0	22·5	36	6·0	8·0	55	3·38	5·02	48
hp/r	16% Co, 0·15% C	18	48·5	38	12·0	27·2	34	7·25	9·25	54	3·90	5·47	45
hs/t	2% W + 2% Mo	15	41	42	9·0	25·0	41	8·25	10·5	50	4·56	5·91	50
hv/w	2% W + 2% Mo + 8% Co	17	44	41	10·5	27·5	43	8·5	11·0	50	5·13	7·14	55
hx/y	1% Nb	15	38	43	9·0	22·5	43	5·75	7·75	33	3·68	4·91	52
hz/ja	2% Nb	16	40·5	35	9·0	23·0	45	6·0	8·25	56	2·46	3·46	67
jt/c	4% Nb	18	46	31	11·5	27·0	50	6·75	9·0	66	3·79	5·36	56
jd/e	1·2% Si + 2% Mo	16	41	40	9·5	23·5	35	7·0	8·25	93	3·35	4·91	50
jh/j	No Ti or Al	17·5	42·5	44	9·75	24·2	37	7·25	9·4	32	4·01	5·58	26
kd/e	1·5% Al	15·6	39·2	47	9·2	22·0	40	5·6	7·2	77·5	3·5	4·3	80
kh/j	3·0% Al	18	43·6	53	—	32·0	32	6·3	7·3	110	3·5	4·2	93
kk/e	5·0% Al	24·5	53·6	38	—	—	—	7·0	7·6	87	3·9	4·4	118
km/o	8·0% Al	—	—	—	—	—	—	—	—	—	—	—	—

H

bility and was only an effective addition at 1000°C, whilst aluminium was only effective at 700°C. Increasing carbon slightly increased stress-rupture properties. Combination of tungsten and molybdenum was promising, and was enhanced by the further addition of cobalt.

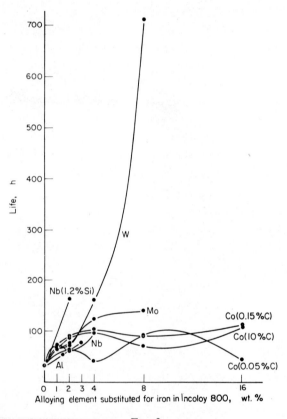

FIG. 3

The effects of alloying additions on stress rupture life at 2750 lbf/in², 1000°C.

Tungsten additions were relatively ineffective for increasing tensile properties at 700° and 900°C but good at 1000°C. Molybdenum, niobium and tungsten additions were all promising and cobalt was useful both by itself and in combination with tungsten and molybdenum. The effectiveness of aluminium again decreased, and of silicon increased, with increasing temperature.

All the additions except cobalt tended to embrittle the material after exposure for 1000 hr at 800°C, the temperature near which embrittling phases are likely to precipitate most rapidly. The embrittling phases produced by tungsten, molybdenum and niobium additions have been determined by X-ray diffraction as μ phase (based on Fe_3W_6), σ phase (Cr Fe Mo N) and Laves phase (based on Fe_2Nb) respectively. An encouraging feature was that the addition of 8 per cent cobalt to a 2 per cent tungsten plus 2 per cent molybdenum alloy greatly improved impact resistance as well as stress-rupture life, indicating that the addition of cobalt and/or increase in nickel content can combat embrittlement.

FURTHER COMBINATIONS OF ALLOYING ADDITIONS

Having established that tungsten, molybdenum and niobium were the most effective strengthening elements and that adjustments such as an addition of cobalt or an increase in nickel content would be necessary to combat embrittlement, the alloys listed in Table 2 and 3 were prepared for testing. These were based on tungsten plus molybdenum contents of 3 and 4 per cent (Table 2) and 4–8 per cent (Table 3) with cobalt contents of 0–16 per cent and nickel contents of 32 and 48 per cent. It was also decided to determine

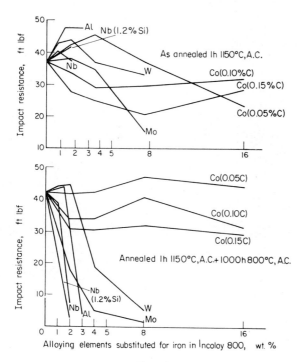

FIG. 4

The effect of alloying additions on impact resistance in as-annealed and annealed plus exposed 1000 hr/800°C conditions.

whether up to 8 per cent manganese replacing iron would reduce embrittlement and to investigate the effect of a $2\frac{1}{2}$ per cent aluminium addition because
of its good corrosion properties.

It was estimated that composition ym (Table 3) would give good properties
and it was decided to go ahead with a full-scale works trial of this alloy,
designated EPE.24, without waiting for results of the experimental heat ym.
This was done mainly to check that such an alloy could be processed from a
12 in. duodecagonal ingot to 4 in. i.d. $\times \frac{5}{8}$ in. wall extruded tube, and whether
the properties of the tube would be comparable with those of bar forged from
a small laboratory ingot.

These alloys were stress-rupture and tensile tested at 900°C and impact

TABLE 2

Combination of Alloying Elements
(Alloy compositions based on 3–4 per cent tungsten plus molybdenum)

Lab. mark	C	Ni	Co	W	Mo	Mn	Al	Ti	Cr	Si	Fe
rb	0·05	32	—	—	—	0·8	0·35	0·4	21·5	0·6	Bal
rc		32	—	3	—	0·8	0·35	0·4	21·5	0·6	Bal
rd		32	—	2	0·5	0·8	0·35	0·4	21·5	0·6	Bal
re		32	—	1	1	0·8	0·35	0·4	21·5	0·6	Bal
rf		32	—	—	1·5	0·8	0·35	0·4	21·5	0·6	Bal
rg		45	—	3	—	0·8	0·35	0·4	21·5	0·6	Bal
rh		45	—	2	0·5	0·8	0·35	0·4	21·5	0·6	Bal
rj		45	—	1	1	0·8	0·35	0·4	21·5	0·6	Bal
rk		45	—	—	1·5	0·8	0·35	0·4	21·5	0·6	Bal
rm		32	—	3	0·5	0·8	0·35	0·4	21·5	0·6	Bal
rn		32	—	2	1	0·8	0·35	0·4	21·5	0·6	Bal
rp		32	—	1	1·5	0·8	0·35	0·4	21·5	0·6	Bal
rr		45	—	4	—	0·8	0·35	0·4	21·5	0·6	Bal
rs		45	—	3	0·5	0·8	0·35	0·4	21·5	0·6	Bal
rt		45	—	2	1	0·8	0·35	0·4	21·5	0·6	Bal
rv		45	—	1	1·5	0·8	0·35	0·4	21·5	0·6	Bal
rw		45	—	—	2	0·8	0·35	0·4	21·5	0·6	Bal
rx		32	2	2	1	0·8	0·35	0·4	21·5	0·6	Bal
ry		32	4	2	1	0·8	0·35	0·4	21·5	0·6	Bal
rz		32	8	2	1	0·8	0·35	0·4	21·5	0·6	Bal
sa		32	16	2	1	0·8	0·35	0·4	21·5	0·6	Bal
sb		32	8	2	1·5	0·8	0·35	0·4	21·5	0·6	Bal
sc		32	8	4	—	0·8	0·35	0·4	21·5	0·6	Bal
sd		45	2	2	1	0·8	0·35	0·4	21·5	0·6	Bal
se		45	4	2	1	0·8	0·35	0·4	21·5	0·6	Bal
sf		45	8	2	1	0·8	0·35	0·4	21·5	0·6	Bal
sg		45	16	2	1	0·8	0·35	0·4	21·5	0·6	Bal
sh		45	8	2	1·5	0·8	0·35	0·4	21·5	0·6	Bal
sj		45	8	2	2	0·8	0·35	0·4	21·5	0·6	Bal
sk		45	8	4	—	0·8	0·35	0·4	21·5	0·6	Bal
sm	0·5	36	15	4·5	—	0·1	—	—	26·5	—	Bal

tested as in the preliminary survey. Stress/log time curves of some of the alloys are given in Fig. 5, tensile results in Table 4 and impact results in Table 5.

The stress-rupture results of even the strongest of these alloys were disappointing when compared with the results for the straight 8 per cent tungsten addition alloy (ek, Fig. 5) tested in the preliminary survey, but in most cases impact results were greatly improved. Cobalt additions were at least as effective as increase in nickel content in the tungsten/molybdenum hardened alloys for improving impact resistance, and generally produced superior stress-rupture properties. Manganese additions did not prevent embrittlement, and the $2\frac{1}{2}$ per cent aluminium addition had a rather severe embrittling effect.

The tube extruded from the works heat of EPE.24 had very promising properties, which were superior to those of the bar forged from the laboratory heat of ym. The structural uniformity, cleanliness and surface quality of the extruded tube was very high.

TABLE 3

Combination of Alloying Elements
(Alloy compositions based on 4–8 per cent tungsten plus molybdenum)

Lab. mark	C	Ni	Co	W	Mo	Mn	Al	Ti	Cr	Si	Fe
yb	0·1	32	—	—	—	0·8	0·35	0·4	22	0·6	Bal
yc		32	—	—	—	4·0	0·35	0·4	22	0·6	Bal
yd		32	—	—	—	8·0	0·35	0·4	22	0·6	Bal
ye		32	—	4	1	0·8	0·35	0·4	22	0·6	Bal
yf		32	—	4	1	4·0	0·35	0·4	22	0·6	Bal
yg		32	—	4	1	8·0	0·35	0·4	22	0·6	Bal
yh		40	8	4	1	0·8	2·5	0·4	22	0·6	Bal
yj		32	16	4	1	0·8	0·35	0·4	22	0·6	Bal
ym		40	8	4	1	0·8	0·35	0·4	22	0·6	Bal
yn		40	16	4	1	0·8	0·35	0·4	22	0·6	Bal
yp		48	—	4	1	0·8	0·35	0·4	22	0·6	Bal
yr		48	8	4	1	0·8	0·35	0·4	22	0·6	Bal
ys		40	8	8	0	0·8	0·35	0·4	22	0·6	Bal
yt		40	8	6	1	0·8	0·35	0·4	22	0·6	Bal
yv		40	8	4	2	0·8	0·35	0·4	22	0·6	Bal
yw		40	8	6	0	0·8	0·35	0·4	22	0·6	Bal
yx		40	8	4	0	0·8	0·35	0·4	22	0·6	Bal
yy		48	—	8	0	0·8	0·35	0·4	22	0·6	Bal
yz		48	8	6	1	0·8	0·35	0·4	22	0·6	Bal
za		48	8	4	2	0·8	0·35	0·4	22	0·6	Bal
zb		48	8	6	0	0·8	0·35	0·4	22	0·6	Bal
zc		48	8	4	1	0·8	0·35	0·4	22	0·6	Bal
zd		48	8	4	0	0·8	0·35	0·4	22	0·6	Bal
gadk		32	8	—	—	0·8	0·35	0·4	22	0·6	Bal

TABLE 4

Combination of Alloying Elements

(Tensile properties at 900°C)

Alloy lab. mark	0·1% PS tonf/in²	0·2% PS tonf/in²	T.S. tonf/in²	Elong. %	R. of A. %
rb	4·5	5·0	8·4	73	76
rm	5·7	7·0	10·4	86	72
rn	5·5	5·8	9·8	73	74
rr	5·7	6·1	10·4	61	67
rs	ND	ND	12·0	79	60
rt	6·3	6·5	11·9	60	65
ry	5·5	6·1	10·0	92	66
rz	6·6	7·0	10·9	90	70
sa	7·2	7·6	12·6	68	66
sb	7·0	7·4	ND	ND	ND
sc	5·8	6·3	11·0	70	70
se	6·3	6·7	11·6	82	63
sf	6·7	7·1	11·9	79	61
sg	7·4	7·8	12·8	76	60
sh	7·1	7·5	12·3	100	75
sj	8·0	8·5	13·5	68	60
sk	7·0	7·5	11·7	77	65
sm	9·1	10·0	15·5	63	55
yb					
yc					
yd	4·6	4·9	7·8	62	74
ye					
yf	6·0	6·5	10·6	71	71
yg	7·2	7·3	10·8	52	56
yh	5·5	6·2	9·8	58	94
yj	6·6	7·1	11·8	64	68
ym	7·9	8·3	12·4	56	64
EPE.24	6·1	6·4	8·6	74	64
yn	7·4	7·9	12·3	97	60
yp	6·4	6·8	10·7	50	60
yr	6·2	6·5	11·4	78	61
ys	6·7	7·1	11·3	46	63
yt	6·9	7·2	10·6	63	60
yv	7·5	8·0	12·2	93	72
yw	7·6	7·8	11·1	78	58
yx	5·5	5·7	9·2	66	55
yy	6·2	6·6	10·1	66	55
yz	6·5	7·1	12·3	78	63
za	5·9	6·5	8·9	49	58
zb	6·0	6·4	8·9	66	60
zc	6·1	6·5	8·7	66	60
zd	5·2	5·6	10·7	70	66
gakd	3·9	4·2	8·9	81	65

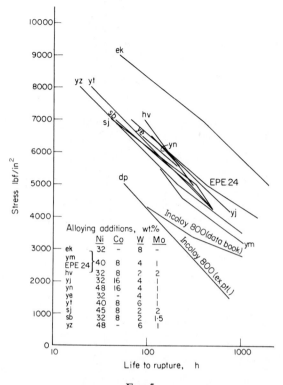

FIG. 5

Stress/log time curves for some alloys containing various combinations of tungsten, molybdenum, nickel and cobalt at 900°C.

DISCUSSION

At present it seems clear that Incoloy 800 type alloys can be greatly strengthened by additions of tungsten with smaller additions of niobium and/or molybdenum. However, these strengthening additions produce embrittling phases at service temperatures. These can be partially or wholly eliminated by increases in nickel content and/or additions of cobalt, depending on the amounts added. However, the addition of excessive amounts of nickel plus cobalt appears to reduce stress-rupture properties somewhat, indicating that it may be difficult to develop a completely non-embrittling alloy as strong as the straight 8 per cent tungsten addition alloy ek, probably because part of the creep resistance of this alloy was almost certainly attributable to precipitation hardening by the embrittling μ phase. Nevertheless, it should be possible to make tungsten-strengthened alloys closely approaching ek in stress-rupture properties by only slightly increasing the total nickel plus

TABLE 5

Combination of Alloying Elements
(Impact properties as-annealed and annealed plus exposed
for 1000 hr/800°C)

Alloy lab. mark	Impact resistance as-annealed 1 hr, 1150°C, a.c. ft lbf	Impact resistance annealed plus 1000 hr, 800°C ft lbf
rb	48	42·4
rm	48	23·9
rn	48	17·5
rr	48	44·2
rs	48	41·5
rt	48	42·9
ry	48	22·5
rz	48	41·6
sa	48	44·5
sb	48	31·2
sc	48	32·5
se	48	47
sf	48	44·2
sg	48	44·5
sh	48	42·3
sj	48	21·8
sk	48	42·8
sm	48	20·4
yb	47·9	37·6
yc	47·9	36·2
yd	47·9	18·3
ye	47·9	7·0
yf	47·9	3·0
yg	34·7	17·5
yh	32·0	0·8
yj	45·8	25·0
EPE.24	44·3	38·0
ym	42·0	17·8
yn	47·5	37·0
yp	19·2	25·5
yr	36·0	39·4
ys	39·8	43·0
yt	34·0	15·4
yv	41·1	35·5
yw	44·6	26
yx	35·1	37·3
yy	34·8	15·5
yz	39·5	17·0
za	36·0	27·0
zb	38·9	23·8
zc	38·1	38·0
zd	43·8	42·9
gakd	46·7	13·1

cobalt content of Incoloy 800. This would probably necessitate acceptance of a small degree of embrittlement during long-time exposure at temperatures in the lower end service range, but this should be less than in HK type steels for instance. It would be most useful to receive comments from manufacturers and operators of reforming plant concerning the degree of μ phase or sigma phase embrittlement that they would be willing to accept.

The welding of the type of alloy being developed does not appear to be any more difficult than the welding of Incoloy 800, although it may be necessary to develop a stronger filler metal than those currently available for customers not employing flash-butt welding.

Another series of alloys has been made with tungsten additions of 4–8 per cent with small additions of molybdenum and/or niobium. Nickel contents of 32, 36 and 40 per cent will be combined with cobalt contents of 0, 4, 8, and 12 per cent to give 32–48 per cent total nickel plus cobalt. Several other compositional variations are also to be investigated.

As the compositional field is narrowed towards the final composition testing will become more intensive. Alloys will be stress-rupture tested for up to 10,000 hr, corrosion testing is being increased as previously mentioned and embrittlement during exposure at temperatures between 700–1100°C will be more thoroughly investigated.

It can be seen that there are grounds for reasonable confidence that we can develop in the near future an alloy capable of carrying almost twice the load that Incoloy 800 can carry at 900–1000°C. The strength-to-cost ratio should be favourable.

WELDING METALLURGY OF CAST
AUSTENITIC MATERIALS

R. G. Baker and D. M. Haddrill

INTRODUCTION

CENTRIFUGALLY cast austenitic steel tubes and headers have found wide-spread application in reformer plant where they are used to contain inflammable gases in a temperature range 700–900°C. The materials in most common use have nominal compositions 18% Cr/37% Ni and 25% Cr/20% Ni respectively with carbon contents usually in the range 0·3/0·4 per cent. They have the advantage of being relatively inexpensive compared with alternative wrought alloys of similar or higher creep strength, but knowledge of their basic metallurgy is much less complete than that of wrought alloys. It is not fully understood how compositional and production variables affect the metallurgical properties. In particular there is a need to define the factors influencing the behaviour of the steels during welding and repair welding and the behaviour of welded details in service.

The fabrication of reformer plant may involve the following types of joint:
- (a) Butt welds in furnace tubes made by metal arc (consumable or non-consumable) or flash butt welding processes.
- (b) Butt and fillet welds for the fabrication of header assemblies using manual metal arc and consumable electrode metal arc processes.
- (c) Welds for the attachment of supports to furnace tubes and headers and for welding-in stub pipes and instrument points.
- (d) Joints between dissimilar metals.

Problems have been experienced in connection with many of these different types of joint during welding and also in service. It is true to say that with regard to the total number of joints welded, the incidence of problems in existing plants is very small. However, when problems do occur they may be costly because of plant down-time involved. Repair welding may be difficult and the actual technique adopted must often be decided on a trial-and-error basis.

An attempt is made in the present paper to review potential welding problems in cast austenitic materials and to indicate where further research work is needed. A limited programme of research work was carried out at BWRA for ICI Ltd.* and the results have been quoted where appropriate.

* Confidential Reports LD1127/1/62 and LD1199/1/62.

2. PREVIOUS WORK

Much of the information available on cast austenitic alloys has been obtained by Avery *et al.* This work was reported some 12 to 17 years ago and contains a great deal of information concerning the creep and stress rupture behaviour of three basic alloy types:

15% Cr/35% Ni (HT*[1]), 26% Cr/20% Ni (HK[2]) and 21% Cr/9% Ni (HF[3]).

The results showed that creep strength was related to carbon content and that room temperature ductility was reduced on ageing. A limited amount of metallographic work was done using the light microscope and it was found that there was a decrease in ductility on ageing which could be attributed to precipitation of carbides.

There was little published work on these alloys subsequently prior to the publication of the paper by Edeleanu and Estruch.[4] They reported further creep data and ageing characteristics and defined a number of outstanding problems in respect of the relation between metallurgical structure and behaviour.

Whilst a body of practical knowledge has grown up as a result of experience in welding cast austenitic materials, there is virtually no published information. The following questions, amongst others, remain open:

1. What potential welding problems may be anticipated to occur as practical problems in cast austenitic materials?
2. In what circumstances are such practical problems likely to arise?
3. What are the important metallurgical factors leading to such problems?
4. How far can such problems be controlled by choice of welding process, alteration of process variables or joint design?
5. Can such problems be controlled by alteration of material variables such as structure or composition?
6. On what grounds should choice of weld metal composition be based?
7. How close a control is necessary over possible defects associated with welds?

3. POTENTIAL WELDING PROBLEMS IN AUSTENITIC MATERIALS

Whilst very little information is available about the welding metallurgy of cast austenitic materials, a great deal is known about the potential problems connected with the welding of wrought austenitic materials. Thus it is possible to go part of the way towards answering the first of the questions posed above by discussing these problems, as they would be expected to apply to cast materials also.

* Alloy Casting Institute Designation.

3.1. *Weld Metal Solidification Cracking*

During the solidification of a weld metal behind the moving source of heat, the solid crystals grow inwards towards the centre of the run. The last liquid metal to solidify will, in general, be enriched in alloying elements which will lower its freezing temperature. As the surrounding solidified metal cools, thermal contraction will take place tending to pull the opposite sides of the weld apart. Solidification cracking occurs if the strength of the

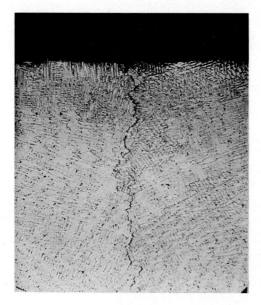

Fig. 1

Solidification crack in fully austenitic weld metal. × 75.

partially solidified portion of the weld is insufficient to resist the contraction stresses and if there is insufficient remaining liquid metal to fill the void that results. Fully austenitic weld metals are generally susceptible to this type of welding problem (Fig. 1). The susceptibility can be substantially reduced by adjusting the weld metal composition so that the solidified structure contains some ferrite. Nevertheless, this is not a universally applicable means of avoiding the problem.

Limitation of impurity elements and control of the balance of the principal alloying elements may improve the performance of fully austenitic deposits in respect of this problem. Limited control of the problem is also possible by variation of welding procedure. Cracking is most likely if heat input is large and if the gap to be bridged by the bead is also large. In general the greater the degree of movement which may take place in a direction transverse to the weld, whether as a result of thermal contraction or not, the greater the risk of cracking.

Both the behaviour and properties of many of the weld metals at present being used for welding austenitic materials are well understood. However, in the development of new welding materials, hot cracking susceptibility is one of the factors to be considered and further research work is necessary to define the metallurgical factors involved in the problem. This need is by no means unique to cast austenitic materials but is general as regards the development of austenitic filler materials.

3.2. *Microcracking in Weld Metal*

Solidification cracking of the type described above occurs in the form of major cracks running longitudinally along the centre of the weld run or sometimes as transverse cracks across the weld run and is a defect which can usually be detected by visual inspection. A far more insidious defect which may occur is that of microcracking in multi-run weld deposits. Such cracking commonly occurs in underlying weld runs and the cracks themselves, as the

FIG. 2

Microcracking in multi-run fully austenitic weld deposit. ×8.

name suggests, are quite small. The length seldom exceeds 2–3 mm (in a transverse section) and the cracks are very difficult to detect (Fig. 2). Dye-penetrant only reveals cracking of this type if the top runs are completely ground away and even then the absence of a definite indication does not guarantee their absence. They are not always universally distributed throughout the weld depth, and they are easily lapped over during the surface preparation. They are not easily revealed by radiography or ultrasonics due to their very small size.

Microcracks can occur by at least three well-defined mechanisms:—

(a) Due to local melting of solidification segregates in underlying runs followed by the opening-up of these regions under the influence of contraction stresses. This mechanism is termed hot tearing and may also occur in the parent material adjacent to the fusion boundary.

(b) Certain weld metal compositions when heated in a temperature range of between 850–1150°C exhibit a sharp fall in ductility and, if the thermal stresses are sufficiently high, cracking may occur.[5] The cracks appear to form in the parts of previous weld runs which are reheated by subsequent runs to the above temperature range and not, as in the case of hot tearing, immediately adjacent to the fusion boundary.

(c) If the silicon content of the weld metal is sufficiently high, a further form of microcracking may occur due to the segregation of films of silicate inclusions between the solidified metal crystals.[6] This form of cracking is not very common since weld metal silicon contents are normally too low.

The above three problems are general in the welding of austenitic materials and there is no evidence that dilution from cast austenitic parent materials

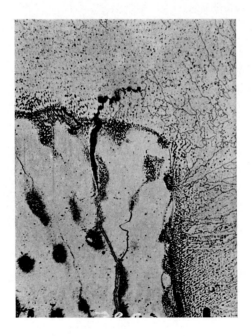

FIG. 3

Hot tearing at fusion line of weld in cast austenitic steel. × 100.

necessarily renders any of them more acute than when welding wrought steels. The possible effect of microcracking on the properties of joints in cast materials has not been established and this is one of the open questions requiring investigation.

3.3. Parent Metal Hot Tearing

When cast austenitic materials are welded, the eutectic between the grains becomes molten for a significant distance beyond the fusion boundary. Since the liquated zone is comparatively broad, if the liquid region is substantially opened under thermal stresses, liquid metal can be supplied from the main weld pool to fill any cavity produced provided the weld metal solidification temperature is not too high. It is, however, possible that if the carbon level were low either due to decarburization or because the general level was low, the "feed" of liquid metal from the weld pool might be interrupted and hot tearing might result. A typical hot tear is shown in Fig. 3. It follows that a weld metal with a solidus temperature significantly above that of the parent material might be expected to increase the tendency towards hot tearing.

In the event of hot tearing occurring in the heat affected zone, the service behaviour of the joint might be directly affected and the hot tearing could also play a significant role in the development of further cracking.[7, 8] These possible effects require further investigation.

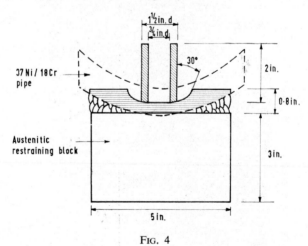

FIG. 4

Elevation of BWRA ring test modified for testing pipe material.

3.4. Cracking during Reheating

It has been shown that many wrought austenitic materials are susceptible to cracking in the HAZ during post-weld heat treatment.[8] Solution of carbides occurs in the HAZ under the high-temperature conditions associated with welding. During reheating, supersaturated solid solution of carbon decreases with the precipitation of carbides and this results in a fall of HAZ ductility. The fall in ductility may be sufficiently great for cracking to occur as a result of the creep associated with the relief of residual stress. Cast austenitic materials are potentially liable to this form of cracking and it has been shown that such cracking can occur in practice under sufficiently high restraint. A section of cast 18% Cr/37% Ni pipe was welded to a thick stainless steel block and a stub pipe welded to the prepared surface of the cast austenitic material as shown in Fig. 4. Cracking occurred when the block was reheated at 750°C (Fig. 5). It was confirmed metallurgically that copious

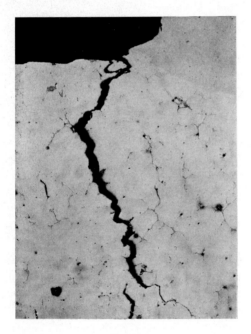

FIG. 5

Cracking in cast austenitic steel after post-weld heat treatment. × 50.

precipitation had occurred within the grains of HAZ parent metal (Fig. 6). It has been shown in previous work[9] that the likelihood of this form of cracking taking place is reduced if geometrical discontinuities at the toe of the fillet weld are removed by grinding prior to reheating and if the joint is raised to a comparatively high temperature relatively quickly. The likelihood of cracking may also be reduced by choosing a weld metal of minimum hot strength consistent with performance. It is not known to what extent this problem might occur in welding cast austenitic materials in practice but it seems likely that it is not a serious practical problem at this time. The risks of a potential problem of this type becoming a practical problem would be increased (a) if material thickness were increased, (b) if operating temperatures were reduced.

It is likely that effective methods of control would be similar to those used with wrought materials but this would require confirmation by experiments.

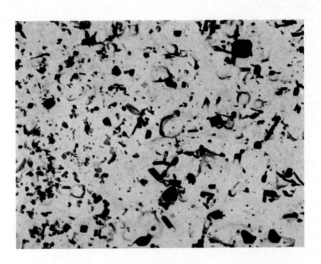

FIG. 6

Precipitation of $M_{23}C_6$ carbide in HAZ of weld in cast austenitic steel after post-weld heat treatment. Electron micrograph. ×40,000.

3.5. *Progressive Embrittlement of the Parent Material*

The microstructure of the cast austenitic steels consists of very large primary grains having a sub-structure of austenitic dendrites with a eutectic infilling. The eutectic is composed of relatively large carbides and austenite. Carbides have a different coefficient of expansion from that of the matrix. Thus, when the material is heated, local deformation takes place generating dislocations in the parent material around the carbides.

This process is, of course, equally liable to occur in wrought alloys which contain carbides. However, in most wrought alloys nearly all of the carbides are taken into solution if the temperature is raised to about 1050°C and recovery and recrystallization can occur. Thus such a material is soft and ductile after cooling. The very much higher carbon contents usually found in the cast materials mean that a large proportion of the carbides remain out of solution at 1050°C and recovery and recrystallization is therefore impeded by their presence. Furthermore, on cooling more dislocations are generated as a result of the differences on the expansion coefficient of carbides and matrix and the matrix becomes harder and less ductile. Intragranular precipitation from carbon in supersaturated solution would be expected to have a further deleterious effect.

This progressive embrittlement might lead to cracking in service if:

(a) The ductility became sufficiently low.

(b) Applied stresses due to system loading or of thermal origin were sufficiently large.

(c) There was a point of stress concentration of adequate intensity (such as might be provided by the toe of the weld bead or by a weld defect).

The problem is similar in many respects to the brittle fracture problem which exists in ferritic materials and is potentially capable of analysis in the same way, by a fracture mechanics approach. The use of such an approach might permit the relative importance of material properties, applied stress and type and size of stress concentration to be defined.

One particular aspect of this problem leading to practical difficulties may arise during the repair welding of cast materials. It has been shown that

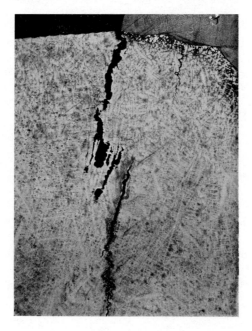

Fig. 7

Cracking that occurred at the toe of the weld during welding in a cast austenitic steel pipe. ×7.

cracking can occur during welding under the influence of the induced thermal stresses if the material is sufficiently brittle. In welding tests carried out on 18% Cr/37% Ni material which had been in service and which showed an elongation of only about 0·5 per cent in a tensile test, cracking occurred during welding as shown in Fig. 7. Heat treatment of this material at 1050°C produced no improvement in ductility and it was not until the heat treatment temperature was raised to about 1200°C that the ductility was recovered and welding could be carried out satisfactorily.

3.6. *The Creep of Welded Details*

There is substantial information available on the creep behaviour of cast austenitic materials but very little, if any, on the creep behaviour of welded details. It is, however, considered likely that the risk of creep failures occurring would be greater at the geometrical discontinuities provided by welds than in the pipe walls remote from welds. The important factor in failure by creep is considered to be the amount of strain which takes place at a given point and thus it is worthwhile paying attention in both design and practice to details at which there might be an accumulation of creep strain during service.

However, until more information accumulates on the behaviour of plant fabricated from cast materials or until creep tests are carried out on welded details it is not possible to say whether any of the details at present in use impose an important limitation on the creep life of the structure as a whole.

4. SUMMARY AND CONCLUSIONS

An attempt has been made to summarize the potential problems which may occur during welding of cast austenitic materials and to discuss them both in respect of the difficulties which might occur during welding or in service after welding.

Much of the substance of the paper is speculative and it would be a great pity if it led to undue despondency about the materials. It might be as well to reiterate here that the incidence of problems so far arising from welding is small. However, there is a clear need for further research to form a rational basis on which future developments in plant materials can take place, and to define the metallurgical factors which may result in practical problems so that these problems may be anticipated and avoided.

ACKNOWLEDGEMENTS

The experimental work quoted in the paper was carried out for ICI Ltd., as part of a small exploratory programme from December 1961 to May 1962. The authors are grateful to ICI Ltd. for permission to publish these results. The work was carried out by R. N. Younger who was at that time with the Association and is now with the Davy Ashmore Group.

REFERENCES

1. H. S. AVERY and N. A. MATTHEWS, *Trans. A.S.M.* **38**, 1947.
2. H. S. AVERY and C. R. WILKS, *Trans. A.S.M.* **40**, 1948.
3. H. S. AVERY, C. R. WILKS and J. A. FELLOWS, *Trans. A.S.M.* **44**, 1952.
4. C. EDELEANU and B. ESTRUCH, Conference on high alloy steels, Scarborough, June 1964.
5. D. M. HADDRILL and R. G. BAKER, BWRA Confidential Report B5/20/63, to be published.
6. O. R. CARPENTER and N. C. JESSON, *Welding Journal*, **26**, 727s–741s (1947).
7. R. N. YOUNGER and R. G. BAKER, *J.I.S.I.* **196**, October 1960.
8. R. N. YOUNGER and R. G. BAKER, *B.W.J.* **8**, 1961.
9. R. N. YOUNGER, D. M. HADDRILL and R. G. BAKER, *J.I.S.I.* August 1963.

THE WELDING OF HIGH ALLOY MATERIALS RELEVANT TO PRESSURE STEAM-REFORMING OF NAPHTHA

F. P. Hahn

THIS paper gives an account of the welding processes and materials used in the construction and repair of the primary reformer furnaces designed and built by ICI Agricultural Division. The general form of the equipment is indicated in the paper by Clark. Basically, it is true to say that while initial fabrication, and especially repair by welding was approached with some trepidation, the difficulties have been much less than might have been expected.

1. BASIC PROCESSES AND MATERIALS

1.1. *General*

Every care has been taken to obtain a high quality of weld and all butt welds have been radiographed. There has been some trouble with cracking of root runs and of parent metal, and it has been routine to check both root runs and the finished welds by the dye penetrant technique, and all techniques have been qualified on the basis of micrographic examination and mechanical tests. Regarding root runs, it was early found that cracking was especially liable to occur if no or too little filler metal was added and this has some bearing on the choice of process.

1.2. *Materials*

Table 1 gives the analyses of the deposits made by the various electrodes and filler wires which have been used. Comments on the different types are made below. The base metal has in general been high carbon 18/37 or 25/20 Cr–Ni castings of $0 \cdot 2$–$0 \cdot 5$ per cent carbon content, as discussed by Estruch, with small tube of Incoloy DS or Incoloy 800 for pigtails.

No material has been bought by ICI with a requirement that it be proved suitable for welding prior to acceptance. Up to date we have had no trouble in the U.K. which would have been avoided by such a requirement, though we believe that acceptance tests of this type are used in the U.S.A. There is reason to believe that the carbon silicon ratio is important. Thus the length of

TABLE 1

Welding Alloys—Analysis of Weld Deposit

	Metal arc electrodes						Filler wires			
	Incoweld A	Inconel 182	Murex Nicrex 3	ESAB SP133	Dew 16/36	Chromex 19/38/0.45	Inconel 92	Inconel 82	NC 82	S
Ni	bal	bal	60	33·9	30·8	33·9	67 min	67 min	bal	21
Cu	0·5	0·5		0·02			0·5	0·5	0·2	
Mn	1–3·5	5–9·5	0·5	1·7	1·30	0·7	2–2·75	2·5–3·5	1·2	2·0
Fe	6–12	6–10			bal	bal	10	3	0·5	
Si	0·75	1·0	0·1	1·3	0·38	0·7	0·35	0·5	0·5	1·5
C	0·15	0·1		0·6	0·25	0·48	0·1	0·1	0·26	0·4
S	0·02	0·015					0·015	0·015	—	
Cr	13–17	13–17	13–15	18·8	18·8	17·4	14–17	18–22	18–21	26
Ti	—	1·0				0·02	2·5–3·5	0·75	—	0·08
Al	—							2–3	—	
Nb	1–3	1–2·5	0·8			0·05		—	—	
Mo	0·5–2	0·12			2·0	0·08		0·1	—	
Co	—	—		0·10					—	
Total impurities									0·5	
Cost/in.³ of weld metal	6/2	10/-		5/10	5/6		9/6	12/10	5/3	

cracking in the root runs of three tubes of similar alloy content were as shown in Table 2.

TABLE 2

Cracking as a Function of C and Si Content

Tube No.	Carbon	Silicon	Si/C ratio	Length of cracking
1	0·32	1·22	3·7	10¾ in.
2	0·40	0·93	2·3	1⅞ in.
3	0·52	0·90	1·7	nil

Available data on the rupture strength of the parent metal and weld deposits is discussed by Estruch.

1.3. Argon Arc Welding

1.3.1. *General.* Argon arc welding involves no flux. This is a very major advantage as the flux or slag from all coated high alloy electrodes can catalyse severe oxidation of the base metal at temperatures over about 500°C if there is a supply of oxidizing gas (and the process gases are sufficiently oxidizing). Argon arc welding is, therefore, essential whenever it is not possible to remove welding slag, i.e. for the root runs of pipe butt welds when it is not possible to clean out the pipe bore, for fillet welds or bracket attachments not having full penetration welds and not welded all round, and for repairing cracks which have penetrated to the bore.

The manual tungsten arc process (TIG) has mainly been used. It is slow, and demands much skill on the part of the welder in those cases where the deposit cracks unless a copious amount of filler is added continuously, and crater cracks are very easily caused by lack of addition of filler at the end of a run.

No furnace tubes or headers made by automatic or semi-automatic welding have yet entered service in pressure steam reforming plants in England although a number of tubes made by automatic TIG welding with and without filler wire are being installed.

Experimental MIG welds (inert gas shielded metal arc) show that the process can produce sound high quality welds, but some detail development work is necessary to bring the fully automatic installations up to a high degree of reliability.

Problems are associated with arc length control when tungsten electrodes are used and control of guide-tube to weld-pool distance with consumable electrodes. Weld pools must be kept relatively small, particularly on the furnace tubes, which have a small outside diameter, and the automatic adjustment of weave or of number of passes per layer as the preparation opens out is complicated. Gas mixtures appear preferable to pure argon for MIG welding.

1.3.2. *Technique.* Details of technique are particularly important if any repair welds have to be done or for any reason the material is particularly crack sensitive. The filler wire diameter is important, 10 s.w.g. or 12 s.w.g. are satisfactory, but nothing smaller should be used as the operator cannot then ensure sufficient addition to avoid cracking troubles and will have to change wire or slide the wire through his hand too often, both of which operations interrupt wire addition to the pool.

The welder very often stops adding filler to the weld pool when he is about to break the arc at the end of a length of root run and as a result crater cracks develop. These can be reduced by leaving a thick end to the section of root pass and bringing the weld pool back along the deposited weld metal for about $\frac{3}{8}$ in. continuing to add metal and then breaking the arc sharply. A blob of filler, perhaps with a crater pipe, is left and must be removed, but removal requires less work than cutting out a crater crack.

The rightward technique permits building up a thicker root pass than the leftward method and can reduce the incidence of cracking. The weld bead tends to be convex, but the grooves at the side do not trap slag from electrodes deposited between the 12 o'clock and 3 o'clock positions. Up to the present we have been able to avoid making repairs in the overhead position, but if we do have to make such repairs we will probably have to tolerate quite a lot of slag inclusions in the root area.

Provision of adequate argon shield without too great an expenditure on gas gives scope for ingenuity. It is seldom necessary to fill long lengths of pipe with argon, for example, on one job stiff cardboard discs were inserted into the ends of the two sections of pipe before they were aligned, far enough away (about 6 in.) for them not to catch fire when welding was carried out. The pipes were aligned with about $\frac{1}{8}$ in. root gap and argon was introduced through this gap by a piece of flattened thin-walled copper tube. The gap was sealed with tape, except where the tube was inserted and for a short distance opposite the tube.

Purging was continued until the gas escaping through this gap would extinguish a burning match.

Welding started opposite the tube and was continued in both directions towards the tube, an assistant pulling the tape away from the gap ahead of the welding arc.

Finally, the copper tube was withdrawn and the gap left in the root run closed relying on the argon inside the pipe to prevent contamination. The cardboard discs burn away when the plant is put on stream.

1.3.3. *Filler wires for* 18/37 *alloy.* The two filler wires used have been Inconels 82 and 92. The 92 wire has been used extensively for root runs on header systems and has been trouble free, but examination of a special furnace tube after 8000 hr service showed that the 92 root run had hardened and cracked, presumably because of lower creep ductility. Some preference is therefore felt for Inconel 82, which is less likely to age harden, though there is little evidence to suggest that its rupture strength is lower than that of the parent metal. Supplies have, however, been short and it has been reserved for repair work on metal embrittled in service. The reinforcement bead is reckoned to counteract the lower strength.

The relative merits of Inconels 92 and 82 are summarized in Table 3.

TABLE 3

Relative Merits of Certain Welding Materials

	Metal arc		TIG	
	Incoweld A	Inconel 182	Inconel 92	Inconel 82
Resistance to weld cracking	Good	Excellent	Moderate	Good
Liability to cause parent metal cracking	Moderate	Small	Moderate	Small
Susceptibility to silicon pick-up from parent metal	Moderate	Slight	Highly susceptible	Slight
Availability	Good	Moderate	Good	Poor
Cost	High	Very High	High	Very High
Welding characteristics	Good	Excellent	Moderate	Good

1.3.4. *Filler wires for* 25/20 *alloy.* A wire of composition S (Table 1) has been used successfully for TIG welds and successful welds have also been made by the MIG process using Inconel 82.

1.4. *Coated Metal Arc Electrode Welding*

1.4.1. *General.* This has been used very extensively, either for complete welds where it is possible to remove all the internal slag, or for filling up welds on top of an argon arc root run. The dangers of the slag causing oxidation have been noted above: considerable care is required as, for example, a bellows (in a low pressure plant) was holed in a few days as a result of fragments of slag brushed from an adjacent weld being left on it. Fortunately, slag pockets sealed in completely are not dangerous.

Major advantages, as compared with manual TIG, are speed and the fact that the amount of filler metal deposited is not under the control of the welder and hence root runs are less liable to crack because of inadequate addition.

1.4.2. *Choice of electrode for* 18/37 *Cr–Ni.* The first batches of furnace tubes were of low carbon 18/37 Cr–Ni and were flash butt welded, but a number of surface defects were repaired with Incoweld A and these repairs have given no trouble. The headers have all been of high carbon 18/37 and very large quantities of Incoweld A were used in this fabrication and for the attachment of brackets, etc. No troubles have arisen from these welds.

A variant of Incoweld A, having a pure nickel core wire in place of the more usual nickel chrome alloy wire, has been tested. This electrode does not overheat so rapidly, but is not as good for positional welds.

A small number of welds using Inconel 182 are in service and give no trouble. This electrode appears less liable to cause parent metal cracking than Incoweld A, perhaps because it is less strong when hot and induces lower contraction stresses. The merits of Incoweld A and Inconel 182 are compared in Table 3 above.

All the above deposit metals contain about 67 per cent nickel. Nicrex 3 contains less nickel (60 per cent) and is relatively cheap and easily available, but its use has been delayed because of lack of data on its strength.

It has been an objective to get an electrode of composition nearer to that of the 18/37 parent metal, both because of possible savings in cost, and also because the high nickel electrodes are presumably somewhat more sensitive to sulphur in flue gas or the process gas, and it was thought at one time that this might be important. Experimental welds have been made with ESAB SP133, DEW 16/36 and Chromex 19/38/0·45, which approximate to the 18/37 analysis. The Chromex electrode gave better welds than the other two and though inferior as regards radiographic quality to Incoweld A and Inconel 182, we would accept it, but it offers insufficient financial economy to evoke much interest.

1.4.3. *Choice of electrode for* 25/20 *Cr–Ni.* The majority of fusion welds in cast 25/20 furnace tubes have been made with a weld deposit of matching composition. Initial attempts to use the low carbon 25/20 electrode designed for wrought alloys had limited success, but provided that one does not expect the perfection possible in mild steel and austenitic steel deposits, high carbon 25/20 electrodes are usable with very little difficulty and large quantities are now being consumed. A carbon content in the 0·45–0·5 per cent region provides a very crack-resistant deposit.

1.5. *Flash Butt Welding*

ICI Agricultural Division installed two flash butt welding machines about 30 years ago for high-pressure mild steel pipe. A great amount of experience was gained in the use of the equipment and welds proved so reliable in service that for a long time they were the only type permitted in high pressure plant. The use of the process was extended to austenitic steel pipe and when the steam reforming process was started it seemed only natural to try out flash butt welding on the spun cast furnace tubes. Low carbon and high carbon 18/37 alloys welded without great difficulty and large numbers of furnace tubes were welded up and put into service.

Radiography was known to be of doubtful value for inspecting flash butt welds and ultrasonics were found ineffective on the cast alloys. Reliance was placed for quality control on destructive examination of test welds at regular intervals and on the comparison of traces produced by machine instrumentation with traces produced during the manufacture of welds subsequently proved satisfactory by destructive examination.

A few early welds have failed. In some cases it has been possible to correlate failures with a feature on the traces which should have caused the weld to be rejected—a break in flashing current just before upset. When welding mild steel this is not important as the oxides of iron formed when air reaches the hot faces melt at a lower temperature than the metal and are readily squeezed out when upset pressure is applied. With high alloy materials, however, refractory oxides are formed and a break in flashing current can result in a thin film of oxide being left in the completed weld.

Some other weld failures are associated with traces which do not show this particular feature, but which show a delay between the slide movement occurring at upset and the rise of upset pressure to its full value. This could indicate that the work has slipped in the dies at the moment of upset.

In view of the success of flash butt welding 18/37 alloys we went ahead with plans to flash butt weld 25/20 tubes when it was decided to use this alloy for furnace tubes. Routine dye-check, however, showed faults in some welds, not on the weld line, but about $\frac{1}{8}$ in. away from it on each side. Micro-examination showed that these faults were associated with planes of carbide agglomeration and, while we have made welds which do not show the defects we want to be more certain of the causes and range of settings over which the trouble is encountered before carrying out production welding of high carbon 25/20 material.

2. WELDING SPUN CAST TUBING

This falls into two groups: furnace tubes, usually about 5 in. O.D., and header and transfer lines which may be 10–16 in. O.D.

Most of the 18/37 furnace tubes have been flash butt welded, but sufficient fusion welds have been done to show that no particular problems arise. All the 25/20 tubes have been fusion welded, using various processes, some mechanized, and again no troubles have arisen. It is possible that further development will open the way to flash butt weld these tubes.

All the ICI headers are of spun cast 18/37, with some sand cast tees, etc., and in general have been fusion welded, although tests have shown that flash butt welding is practicable if the thickness is reduced locally to bring the total area within the capacity of the machine. As discussed above, Incoweld A has been used where the root slag can be removed, and a root run by TIG with 92 Inconel and then built up with Incoweld A, has been used in other cases. Large lobsterback bends have been made by this technique.

3. WELDING OF SAND CASTINGS (18–37)

Early in the furnace construction programme some very heavy castings were welded without any real difficulty, but later experience showed that major difficulties could arise.

The Heysham furnace headers had two 10–12 in. tees and one 12–16 in. tee. These were required of radiographic quality, but no supplier could offer to make them. They were finally obtained as pairs of half castings, requiring a "U" weld to produce the complete tee, and the section to be welded was as much as 2 in. thick. Incoweld A was used and no trouble experienced, though destructive examination showed that there were a few interdendritic cracks up to $\frac{1}{8}$ in. long. These tees have now some 3 years' service. All furnaces have sand cast end caps on headers and a large cone which connects the header to the secondary reformer and ICI have had no trouble so long as the casting was sound adjacent to the weld preparation. In a few cases it has been necessary to cut back to sound metal and build up.

In a small number of cases a maze of cracks has appeared on the weld preparation near the weld and have spread on attempting to grind them out. This trouble has been tentatively attributed to material being in an unsuitable metallurgical condition resulting from slow cooling through the 800°–600°C range. If a casting showing this trouble is heated to 1250°C for about $\frac{1}{2}$ hr and is then withdrawn from the furnace and rapidly air-cooled there is then a very good chance of being able to weld it without trouble.

If a casting is stripped from the mould while still about 800°C and rapidly air-cooled it is generally weldable. We have found that a casting having a hardness above 200 VPN usually cracks during attempts to weld, but a low hardness figure does not necessarily indicate that a casting can be welded.

No 25/20 sand castings have been used for ICI steam-reforming plants to date.

4. WELDING OF TUBES AND HEADERS AFTER SERVICE

4.1. General

There have been a number of failures in service of varying importance and it has been found possible to repair 18/37 headers without undue difficulty. The earliest case occurred where a gas leak from a faulty weld at a branch melted the aluminium cladding of a header and a pool of molten aluminium ate some $\frac{3}{16}$ in. into the header. It was ground out and built up with 182 Inconel and no cracking resulted. There have also been one or two leaks at weldolets and these have necessitated welding the base tube, again without trouble.

The major amount of experience has, however, been in relation to the hanger at the top of the vertical leg of the transfer line, where the original design was unsatisfactory and one header leaked and fired and all the others were found cracked. Details of the original and improved design are given elsewhere (Hahn, Failure of header support bracket assemblies).

On the occasion of the original failure, it was desired to start up as soon as possible. The hanger plates and fillet welds were cut back to clear the crack, which was chipped out. It was then found possible to weld up the cracks (about 6 in. long). In the case of the header which had leaked, a good root run could not be obtained because of the oxidation/carburization of the inner skin of metal and this header had a new section welded in as soon as possible. Examination of this and the other repair welds when finally withdrawn from service showed no signs of impending failure.

The following points on technique are based in part on experience in repair on material which has been in service and in part on experience in welding new material (especially sand castings) which have shown serious cracking during fabrication.

4.2. TIG Welding

It is essential to follow the advice given in 1.3.2 above, otherwise serious trouble will arise. No relevant experience with MIG welding is available.

4.3. Metal Arc Welding

In several cases repairs have been carried out by metal arc welding without any special precautions being necessary, although most of these involved complete circumferential welds where a length of new material has been inserted into an existing line. There is some evidence that restraint has an effect and when replacing a length of pipe it may be preferable to insert two pieces of new material, welding each to the existing pipe first and then making the restrained closing weld between the two pieces of new material.

However, when making local repairs and in some cases when making complete welds, weld or parent metal cracking has caused a great deal of trouble. The following techniques help, although very often repair work involves cutting out half the weld metal deposited to get rid of cracks.

(a) Use stringer beads of width about equal to depth in preference to weave runs.

(b) Do not allow the interpass temperature to exceed 150°C.

(c) Peen each run immediately after deposition and while still hot. Immediately the welder breaks the arc an assistant should deslag the weld starting at the end at which the welder started. This gives the slag at the end of the run time to cool below red heat and become brittle before the deslagging tool reaches it. A pneumatic needle gun is a considerable help in this operation, but not essential. Immediately the slag is clear the welder should peen the weld with a pneumatic chipping hammer weighing between 5 and 8 lb, fitted with a ball peen point. A $\frac{3}{4}$ in. radius point is about right and it is useful to have two or three points of different end diameters. Small diameters are necessary to get down to the root area, but larger diameters are more easily kept on the weld bead when the weld is wide. Do not overpeen. There should be individual indentations on the surface, not grooves.

There is an indication that condensed moisture can be a source of trouble and when welding in very cold damp conditions preheating until the metal is warm to the touch is thought to be advantageous. It appears that the best parent metal temperature is in the range between just feeling warm to the hand and being too hot to touch and, depending on ambient conditions, the weld zone may have to be heated or cooled to maintain these conditions.

It has been suggested that the hot strength of the weld metal has considerable influence on parent metal cracking. If the hot strength is low the weld metal will deform plastically as it cools without building up very high residual stresses or applying high forces to the heat affected zone of the parent metal while it is cooling through a hot short range from the maximum temperature attained during the welding operation.

The desirable weld metal will, however, have high strength at the operating temperature. 182 Inconel approaches this ideal as the strength falls off very suddenly around 1100°C. Unfortunately, the creep strength in the 850°C range is somewhat lower than that of high carbon 18/37 alloy.

Up to the present trial welds with high carbon 18/37 weld metal have cracked badly in the parent metal which lends weight to the theory, but information from the States suggests they can be used for repair work if about 400°C preheat is applied.

FAILURES OF HEADER SUPPORT BRACKET ASSEMBLIES

F. P. Hahn

The failures that have caused most inconvenience on the high-temperature parts of the steam-reforming plants have been associated with the attachments taking the weight of the vertical leg of the pipe taking gas from the primary reformer to the top of the secondary reformer.

On the earliest plants cast 18/37 alloy brackets were welded to the pipe as sketched in Fig. 1. Full penetration manual metal arc welds were made using Incoweld "A" electrodes (Fig. 1A).

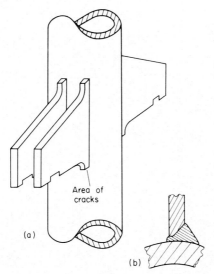

Area of
cracks

(a)

(b)

Fig. 1A
Support brackets on earliest furnaces materials: cast 18/37 electrodes: Incoweld A.

Fig. 1B
Form of weld.

After about a year in service, involving about 30 thermal cycles from operating temperature to ambient and back again, a crack through the wall of the pipe permitted a leak which ignited. The plant was shut down about

15 hr after the leak had first been observed and, when cool, cracks generally as shown in Fig. 2 were found.

The brackets were cut down in size as shown in Fig. 3 and the cracked areas were cut out. Some arc air gouging was tried, but as this appeared to cause the cracks to grow the majority of the work was carried out by chipping and grinding. Before we cleared the cracks we had broken through to the wall in three places. We started to fill the first cavity using 182 Inconel electrodes, but a new crack immediately opened out about $\frac{1}{4}$ to $\frac{1}{2}$ in. away from the edge of the groove and running longitudinally along the pipe. This new crack was cut out and cleared at a depth of about $\frac{3}{8}$ in. We then started using the peening technique described in one of the other papers and achieved a repair reasonably free from cracks.

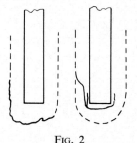

FIG. 2

Enlarged view of cracking on side away from furnace.

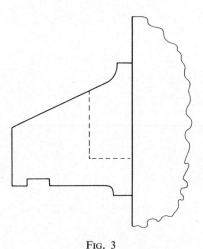

FIG. 3

As the brackets were now too short to connect up with the suspension bars an 18/8/Ti collar was made and fitted as shown in Fig. 4. The original brackets projected through the thermal insulation and the outer edges were only warm to the touch when the inner edge in contact with the pipe was at 850°C. Bowing as a result of differential thermal expansion was thought to be a possible cause of the stresses that had led to fracture and the whole of the shortened brackets were encased in insulation.

Inspection of brackets on other plants at convenient shut down periods revealed that cracks had formed in all cases, although in bracket assemblies made from wrought Incoloy "DS" plate, instead of cast 18/37 the main

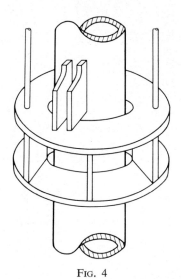

Fig. 4

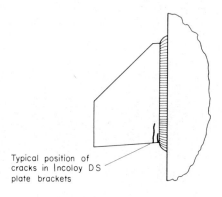

Typical position of
cracks in Incoloy DS
plate brackets

Fig. 5

cracks were in the bracket, not the pipe, as shown in Fig. 5. All brackets were reduced in length and fully encased in insulation. Later examination revealed that cracks were appearing at the toes of the fillet welds, even on the shortened brackets and sections with brackets welded on were cut out and replaced by new pieces with integral rings as sketched in Fig. 6.

This has, we hope, cured the trouble at the brackets, but we have now had an incident which we are hoping does not foretell a new trouble. All circumferential butt welds made by manual metal arc welding on new material have given trouble-free service. However, a weld between a replacement section of new material and material that had been in service for about a year

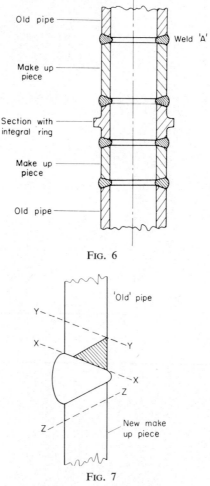

Old pipe

Weld 'A'

Make up piece

Section with integral ring

Make up piece

Old pipe

FIG. 6

'Old' pipe

New make up piece

FIG. 7

Section of weld "A" Fig. 6.

at 700°C was found to be cracked 3 months after completion. The crack first observed was a circumferential crack following the interface X–X, Fig. 7. While it had not been leaking when the plant was on line it was found to penetrate the full wall thickness and the pipe was parted off and re-prepared with the intention of making a new weld. Longitudinal cracks spaced about $\frac{1}{2}$ in. apart and covering the area cross-hatched in Fig. 7 were then found and the new preparation had to be formed on plane $Y-Y$. All old weld metal was cut away and a new preparation formed on the make-up piece in plane ZZ.

When we made the new weld severe cracking occurred, not in the oldest material, but in the make-up piece that had been in service 3 months. This has been attributed to the material having very low ductility as a result of time in service. Ductility against time curves are plotted for two tempera-tures in Fig. 8. It is suspected that most of our previous repairs (on older plants which run at higher temperatures) have been carried out on material which has reached area $P-P$ while in this case we have encountered material in condition Q.

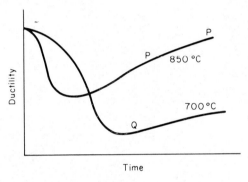

FIG. 8

We hope to overcome this difficulty by cutting out the material that has been in service for 3 months and replacing it by new material, hoping thus to have reasonably ductile material on each side of the weld. We hope to reclaim the section cut out, for further use by heat treatment at 1200–1250°C for $\frac{1}{2}$ hr followed by rapid air cool.

It is apparent, however, that one must select carefully the point in time at which to carry out the installation of new sections.

FABRICATION OF PIGTAIL ASSEMBLIES

F. P. HAHN

1. GENERAL

A PRIMARY reforming furnace tube increases in length by about $4\frac{3}{4}$ in. as the plant comes up to working temperature from cold. Header systems increase in overall dimensions by as much as 12 in. as they heat up. Temperature changes do not necessarily keep in step.

The considerable relative movement that occurs as the plant comes up to operating temperature has been accommodated by making the connection to the top and bottom of the primary furnace tubes by lengths of wrought tube (termed "pigtails") bent into various forms to provide flexibility. The inlet connections are of $1\% \text{ Cr}/\frac{1}{2}\% \text{ Mo}$ tube and there is a flanged joint between the pigtail and a stub pipe welded to the primary furnace tube. Being of a conventional material the inlet pigtails have presented no unusual problems. The outlet pigtails are of wrought Incoloy DS or Incoloy 800, this latter being now the preferred material and all information given below concerns these two materials. Flanged joints are troublesome at outlet temperatures and the outlet pigtails are welded to the furnace tubes and outlet headers. All plants that have had extended service have "Weldolets" at each end of the outlet pigtails. The Weldolets are welded to the furnace tubes and headers in the workshops and the Weldolet to pigtail welds must usually be made on site.

Newer plants are being built with "Socolets" in place of Weldolets which simplifies site welding to some extent, although bitter experience has shown that the Socolet weld still requires considerable skill and knowhow.

The reasons for the choice of Weldolets for the early plants were:

(a) The Weldolets could be welded to the furnace tube and the weld could be examined both inside and outside thus giving a fair assurance that it was sound and had full penetration. The pigtail could then be butt welded to the Weldolet and this weld radiographed to make sure it was satisfactory.

(b) As compared with a simple set on branch the Weldolets provided some reinforcement for the hole cut in the furnace tube and was thought to provide better stress conditions in the smoother transition from a thick to a thin section.

(c) A perforated plate was fitted at the exit end of each furnace tube to

255

prevent catalyst from getting into the pigtail pipe. By fitting this plate into a hole in the furnace tube larger in diameter than the pigtail bore the area of perforations could more nearly equal the bore area of the pigtail so that the perforated plate did not restrict flow.

(d) It was thought that residual stress in the parent material might cause cracking during initial heating and such stresses are reduced by using butt welds as compared with fillet welds.

(e) Cracking of process gas in stagnant areas to form carbon was feared.

Point (a) was very relevant when starting out to use a relatively unknown material for large scale use. Points (b) and (c) still apply but are equally met by Socolets. We now believe that the symptoms that led us to believe (d) were in fact the result of thermal stresses exceeding the creep-rupture stress and point (e) has been shown unimportant by process experience. As a result of improved knowledge of the materials and process we have now agreed to accept the Socolet constructions.

2. WELDING PROCESSES

Initially we welded Weldolets to primary furnace tubes and headers using argon arc root runs followed by metal arc welding, primarily to reduce the risk of slag entrapment. We found it very difficult to achieve full penetration without producing "icicles" and in addition we had a great deal of trouble with root runs cracking. This we attributed to the root runs being too thin in relation to the surrounding masses of metal.

As the root run is accessible for cleaning, it was decided to use metal arc welding throughout and good penetration beads were obtained with Incoweld "A" electrodes. Small air driven carbide burrs and wire brushes are used to remove the internal slag. It is fairly certain that small pinpoints of slag remain but no troubles have occurred which can be attributed to this.

The root runs of all Weldolet to pigtail welds were made by t.i.g. welding with argon purge as slag removal was not possible. Argon was normally introduced at the furnace tube end by a device inserted from the bottom as shown in Fig. 1 but the consumption of argon has been high. We were initially warned against using nitrogen by the material suppliers but experimental welds made with nitrogen backing have no obvious defects.

Weldolet to pigtail welds have usually been completed by t.i.g. welding as the saving to be obtained by completing with metal arc was outweighed by the cost of having two separate types of welding equipment on site, and the changeover time.

3. FILLER METALS AND ELECTRODES

All metal arc welding on the pigtail assemblies has been carried out with

Incoweld "A" electrodes.* Where root runs of welds between forged Incoloy 800 Weldolets and spun cast furnace tubes were made by t.i.g. welding 92 Inconel was mainly used although a small number of welds have been made with 82 Inconel. Welds made with 92 Inconel joining Incoloy DS pigtails to

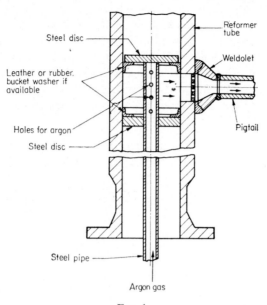

FIG. 1
Gas purge arrangement for welding outlet pigtails.

Incoloy 800 Weldolets were found very prone to crack and "NC82" filler wire was used for these welds in most cases because of availability problems, although "82 Inconel" is preferred in view of its higher strength and better welding characteristics.

4. FAILURES

The pigtail assemblies have been remarkably free from troubles that can be attributed to fabrication although tube defects have resulted in a number of failures.

Three pinhole leaks occurred in pigtail to Weldolet welds and allowed very small quantities of gas to escape and burn, but they did not necessitate unscheduled shut down. The leak areas were cut out and rewelded without difficulty.

The very similar sampling branches connected to the headers, however, have given a great deal of trouble. This has been attributed to a disproportionate

* Refer to Table 1 of Hahn paper for analysis of weld metal.

amount of flexing occurring in the hot part of the pipe adjacent to the header because of the lower yield stress at temperature. As flow is small or intermittent the major part of these pipes is comparatively cold.

Typical failures are creep cracks. Modification to the design is thought to be the only way to avoid these failures and it was proposed to include bellows assemblies to provide greater flexibility, however it was found simpler to attach the sample line at the other end of the header, adjacent to the secondary reformer, where expansion movements are small. The solution of this problem was delayed by incorrect diagnosis of the basic cause of failure. Initially we attributed failure to incorrect weld form and then to strain induced precipitation hardening caused by the temperature being a little below that of the bulk of the header system.

5. ALTERNATIVE METHODS OF ASSEMBLY

While, as mentioned above, no ICI plant has pigtail employing Socolets, some experimental work has been carried out and has shown that Incoloy 800 pigtails can be welded into Incoloy 800 Forged Socolets. T.i.g. welding with 82 Inconel filler has produced successful results without internal gas purge.

The main precautions required are that the pigtail pipe should be a reasonably close fit in the Socolet and that the pigtail should not "bottom" in the socket. The main defect found has been excessive thinning of the pigtail pipe wall caused by holding the arc stationary for too long at the 6 o'clock position. The full thickness of the pipe wall becomes molten and the top surface, in the bore of the pipe, sinks.

Silicate/carbon dioxide bonded sand backing rings can be used to avoid having to use an internal argon purge but they are a nuisance on site as they are fragile and disintegrate if they get wet. The use of two sand rings, one of which is placed on the Weldolet and one in the pigtail pipe can reduce the risk of breaking the backing ring when aligning the two ends to be welded. An alternative is to use a resin bonded ring but these are difficult to remove after welding while the silicate/carbon dioxide ring disintegrates completely in water and can be flushed out.

BLANKING-OFF REFORMER TUBES DURING PLANT OPERATION

B. Estruch and S. Gill

1. INTRODUCTION

When a reformer tube splits during service the loss of gas through the leak is not necessarily intolerable, but the leaking gas ignites inside the furnace and causes overheating of the surroundings. To prevent damage to the refractories and to the neighbouring tubes, it is necessary to isolate the failed tube.

To achieve this, either the design must make provision for shutting off any individual tube or, if simple welded up connections are used, the whole unit must be shut down and cooled so that the failed tube can be cut out and replaced, or the connections plugged by welding.

Because of the expense and complication of fitting individual valves to every pigtail and because no valves are known that would operate at the exit pigtail temperature (700–800°C), the solution normally adopted is an all-welded design. Initially, when an overheated tube leaked, the furnace had to be taken off line losing some 36 hours' production. This represented a serious loss of output. Apart from that, in reformer plants built for the production of town gas, the manufacturing authority is under legal compulsion to maintain a minimum gas pressure and it could hardly afford to shut down a furnace even for only 30 hours, should a tube fail during a period of peak demand. Consideration was, therefore, given to methods of blanking-off leaking tubes, which would not necessitate shutting the plant down.

2. BACKGROUND

It has been standard practice for many years to squeeze mild steel pipes on gas and water service when it is necessary to isolate a line, and a number of devices are commercially available for this purpose. However, the application of gross plastic deformation to pressure equipment containing hot inflammable gases had not been considered. The commercially available devices for low-temperature service are hydraulically operated, which is an advantage, but their frames have to be dismantled and then reassembled on the pipe to be squeezed. This would have been perhaps acceptable for inlet pigtails where the temperature is around 400°C, but the manipulation involved would not be acceptable in the proximity of the hot outlet pigtails (700–800°C). For that reason a G-clamp squeezer was designed so that the unit could be placed on to the pigtail where it runs horizontally adjacent to the reformer tube (Clark and Elmes, this volume, Fig. 2) and all that was required in the way of preparation was to remove the lagging on this section.

3. G-CLAMP SQUEEZER

Details of the squeezer which is the subject of British Patent App. Nos. 33881/63, 2436/64 are given in the photograph of Fig. 1. It is driven by a short 6-ton hydraulic ram, manufactured by Epco Flexi-Force.

FIG. 1
G-clamp in operation.

The main advantages of this design are:
(1) The G shape of the frame reduces manipulation near the pipes before squeezing to hanging the device on to a horizontal part of the pigtail.

(2) The ram is connected to the pump by means of a pressure hose of convenient length so that the operator is at a safe distance while the tube is being squeezed. Experience has shown that even if a failure does occur there is no serious risk.

(3) Should any accident happen to the hydraulic ram, to the hose, or to the pump, the quantity of oil involved is very small (1–2 pints).

(4) After squeezing, the jaws can be fastened together by means of screws to form a permanent clamp to prevent the internal pressure opening up the squeezed pipe. The G-clamp and hydraulic ram can then be removed by simply letting the jaws slide off along the guides shown in the drawing. The jaws are prevented from sliding off while the clamp is being hung and while pressure is being applied by means of ball catches.

(5) Two lateral sheet metal pieces locate the clamp jaws on the pipe, and are crushed away as the squeezing operation is in progress.

4. LABORATORY TESTS

Although from the above considerations it appeared that blanking-off reformer tubes by flattening the inlet and outlet pigtails could be achieved with reasonable safety, it was decided to carry out some preliminary tests on a laboratory scale.

In order to simulate plant conditions, a test rig was arranged in which a length of pipe could be electrically heated by making it an integral part of a circuit connected to a low voltage high current source. One of the ends of the tube was blanked-off and the other connected to a 275 psig steam line. Provision for measuring the steam pressure and for measuring and controlling the temperature during the tests was made. Samples of both Incoloy and Cr-Mo pipe were tested. The clamp itself was tested under a 7-ton load without it showing any permanent set.

4.1. Incoloy Pigtails

Two samples of extruded Incoloy DS tubing $1\frac{11}{32}$ in. o.d. $\times$ 8 s.w.g. as used for the fabrication of the outlet pigtails were used for the trials. One sample was ex-stores, but was aged for 72 hr at 800°C in order to bring it into a condition nearer to that of the pipes after service. The second sample was cut from an actual pigtail which had failed due to the presence of manufacturing defects after a few months in service.

These samples were heated to 800°C before squeezing. During the test as the jaws touched the tube, the temperature dropped about 20°C.

In all, eight trials were performed. The results were completely satisfactory, except in one case, when a number of small cracks developed on the outside of the pipe, but no leak occurred. This cracking was not thought to be significant because the trial was done on a part of the pipe which had been overheated to nearly melting point during the initial attempts to adjust the temperature. Figure 2 shows the general appearance of the tube and Fig. 3 a cross-section through one of the flattened parts.

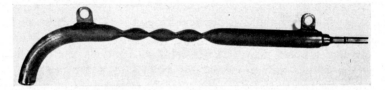

FIG. 2

Outlet pigtail piping (Incoloy DS) squeezed at 800°C.

FIG. 3

Cross-section through pipe shown in Fig. 2.

4.2. Cr–Mo Pigtails

The tests were done at 400°C on a length of 1% Cr–Mo steel pipe $\frac{13}{16}$ in. o.d. × $\frac{5}{32}$ in. wall as used for the inlet pigtails. At this temperature the tube was too strong for the squeezer and a perfect flattening could not be achieved. In order to increase the stress on the pipe, the width of the jaw faces of the clamp was reduced from $\frac{1}{2}$ in. to $\frac{1}{8}$ in., but then the ductility of the material was insufficient and the tube wall sheared. It was found possible to avoid this by carrying out the operation in two stages. In the first, a set of jaws with $\frac{1}{2}$ in. wide and slightly curved faces was used. This spread the deformation over a large area, but still left a gap between the two wall faces. A second pair of jaws with faces $\frac{1}{8}$ in. wide, and semi-circular cross-section was used to close the gap. To achieve this the load had to be increased to 8·5 tons. The clamp withstood this overload well. Figures 4 and 5 show the results of the tests.

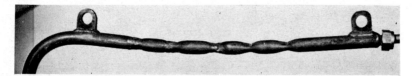

FIG. 4
Inlet pigtail pipe (1 % Cr–Mo) squeezed at 400°C.

FIG. 5
Cross-section of pipe in Fig. 4.

During the tests it was found that the original jaws in 18/8/Ti were too soft and yielded appreciably during operation. This was prevented by protecting the jaw faces with welded inserts of heat-treated FV520 (B) steel whose yield strength is about three times higher than that of 18/8/Ti steel.

5. PLANT EXPERIENCE

The pigtail squeezer has been used successfully on several occasions to isolate leaking reformer tubes. Squeezing the inlet pigtails has proved to be as easy in the plant as it was in the preliminary trials.

On the other hand, with outlet pigtails trouble has been experienced on three or four occasions owing to cracks forming during the operation. It appears that the difficulties are due to a combination of the following factors:

(1) Embrittlement during service. It is known that the ductility of Incoloy DS decreases with time due to an age-hardening process. The use of Incoloy 800 which is now readily available and reputed to be less prone to embrittlement during service will probably improve matters. Another cause of embrittlement is heavy carburization of the bore in over-heated pigtails.

(2) Decrease in temperature. As soon as the flow of hot gas through the pigtail is restricted the metal temperature begins to fall and so does its ductility. The more quickly the operation is completed the less likely it is for trouble to occur. The possibility of increasing locally the temperature of the outlet pigtail prior to squeezing is also being considered.

(3) The occasional presence of score marks on the surface and stringers of inclusions inside the pipe wall which facilitate the initiation and propagation of cracks.

Except in cases of extremely severe carburization of the pigtail it has always been possible to blank-off the failed reformer tube. On some occasions when cracks have appeared in the pigtail its flattening has been achieved at a second attempt.

The use of screwed-on jaws to maintain the pigtail gas tight has proved necessary. Whenever the jaws have been removed, the leakage of gas from the reformer tube has been seen to increase gradually becoming excessive after some time. A second application of the squeezer and permanent clamping of the pigtail has been sufficient to reduce the leakage to a negligible amount.

CONCLUSION

Blanking-off failed reformer tubes without having to shut the plant down, by squeezing the inlet and outlet pigtails at temperature and under pressure is possible. This operation has been successful in more than 95 per cent of the cases attempted. So far no untoward incidents have occurred and provided adequate care is taken, the isolation of the failed tube can be achieved without danger to the operating personnel or to the plant.

EXPERIENCES IN CONSTRUCTION AND OPERATION OF THE ICI TUBULAR REFORMER AT THE EFFING-HAM STREET WORKS OF THE EAST MIDLANDS GAS BOARD

A. G. PRATT

INTRODUCTION

The manufacture of town gas, by a process primarily developed for the chemical industry, may give rise to difficulties due to the essentially different requirements of the two industries.

The chemical industry may require operation at full design rating for the manufacture of low C.V. high hydrogen content synthesis gas, whereas for town gas application a high C.V. coupled with flexible control of output is desirable, since the load expansion is mainly derived from space heating and results in a variable plant load factor.

Whilst the fundamental basis behind the development and utilization of new processes is an economic one common to all industries, the gas engineer's thinking must be conditioned to give additional stress to reliability by the knowledge that a statutory obligation exists for continuity and quality of supply.

If plant failure occurs in private industry, no doubt the economic consequences are viewed very seriously indeed, but the gas industry, in addition to considering these economic consequences, is very much concerned with the continuity of the gas supply itself.

The theme of this paper is an endeavour to describe some of the mechanical difficulties encountered in the construction and operation of the Effingham Street plant, which was one of the first plants to be built which uses the ICI process, originally developed for synthesis gas production, for the production of town gas.

Although the gas industry has been glad to reap the benefits of the development of the ICI process, it is now significant that the gas industry is beginning to use other techniques of light distillate pressure reforming at lower temperatures.

For some years the gas industry has been moving away from the usage of coal to medium fuel oil and light distillate, at first in low pressure plants, and the increasing quantities of light distillate available, together with the high pressure processes, have accelerated this move.

The installation of plant at the Effingham Street works of the East Midlands Gas Board was considered in relation to the need for increased gas production in Sheffield and the availability of imported liquefied natural gas. The adoption of the ICI process was a logical development in order to use the natural gas at 100 per cent efficiency by cold enrichment and to produce a larger quantity of gas than by merely reforming the methane alone.

It was necessary, however, that the plant should be capable of operating solely on methane in order to meet variations in consumer gas demand and contractual commitments for methane supply. A turndown to 20 per cent of total output was chosen as the probable practical operational minimum but, in practice, this has not yet been achieved. Turndown to about 30 per cent of maximum has, however, been operated as a regular practice.

SUMMARY

A description is given of the materials used for the tubular reformers at Effingham Street and also details of the weld preparations, welding rods and inspection techniques.

A section is included on the materials and methods being adopted at the Board's new Killingholme plant.

Various occurrences affecting the methods of construction which became apparent during construction and after commissioning are described.

DETAILS OF MATERIALS, WELD PREPARATIONS, WELDING RODS AND INSPECTION TECHNIQUES

Effingham Street

Furnace Tubes

(1) Tube (Top 3' 6" section)—18% chrome—8% nickel centri spun casting.
(2) Tube (Centre 26' 11" section)—25% chrome—20% nickel centri spun casting.
(3) Tube (Bottom 10¾" section)—carbon steel B.S.1503—161—Gr.B.
(4) ½" Sockolet in top section—1% chrome—½% molybdenum wrought form.
(5) ¾" Branch in top section—18% chrome—8% nickel centri spun casting.
(6) 1" Weldolet in centre section—37% nickel—18% chrome sand casting.
(7) 5" N/B flanges 300 lb/in.² W.N.R.F.—carbon steel forging to B.S.1503 —161—Gr.B.

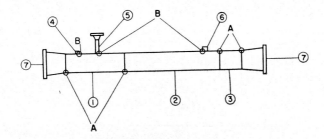

Welding Procedure Specification for Reformer Tubes
Procedure specification for manual metallic arc welding.
Specification No. A.S.M.E. pressure vessel code.
    Section 9
    Date: 14.11.62

Weld Deposit
The chemical composition of the weld metal deposit used in various combinations of base materials will be as follows:

25/20 to 25/20   E.S.A.B. Exp. 2936.
                    Carbon $0.35-0.45\%$ Phos. 0.04% Max. silicon 2.0%.

25/20 to 18/8   Max. manganese 1.5% Sulphur 0.04% Max. nickel $19-22\%$
                    Chrome $23-27\%$.

25/20 to 5″ Sh.80 Tube   Argon fuse root run   Nickrex 1 electrodes
                            with N.C.82.

25/20 to 37/18   N.C.82. Filler wire   Incoweld "A" electrodes
                    root run.   for subsequent passes.

18/8 to 18/8   Nicrex N.D.R.   Carbon $0.05-0.1\%$, Chrome 19.0% Max.
                    nickel 8.5%.

1% Cr ½% Mo to 18/8   First run. N.C.82. Filler wire.
                        Incoweld "A" electrodes.

BS.1503—161 Grade B to 18/8   Armex No. 2.   Carbon $0.07-0.12\%$, Cr
Root run argon with little N.C.82. 20.5%, Hi 8.5%, Mo $3.0-4.0\%$.

B.S.1503—161 Grade B to 5″ dia. Sh.80″ Tube   Queen Arc. Carbon 0.08%.
                                                Silicon 0.23%, Sulphur 0.24%,
                                                Phos. 0.02%, Mang. 0.46%.

Position
The welding shall be done in the position as shown in Figs. 1–7.

Heat Treatment
Pre-heat temperature sufficient to exclude moisture in material.
Post-heat treatment—None.

Preparation of Base Materials

The edges or surface of the parts to be joined shall be prepared by machining as shown on attached sketches and shall be cleaned of grease, scale or inclusions and checked for cracks using dye penetrants.

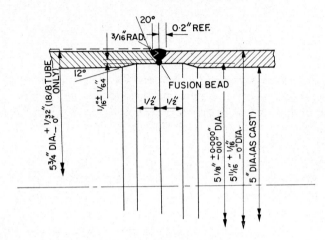

Fig. 1

Welding standard joint details. Pipe axis: Horizontal. Weld axis: Vertical. A.S.M.E. Code Position 1.G. 25/20 to 25/20 tube—25/20 to 18/8 tube. Fusing run done using 2 per cent thoriated rod $\frac{1}{8}$-in. dia with $\frac{1}{16}$-in. arc and argon gas shield.

Pass	Electrode details			Current (amps)	Mean voltage	Progression	Weave or Bead
	Size	A.S.M.E. ser.	Trade name				
To 4	$\frac{1}{8}''$		E.S.A.B. Exp 2936	85– 90	30		Bead
	$\frac{1}{8}''$		E.S.A.B. Exp 2936	100–105	30		Weave

Fusing of Base Materials

Both parts to be fused together shall be held in proper alignment during fusing and fused using the inert gas-shielded tungsten arc process with inside of tube flooded with inert gas flowing at 4 ft³/hr. Type of electrode 2 per cent thoriated tungsten carbide $\frac{1}{8}$ in. dia. arc length $\frac{1}{16}$ in.

The base material shall be on the positive side of the line.

Backing Strip

The welded joints shall not utilize a backing strip.

Joint Welding Procedure

The welding technique, such as electrode sizes and mean voltages, current for each size of electrode and direction of progression for vertical welds shall be shown on attached sketches. (Preparation of base materials.) W.D.1.

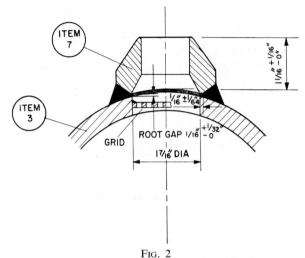

Fig. 2

Welding standard joint details. Weldolet axis: Vertical. Weld axis: Horizontal. A.S.M.E. Code Position 2.G. 37/18 weldolet to 25/20 tube. Grid to be welded in position using N.C.82 filler rod with argon gas shield.

Pass	Electrode details			Current (amps)	Mean voltage	Progression	Weave or Bead
	Size	A.S.M.E. ser.	Trade name				
First	$\frac{1}{16}''$		N.C.82 Filler Wire	85– 90	30		Bead
Subsequent passes	10G		Incoweld "A"	100–105	30		

N.C.82 filler wire deposited using tungsten arc argon gas-shielded process.

Welding Process

The welding shall be done by manual metallic arc using Metro-Vickers d.c. motor generator.

The manner of depositing the weld metal shall be such as to ensure complete penetration and fusion. When welding is stopped for any reason, care shall be taken in restarting to ensure that the required penetration and fusion are obtained.

Electrical Characteristics

The current shall be d.c.

The base material shall be on the negative side of the line.

Appearance of Welding Layers

The welding current and manner of depositing the weld metal shall be such that there shall be practically no undercutting on the side walls of the welding grooves or the adjoining material.

Cleaning

All slag or flux remaining on any bead of welding shall be removed before laying down next successive bead.

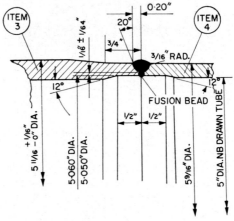

FIG. 3

Welding standard joint details. Pipe axis: Horizontal. Weld axis: Vertical. A.S.M.E. Code position 1.G. 25/20 tube to 5-in Sch. 80 tube. Fusing run done using 2 per cent thoriated rod, argon gas shield and addition of N.C.82 wire.

Pass	Electrode details			Current (amps)	Mean voltage	Progression	Weave or Bead
	Size	A.S.M.E. ser.	Trade name				
Subsequent passes	$\frac{1}{8}''$		Nickrex 1	85– 90	30		Bead
	$\frac{1}{8}''$		Nickrex 1	100–105	30		Weave

Defects

Any cracks, pin holes, excessive undercutting, or other welding defects shall be removed by chipping, grinding or gouging before depositing the successive bead of weld.

Inspection: Root Run (inert gas shielded arc)

100 per cent inspection of all fused joints shall take place using dye pene-

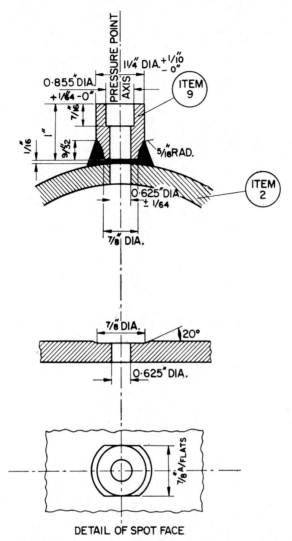

DETAIL OF SPOT FACE

FIG. 4

Welding standard joint details. Point pressure axis: Vertical. Weld axis: Horizontal. A.S.M.E. Code Position 2.G. 1% Cr, ½% Mo. Pressure point to 18/8 tube —to be set with $\frac{1}{16}$-in. gap. First run N.C.82 filler wire and argon gas, other runs Incoweld "A" electrode.

| Pass | Electrode details | | | Current (amps) | Mean voltage | Progression | Weave or Bead |
	Size	A.S.M.E. ser.	Trade name				
Subsequent passes	10 g		Incoweld "A"	100–105	30		Weave

trants as a crack detector. Any crack so found shall be rewelded using the inert gas-shielded tungsten arc process.

A further test shall be made after rectification.

The bores of tubes having been fused using inert gas-shielded tungsten arc process will be examined internally by means of a boroscope.

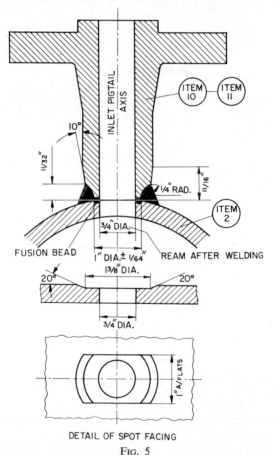

DETAIL OF SPOT FACING

Fig. 5

Welding standard joint details. Inlet pigtail axis: Vertical. Weld axis: Horizontal. A.S.M.E. Code Position 2.G. 18/8 inlet pigtail to 18/8 tube. Fusion run done using 2 per cent thoriated rod $\frac{1}{8}$-in. dia with $\frac{1}{16}$-in. arc and argon gas shield.

Pass.	Electrode details			Current (amps)	Mean voltage	Progression	Weave or Bead
	Size	A.S.M.E. ser.	Trade name				
First	10 g		Nickrex N.D.R.	90– 95	30		Bead
Subsequent passes	10 g		Nickrex N.D.R.	100–105	30		Weave

Finished Welded Joints

Completed joints shall be subjected to 100 per cent visual check and 100 per cent check using dye penetrant as crack detector. Radiographic examination of the first twenty completed welds will be carried out and, if results are satisfactory, the level will drop to 20 per cent of all completed welds. Radiographic standards shall meet the requirements of 1959 A.S.M.E. Code U.W.—51 except that elongated slag inclusions will not be acceptable.

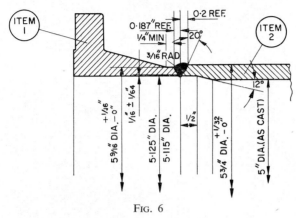

FIG. 6

Welding standard joint details. Pipe axis: Horizontal. Weld axis: Vertical. A.S.M.E. Code Position 1.G. 5 in.—300 weld neck flange to 18/8 tube. Fusion run done using 2 per cent thoriated rod ⅛-in dia, argon gas and a little N.C.82 wire.

| Pass | Electrode details | | | Current (amps) | Mean voltage | Progression | Weave or Bead |
	Size	A.S.M.E. ser.	Trade name				
First	10 g		Armex No. 2	90– 95	30		Bead
Subsequent passes	8 g		Armex No. 2	100–105	30		Weave

The techniques employed for radiographic examination of the welds will be as follows:

For the circumferential welds on the 5 11/16-in. dia. tubes, a panoramic shot will be taken locating the source in the centre of the tube and the films wrapped around the outside. For the welds on the branches the film will be cut down and wrapped round the welded joint and the source located against the inside of the main tube opposite the branch. Using these methods a sensitivity of 2 per cent will be obtained.

The source of the rays is irridium-192.

Pressure Test

All complete assemblies shall be subjected to a hydraulic test of 1100 lb/in.^{2} Test pressure to be maintained for 10 min.

Rectification

Any flaw defect or leaking revealed by either visual check dye penetrants, radiography or pressure test shall be ground or shipped out and rewelded to finished sizes. The appropriate test will then be reapplied.

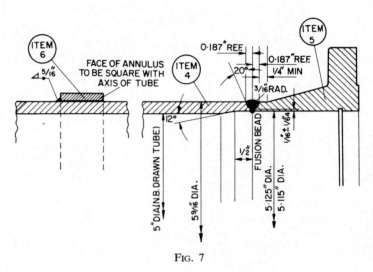

FIG. 7

Welding standard joint details. Pipe axis: Horizontal. Weld axis: Vertical. A.S.M.E. Code Position 1.G. 5-in. dia Sch. 80 tube to B.S.1503—161 grade "B" flange. Fusion run done using 2 per cent thoriated rod $\frac{1}{8}$-in. dia with $\frac{1}{16}$-in. arc and argon gas shield.

Pass	Electrode details			Current (amps)	Mean voltage	Progression	Weave or Bead
	Size	A.S.M.E. ser.	Trade name				
Subsequent passes	10 g 8 g		Queenarc Queenarc	100–105 130–150			Bead Weave

Electrodes

All metallic arc electrodes will be oven-dried immediately prior to use at a temperature of 100°C for a period of not less than 30 min.

A temperature of 200°C for a period of not less than 1 hr for Incoweld "A" rods.

All electrodes shall be stored under consistently warm and dry conditions and shall not be left lying in the open.

All electrodes shall be returned for proper storage at the end of each working day.

Outlet Headers:

(1) Tube sections ⎱
(2) End cap   ⎬   37% nickel—18% chrome centri spun castings.
(3) Taper section ⎰
(4) Sockolets   37% nickel—18% chrome wrought.

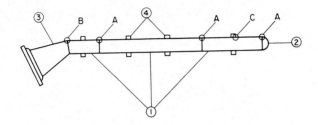

Note

Item (4) Sockolets were in the initial stage sand castings but after faults were discovered in these, the headers were returned for their removal and replacement by sockolets of a wrought form. The removal and replacement was carried out as follows:

The cast sockolets were burnt off by arc-air gouging keeping well clear of the main header, after which the remaining material was ground down to the outside diameter of the headers and the finished surface dye penetrant checked for faults. Wrought sockolets were then fitted and tacked in place and prior to any further work these were then inspected both by ICI and the contractors.

Welding of the replacement sockolets was as follows:

The root run on the 7-in. header was done by the argon arc process using Inconel 82 filler rods with a tungsten electrode and the weld was then dye-penetrant checked.

The root run on the 10-in. header was done by the metal arc process using an Incoweld "A" rod, here again the weld was dye-penetrant checked. The welds on both headers were then completed by the metal arc process using Incoweld "A" rods.

The difference in procedure between the two header sizes with regard to the root run, i.e. argon arc and metal arc, was due to the fact that the 10-in. header could be internally shot-blasted to remove slag (a product of metal arc welding) whereas the access in the 7-in. header did not allow shot-blasting, thus the use of argon arc with its slag-free deposit.

Weld Preparations

Weld preparation A—Header tube preparation is a butt weld—preparation as shown:

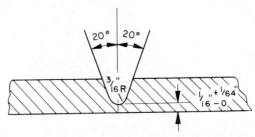

Weld preparation B—Header tube to taper section is a butt weld—preparation as shown, 45° chamfer with a $\frac{1}{16}$-in. root:

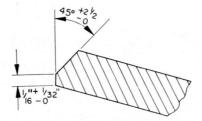

The above is a hand-prepared weld preparation due to the section being angled making it impossible for a machined preparation.

Weld preparation C—Sockolets have 35° increasing to 50° chamfer with a 30° fillet build-up as shown:

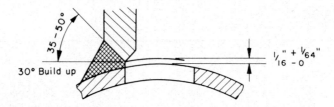

Welding Rods

Header tube sections (1) end cap (2) and taper section (3) welds are as follows:

Argon arc first run using Inconel 82 rods and tungsten electrode with subsequent metal arc filling runs using Incoweld "A".

Sockolets (4) are welded to the header as described in a previous paragraph.

Inspection Procedure

Weld preparations A and B—Root run dye-penetrant tested. Final welds 100 per cent radiograph examination. Internal beads intrascope inspected.

Weld preparation C—Root run dye-penetrant tested. Final welds smoothed by grinding and dye-penetrant checked to the extent of approximately 70 per cent of the total.

Pigtails

Material 32% nickel—20% chrome (Incoloy 800) extruded tubing made from one complete length.

Weld Preparation and Rods

Pigtails to sockolets fillet welds as shown, using the argon arc process with tungsten electrode and 82 Inconel filler rod.

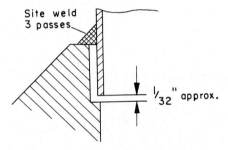

Pigtails to reformer tube weldolets butt weld as shown, using the argon arc process with tungsten electrode and 82 Inconel filler rod.

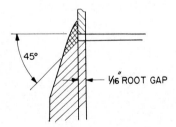

Inspection Procedure

All tacks inspected, root run dye-penetrant checked. All completed welds dye-penetrant checked and radiographically inspected.

Note

For details of welding procedure and equipment see notes given at the end of the Killingholme section under the sub-heading of "General Details".

Killingholme

Reformer tubes

(1) Tube material—25% chrome—20% nickel centri spun castings.

(2) Pigtail outlet connection—37% nickel—18% chrome forging.

(3) Cast branch—18% chrome—8% nickel titanium stabilized centri spun casting.

(4) Pressure connection—carbon steel forging to B.S.1503—161 Gr.B. (see material specifications).

(5) Main flanges—carbon steel forgings to B.S.1503—161 Gr.B.

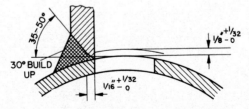

Weld Preparations

Weld preparation A—Butt weld—Preparation chamfer with $\frac{1}{16}$-in. root face as shown:

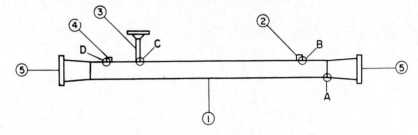

Weld preparation B—Butt weld 35° chamfer increasing to 50° having a 30° fillet build-up as shown:

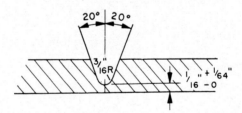

Weld preparations C and D are as for B.

Welding Rods

Fittings 2, 3 and 4 are welded by means of the metal arc process using Incoweld "A" filler rods and tungsten electrode.

The flanges, Item 5, are attached to the main tubes using an argon arc first run, the rods being Inconel 82 with tungsten electrode subsequent metal arc filler runs using Nitrex I rods.

Inspection Procedure

Inspection of the root run in all cases is to be carried out using the dye-penetrant method.

Intrascope inspection of the internal bead to be carried out to ensure full penetration has been achieved.

On completion of all welds a final dye-penetrant test is to be carried out followed by radiographic inspection as follows:

100 per cent for the first ten welds of each operation and 10 per cent of the remaining welds. Radiography acceptance to be to A.S.M.E. Section VIII except elongated slag inclusions are not acceptable.

General Notes

It is proposed to use 10 tubes of a 20% nickel, 20% chrome analysis on Killingholme 2nd Stream on an experimental basis. These will take the form of cast and wrought materials on a 50/50 basis.

Outlet Manifold (header)

(1) Header tube body—37% nickel—18% chrome centri spun casting.
(2) Header end cap—37% nickel—18% chrome casting.
(3) Taper piece—37% nickel—18% chrome centri spun casting.
(4) Inlet connection (sockolet)—37% nickel—18% chrome forgings.

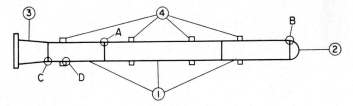

Weld Preparations

Weld preparation A—Butt weld preparation chamfer with $\frac{1}{16}$-in. root face as shown:

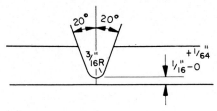

Weld preparations B and C as A.

Weld preparation D—Butt weld 35° chamfer increasing to 50° having a 30° fillet build-up as shown:

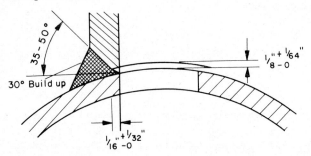

Welding Rods

Welding of Items 1, 2, 3 and 4 is carried out by use of an argon arc, first run using Inconel 82 filler rods and tungsten electrode with subsequent metal arc filler runs using Incoweld "A" rods.

Inspection Procedure

Inspection of the root run and final weld in all cases is to be carried out using the dye-penetrant method to the following extent:

20 per cent selected at random (minimum).

The welding preparations A, B, and C are to have 100 per cent radiography of the final weld.

All machined weld preparations to be dye-penetrant tested prior to welding and all surfaces adjacent to the area to be welded to be free from scale, paint, oil or grease.

Intrascope inspection of the internal bead of all welds to be carried out to ensure full penetration has been achieved.

Radiography is to be gamma, using a 1×1 mm ray source using a sensitivity of 2 per cent or better. Photographs obtained used against an assessment of Weld Quality Table supplied by manufacturer.

Pigtails

Materials, 32% nickel, 20% chrome (Incoloy 800) extruded tubing made from one complete length.

Weld Preparations

Pigtails to sockolets fillet weld as shown.

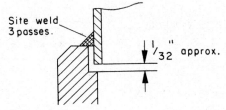

Welding Rods

Argon arc process using Inconel 82 rods with a tungsten electrode.

Inspection Procedure

All pipe bevels and surfaces adjacent to the area to be welded shall be free from scale, paint, oil or grease and shall be dye-penetrant checked for defects before welding commences.

Pigtail pipes must not in any way be forced into position and misalignment must be avoided. All pigtails must be supported throughout the entire welding operation.

Root run to be dye-penetrant checked before the second and subsequent run.

All completed welds shall be dye-penetrant checked for defects and gamma radiographically inspected.

General Details

Following is a brief description of welding equipment, methods used and precautions to be taken during site welding of the pigtails.

All welding to be carried out using the argon arc process. The electrode, thoriated tungsten shall be non-consumable and supplies may be obtained from Saturn Industrial Gas Ltd.

The argon gas shall be of 99·8 per cent minimum purity and when ordering supplies "Welding Quality Argon" must be quoted.

Argon torch pressures shall be as follows:

H1 Weldolets	12 ft³/hr
H2 Weldolets	16 ft³/hr

Note

Back purging shall be carried out on the welding of weldolets only, purge pressure being at the rate of 8 ft³/hr.

The thoriated tungsten sizes shall be as follows:

J1 Weldolets	$\frac{1}{16}$-in. dia.
J2 Sockolets	$\frac{3}{32}$-in. dia.

Filler metal shall be Inconel 82 and the size $\frac{1}{16}$-in. dia. No other filler metal shall be used.

Note

Each length of filler wire shall be wiped clean with stainless steel swarf before commencing to weld.

Welding in Bad Weather

It is extremely important to protect completely the welding operations during adverse weather conditions. Wind and/or rain are the main hazards

K

and flameproof tarpaulin sheets should be used as protection. When the ambient temperature falls to 32°F or below, any joints to be welded should be slightly preheated to approximately hand warm.

No metal stamping, chiselling or hammering is allowed on this material.

SUMMARY OF MATERIAL SPECIFICATION

37% Nickel—18% Chrome

C	0·4–0·5 per cent max.	Mo	0·5 per cent existing as an
Mn	1·5 per cent max.		impurity.
Si	1·5 per cent max., 1 per cent	Cr	18–20 per cent max.
	preferred.	Ni	33–37 per cent max.
Ph	0·04 per cent max.	Fe	Balance.
S	0·04 per cent max.		

25% Chrome—20% Nickel

C	0·35–0·45 per cent max.	Mo	0·5 per cent max. existing as
Mn	2 per cent max.		an impurity.
Si	1–2 per cent increasing with	Cr	24–28 per cent max.
	C and vice versa.	Ni	18–22 per cent max.
Ph	0·04 per cent max.	Fe	Balance.
S	0·04 per cent max.		

32% Nickel—20% Chrome (Incoloy 800)

C	0·1 per cent max.	Copper	0·5 per cent max.
Mn	1·5 per cent max.	Ni	30–34 per cent.
Si	1·0 per cent max.	Cr	19–22 per cent.
S	0·03 per cent max.	Fe	Balance.

18% Chrome—8% Nickel Titanium stabilized

C	0·08 per cent max.	Cr	17–19 per cent max.
Mn	2·0 per cent max.	Ni	9–12 per cent max.
Ph	0·045 per cent max.	Ti	5×C with a max. 0·7 per
S	0·03 per cent max.		cent stabilizing element.
Si	1·0 per cent max.	Fe	Balance.

B.S.1503—161—Gr.B.—Carbon Steel

C	0·25 per cent.	Mo	0·15 per cent max.
Si	0·1–0·35 per cent.	Cu	0·4 per cent max.
Mn	0·9 per cent max.	S	0·05 per cent max.
Ni	0·4 per cent max.	Ph	0·05 per cent max.
Cr	0·25 per cent max.	Fe	Balance.

1% Chrome—½% Molybdenum Alloy Steel

C	0·1–0·2 per cent max.	Si	0·1–0·6 per cent max.
Mn	0·3–0·8 per cent max.	Cr	0·8–1·25 per cent max.
Ph	0·04 per cent max.	Mo	0·44–0·65 per cent max.
S	0·04 per cent max.	Fe	Balance.

WELDING ROD SPECIFICATIONS

Inco-Weld "A" (Metal Arc)

Nl	Balance.	S	0·015 per cent max.
Cu	0·5 per cent max.	Cr	13–17 per cent.
Fe	6–10 per cent.	Ti	1·0 per cent max.
Si	10 per cent max.	Niobium	1·0–2·5 per cent max.
C	0·1 per cent max.	Mo	0·12 per cent max.

Inconel 82 (Inert Gas)

C	0·1 per cent.	Ni	67 per cent min.
Mn	2·5–3·5 per cent.	Ti	0·75 per cent.
Fe	3·0 per cent.	Cr	18–22 per cent.
S	0·015 per cent.	Niobium	2–3 per cent.
Si	0·5 per cent.	Cobalt	0·1 per cent.
Cu	0·5 per cent.		

Nitrex I. Low carbon 25 per cent chrome, 20 per cent nickel, rod analysis is as for material, excepting carbon usually limited 0·1 per cent max.

Practical Experiences

The installation of the plant at Effingham Street proceeded normally, with the intention of gas making in December 1963, until on Wednesday, 27 November 1963, some cracking was observed by dye-penetration tests at welds on the sockolets on the main outlet headers from the reforming tubes on No. 2 furnace. Some cracking had penetrated into the base metal of the sockolet. Co-incident with the above occurrence a weld section prepared at ICI Billingham Works and subjected to dye-penetration and micrographic examination, showed positive evidence of weld cracking and microscopic examination revealed poor grain structure in the heat-affected zone adjacent to the weld.

All outlet headers were removed and delivered to ICI Billingham Works by Friday, 29 November. The main plant contractors requested permission to use arc-air cutting to facilitate removal of the sockolets but this was refused pending an examination in view of the fact that arc-air cutting might recreate a heat-affected zone and perhaps promote further cracking which might carry into the headers themselves.

A specimen sockolet was cut using the arc-air process and it was found that the amount of heat penetration was so small that this method could be used.

It was decided, however, that the cut should be made $\frac{1}{8}$ in. above the surface of the main header and the remaining material ground off.

The sockolets were sand-cast material to the same specification as the main headers, i.e. 37/18 nickel chrome, and evidence of cracking was present on a large percentage of the sockolets removed.

The rough-cast finish of the sockolets rendered crack detection difficult.

In order to ensure, as far as possible, satisfactory refabrication of the sockolets to headers the following procedure was adopted:

(1) Forged sockolets of more uniform quality and grain structure were substituted for the previous cast sockolets.

(2) Weld preparation was to be by machining and the surface to be such as to permit satisfactory and accurate crack detection by dye-penetration methods.

(3) The headers were cleaned and ground smooth in the areas where the sockolets were removed to permit satisfactory dye-penetration testing.

(4) The sockolets were attached to the headers with a root run which on completion was cleaned, ground smooth and dye-penetration checked.

(5) If the dye-penetration checks on the root run were satisfactory then welding proceeded to completion. After completion the sockolet was cleaned up and subjected to further dye-penetration checks.

It was also necessary to lay down similar stringent welding and test procedures in respect of the site welds when the outlet pigtails were secured to the sockolets.

As a result of the delays one unit of the plant was commissioned to gas making on 17 February 1964.

A serious incident occurred on 15 June when the plant tripped due to an electrical fault on the light distillate feed pump. During the restart procedure a drift to high gas temperature occurred and before corrective measures could take effect the gas temperature at the outlet end of the header assembly rose to approximately 930°C compared with a normal gas temperature of 700–750°C and an agreed maximum of 850°C.

A leak in the 7-in. header assembly caused a fire in the header insulation box and the plant was shut down. It was found that the end pigtail had cracked adjacent to the fillet weld joining the tube to the main header sockolet. The particular tube was at the free end of the header where the thermal expansion of the header is at a maximum and consequently the deflection in the pigtail is greatest. The movement is about 6 in. during heating to normal operating temperature.

Independent laboratory investigation of the cut out fracture specimen showed marked evidence of severe bending stress, and taken with the severe distortion of end pigtails on the 10-in. header, this would be fair confirmation that the failure occurred quickly as a result of temperature rise rather than having been initiated by thermal cycling up to operating temperatures during earlier operations. It was evident, however, from the severe bending that some restriction to free movement of the pigtails had occurred.

Similar bending of the end pigtails was found in the 10-in. header, and after further tests it was found that the restraint was due to the vermiculite with which the insulation boxes were packed. The use of vermiculite filling in the boxes was therefore discontinued and gas making recommenced on 5 July 1964.

Since then there have been no serious interruptions to gas production on this unit and outputs of 33 to 100 per cent of rated capacity have been achieved.

After applying the experience obtained in the construction of the first unit to the second unit the latter was in the final stages of initial commissioning on 13 May and lean gas was being produced to vent stack when a loud report was heard. It was found that the 37/18 taper transition piece connecting the 7-in. diameter collection header to the refractory-lined carbon steel connections leading to the make-gas waste heat boiler had fractured discharging lean gas to atmosphere and the plant was shut down as quickly as possible. By the time some cooling had taken place the gap at the fracture had opened up from about $\frac{1}{16}$ in. to about $1\frac{1}{2}$ in.

Investigation showed that while the header is suspended freely, upwards of 5 in. of expansion takes place during heat raising, the insulation box around the header is fixed, but designed with adequate clearance to allow movements due to expansion. In fact, insufficient clearance had been left during construction with the result that some restraint was imposed before the full 5 in. of expansion had taken up. One slot in the insulation box was actually torn and as the box is fabricated from $\frac{3}{16}$-in. plate material it was obvious that considerable force had been exerted.

This restraint was applied close to the free end of the header and would subject the header to severe bending stress. It was found that steel plates had been welded, in error, over part of the expansion slots in the base of the insulation boxes. A high tensile stress had been imposed at one side of the angle weld where the taper piece joined the header and calculations showed that the ultimate tensile stress of the materials in the hot conditions had been exceeded by almost 100 per cent. A new taper piece was manufactured and welded in. The header insulation boxes were emptied of vermiculite insulation to facilitate inspection of the headers, and the vermiculite was not replaced. The boxes were lined with additional insulation materials, the pigtails being left free.

After this work was carried out recommissioning commenced and gas making resumed on 15 July.

Future Policy and Trials

It has become only too obvious during the erection and operation of the plant at Effingham Street that considerable liaison is necessary between ICI, the plant licensees and the customer in the main problems which have arisen.

Never can it be truer to say that co-operation between engineer and metallurgist is vitally necessary and this point is well demonstrated by Inglis in the 1964 James Clayton Lecture. It may be true as Inglis said that ". . . a pinch of practical usage is always worth a peck of research investigation because such usage refers back to the researcher the real questions which require an answer". Certainly this seems to be happening with the utilization of the ICI process for town gas manufacture but it is, of course, necessary to continue research whether it be laboratory investigation or full-scale trial.

A stage has now apparently been reached where the centrifugally-cast materials are giving good service with very small failure rate under ICI conditions of operation. However, it may be that all these materials must be regarded as expendable and replacement undertaken depending on:

(a) the number of hours operation at temperature

(b) the number of stress reversals due to plant start-up and cool-down; and

(c) the variations in gas output.

It is obvious, therefore, that two main problems exist as far as materials are concerned:

(1) the type of material to be used; and

(2) the welding problems associated with these high temperature materials.

In order to explore the former the East Midlands Gas Board is carrying out a long-term project which involves the experimental installation at their Killingholme Works (where ICI reforming plants are in course of construction) of five tubes in 21 Cr 25 NiTi cast steel, machined inside and out and five tubes in the wrought condition in 21 Cr 25 NiTi steel. The remainder of the tubes at Killingholme will be of cast 25 Cr 20 Ni material, i.e. similar material to Effingham Street but in addition internally machined, introscope checked and welds dressed externally.

The headers will be cast 37 Ni 18 Cr material similar to Effingham Street machined internally and externally and introscope checked. It may be that the headers should also be utilized in the wrought rather than the cast material particularly as the former facilitates welding.

The problem of welding these materials depends on very careful preparation, complete supervision of the welding and thorough inspection of the welds. There does not appear to be a great deal of information on the welding of 37/18 material but the modified methods adopted at Effingham Street appear to be satisfactory.

Conclusions

This type of plant involves engineering and metallurgical design of equipment in pressure/temperature ranges at the edge of knowledge when using commercially practical metals and all the failures so far experienced in operation at Effingham Street have been the result of inadvertent occurrences of a mechanical nature.

The faults in sockolet castings were in fact discovered by inspection checks during construction and led to the contractors and the Board rejecting them entirely, as they considered it introduced a hazard they were not prepared to accept.

The contractors' investigations in America showed that cast sockolets had been successfully used in similar applications there, and as castings were more readily obtainable than forgings they decided to introduce them in order to expedite the work. The castings as made were thoroughly checked and appeared satisfactory until welding was carried out in attaching the castings to the cast headers, when dye penetrant checks revealed cracks in some sockolets. The faulty ones were cut out and replaced and satisfactory headers with sockolets free from visible fault were accepted from sub-contractors. However, when further welding was attempted at site on the attachment of pigtails, some additional cracking was revealed by dye-penetrant check, and all were rejected. The only difference discovered between the practice adopted by foundry here as compared with American practice is that here castings were cored and machined in bores whereas American practice had been to produce solid castings, the bores being drilled out.

The ICI process, like all continuous processes, is vulnerable in case of failure of its various ancillaries and services and shut down can occur instantaneously. Maintenance of equipment, in particular instrumentation and control gear, is therefore of prime importance if the process is to be reliable.

It is quite fair to say that the ICI tube reformer has certainly given no more in the way of teething troubles than any of the other plants that have been developed over the past years for the gas industry, and any advance of this kind is bound to give some teething troubles.

HIGH TEMPERATURE STRENGTH AND DELAYED FRACTURE IN CERAMIC MATERIALS

J. C. V. Rumsey and A. L. Roberts

INTRODUCTION

This paper briefly summarizes the results of some 3 years' study of silicon carbide as a future constructional material for chemical process plants. Before specific data are given, however, some discussion is advisable not only of present-day problems of the application of ceramics of various types in reforming plant but also of the potential for the large-scale use of non-metals in the future. There are many examples in the chemical industry and elsewhere in which the advantages to be gained from going up to much higher temperatures and pressures than can be tolerated by metals are so great that serious attention has to be given to the possibility, however remote it may seem at present, of developing ceramics as true engineering materials. The steam reformer is a current and outstanding example. Another coming from the gas industry is the development of radiant tubes for furnaces. These are needed in sizes which present difficulties in manufacture, e.g. 6 ft long, 6 in, wide and must be made of material which allows gas to be burned and recirculated inside the tube without contaminating the furnace atmosphere with products of combustion. The material has thus to withstand high temperatures—maybe in this case up to 1500°C. It obviously must be impermeable, immune to chemical attack from inside or outside; it should be mechanically strong at the operating temperature and as resistant as possible to thermal shock. Pressure is not a problem here but there are many potential applications in the major industries in which resistance to high pressures would be an added requirement. For these applications on the large scale, ceramics present their own peculiar problems, not found with metals, although the accompanying papers in this volume may suggest that this statement is too simplified. These are the problems of: (a) finding the right material, and (b) fabricating it into the large sizes and special shapes required; just as with metals there is a limit to the size, but the limitation is far more severe for ceramics. In fabrication the problem of jointing is an added difficulty, although pure-alumina tubes have already been successfully welded in our laboratories.

Finding the right material is not difficult except in the sense that the number of appropriate materials is decidedly limited, in general to pure oxides or compounds, often costly in themselves, even before fabrication. But if a material can be chosen on the basis of its known properties, it is then usual to find that design data appropriate to its use in large-scale plant are non-existent. This is simply because no one so far has envisaged the use of these materials in really large units, mainly because of the difficulties of fabrication. So the problem boils down to, first of all, selecting the material, then establishing design data from systematic tests on small pieces and then, finally, developing methods by which the material can be fabricated into the sizes required while still retaining its intrinsic properties, at least in part.

In ceramics we have another unique problem. They are normally made from compressed aggregates of particles, first moulded to shape and then fired. The moulding process precedes the manufacture of the ceramic itself and can be a serious limitation. Machining *after* firing is possible (as is carried out on rocket nose-cones) but is elaborate and costly. Because of this forming process the tonnage type of ceramic is invariably porous and permeable. Impermeability is essential for the special applications we are discussing and so only those ceramics can be entertained which can be rendered impermeable by sintering at high temperatures or by reaction sintering so conducted that the product is non-porous. This problem by itself imposes its own limitation on the sizes that can be fabricated.

On these grounds one could almost dismiss ceramics straightaway as likely engineering materials, but their potential is so enormous that the admittedly difficult problems must be solved as a matter of some urgency. It is significant that in many places, including our own, the fundamentals of fabrication are being seriously examined; this is particularly true in the U.S.A. There is, however, another drawback to ceramics which arises from their brittle character and their fundamental difference from metals. This is their liability to delayed fracture, a property well recognized in glass and on which much work has been done. For ceramics, very little is known about what is at present an elusive effect.

Considerations of this nature led ICI some 3 years ago to bring the problem of delayed fracture to us, with the remit of examining the general possibility of using ceramics as engineering materials for high temperatures and pressures. Silicon carbide was chosen as a starting material because of its high strength, its resistance to corrosion in general, its resistance to creep and thermal shock and its relatively high thermal conductivity. In addition, silicon carbide of a special type made by reaction sintering is virtually non-porous. On the basis of known properties it was thus potentially a good material, but so far as design data and in particular its tendency to delayed fracture were concerned, very little was known, not even whether it was, in fact, liable to delayed fracture.

EXPERIMENTAL

The following summarizes the work on a special commercial variety of silicon carbide known as KT, which is fine grained, very strong and virtually impervious. Full details will be published elsewhere during 1965.

The material is made by reaction sintering, the pores between the grains of a matrix of silicon carbide being filled by reaction between silicon vapour and the appropriate amount of graphite incorporated in the matrix. The nominal content of silicon carbide is 96·5 per cent by volume, but the samples used in this work were found to contain substantial quantities of free graphite and silicon, actual compositions ranging from 61 to 81 per cent of SiO, 6 to 32 per cent of Si and 1 to 25 per cent of graphite. This variability of composition was an additional factor likely to increase the scatter of results normally encountered when testing brittle materials. Furthermore, for various reasons, the number of specimens which could be tested at each temperature was limited. In strength measurements, however, it was found that the methods of extreme value statistics were applicable and enabled values of the median fracture stress to be determined with reasonable precision on comparatively few test-pieces. A particular advantage of this method is that it identifies the mimimum fracture stress to be encountered and obviates the need to test the large numbers of test-pieces required by conventional statistics. More measurements would, however, be desirable before the values were used for design purposes.

METHODS OF TEST

Accurately-ground specimens (4 × 0·13 × 0·13 in.) were stressed in four-point bending, in bend-test rigs made of magnesite and accommodated, five at a time, in an electrically-heated furnace which could operate at 1200°C and above. Short-term (i.e rapid loading) measurements of fracture stress, made to estimate the maximum stress to be applied in delayed fracture experiments, gave the following median values for tests on ten specimens at each temperature

$$3 \cdot 16 \times 10^4 \text{ psi at } 900°C$$
$$4 \cdot 10 \times 10^4 \text{ psi at } 1200°C$$

the standard deviation being approximately $8 \cdot 2 \times 10^3$ psi. Individual stress values were closely correlated with the content of free graphite as an inverse function and showed that, for maximum strength, free graphite should be avoided. Despite this, however, the median fracture-stress values establish even the present silicon carbide as a material of exceptional strength at temperatures up to 1200°C.

Delayed fracture tests were made, again on five specimens at a time, by first applying a stress too low to cause immediate fracture and then increasing it by a constant amount at 12-hourly intervals until fracture occurred. Tests were run at room temperature, 300, 600, 900 and 1200°C, with stress-increments of $2 \cdot 05 \times 10^3$ psi at 1200° and $1 \cdot 58 \times 10^3$ psi at all other temperatures. No fracture occurred while the stress was being increased, demonstrating that delayed fracture took place at all temperatures of test.

Typical absolute results are shown by long-term tests run at 1200°C, under a stress of $2 \cdot 05 \times 10^4$ psi at the tensile surface of the specimen, as calculated by elastic theory. No specimens fractured within 1010 hr, but creep was detected, the maximum linear creep-strain ranging from $2 \cdot 1 \times 10^{-4}$ to 6×10^{-4}. The occurrence of creep meant that the maximum stress in the specimens at any given time was indeterminate, but a lower and safe limit (S') for the maximum stress could be deduced by considering the stress-relaxation to be so great that the stress was a constant and independent of distance from the neutral axis. The conditions for static equilibrium then give $S' = 2S/3$, S being the observed stress at the delayed fracture. In this, and in other experiments at 1200° for over 1200 hr, the following were the results.

Short-term fracture stress, psi	Maximum stress (S') not causing fracture in 1000 hr, psi
Greater than $2 \cdot 05 \times 10^4$	$1 \cdot 37 \times 10^4$
Greater than $3 \cdot 29 \times 10^4$	$2 \cdot 19 \times 10^4$

Or, in other words, silicon carbide at 1200°C would withstand continuous stress of at least two-thirds of its short-term fracture stress without fracture within 1000 hr.

GENERAL RELATIONSHIPS

Special statistical methods have enabled a general equation to be derived from experiments such as those described above; they obviate the need for large numbers of lengthy tests on individual specimens which in any case would be impracticable at present. Tests at 150, 300 and 500°C have established the following relationship

$$t = B \exp A(S_0 - S)$$

between the fracture time t, the short-term fracture stress S_0 and the applied stress S. A and B are constants independent of structure and composition. The values given below will enable the reader to estimate likely times to fracture under given conditions of stress.

Values of Constants A and B		
Temperature °C	$A(psi)^{-1}$	$B(hr)$
R.T.	$1 \cdot 24 \times 10^{-3}$	$0 \cdot 79$
150°C	$2 \cdot 43 \times 10^{-3}$	$0 \cdot 20$
300°C	$1 \cdot 79 \times 10^{-3}$	$0 \cdot 11$
500°C	$2 \cdot 11 \times 10^{-3}$	$0 \cdot 02$

The equation holds good for times up to 24 hr and there appears no reason to doubt its applicability to far longer times and, possibly, somewhat higher temperatures, although verification is essential. It is the first step towards a general relationship by which the probability of delayed fracture under given conditions may be enumerated for any material.

CREEP

It seems probable that creep plays little part in delayed fracture at low temperatures, although it was detected at 500°C and indicated at 300°C. At higher temperatures, however (e.g. 1200°), it may provide an alternative mechanism for failure, analogous to creep rupture in metals. The present experiments have shown that creep rates at 1200° are measurable but small as compared with those of creep-resistant metals at far lower temperatures and stress. Thus, typically, the maximum linear creep-strain rate under an initial stress of $2 \cdot 05 \times 10^4$ psi was only $1 \times 10^{-6} hr^{-1}$ and it is probable that creep behaviour is primarily associated with the substantial amounts of free silicon found in the material tested.

CONCLUSION

Measurements of its strength and tendency to delayed fracture indicate that the possibility of using impervious silicon carbide as a constructional material in high-pressure and high-temperature processes is far from remote. Much work remains to be done before design data can be suggested, including especially the effect of atmosphere on properties. The present studies are being continued and extended with support from the Science Research Council.

SOME PRINCIPLES GOVERNING THE PERFORMANCE OF REFRACTORY CONCRETES (REFRACTORY CASTABLES)

T. D. Robson

I. INTRODUCTION

THIS discussion will deal with only certain aspects of refractory castables, particularly with those points on which some controversy seems to have arisen in recent years. For example, a curing method which is different from the classical method of cooling by water-spraying has lately been recommended after extensive testing in the field,[1] and some revision of existing ideas on the temperature range at which gunned castables may have their minimum strength has been suggested.[2] It is believed that a study of the properties of the cement hydrates allows one to reconcile some apparent anomalies, and to present a simplified hypothesis capable of explaining the critical factors which determine the physical properties of a castable, both before and after firing.

Only castables containing high-alumina cement (HAC) will be considered and it may therefore be helpful to mention the two main types of this cement which are used. The first type of HAC is the ordinary grey-to-black variety, made by fusion from red bauxite, and hence containing variable (but often substantial) proportions of iron oxides, together with 3–8 per cent silica. The second type of cement is made from alumina and is white in colour with only minimal proportions of iron oxide and silica. The alumina content is high (72–80 per cent), and practically all the remainder consists of calcium oxide. HAC cements made from low-iron bauxites, or from red bauxite by reductive fusion, have iron oxide contents intermediate between the above main types, but they are always distinguishable from the white, pure cements by their residual contents of silica and titania.

In all commercial high-alumina cements the important hydratable compound present is monocalcium aluminate or CA.* Some of the white, pure cements may also contain substantial quantities of calcium dialuminate (CA_2) and it will be seen later that the presence or absence of this compound may modify the physical properties of refractory castables in certain conditions.

* The usual shortened formulae for cement compounds will be used. Thus $C = CaO$, $A = Al_2O_3$, $H = H_2O$.

II. THE HARDENED CASTABLE BEFORE FIRING

A refractory castable mix which has been gauged with water and allowed to harden consists of a graded refractory aggregate bound together by the products of cement hydration. As far as the binder is concerned there is therefore no difference, at this stage, between the hardened castable and an ordinary shingle/sand HAC concrete designed for load-bearing structural purposes. Factors affecting the physical properties of one will have a similar effect on the other and, until the castable is fired in service, the principles which will be discussed apply to both types of concrete.

The hydrates formed by reaction of water with the cement comprise:

(i) the so-called "hexagonal" hydrates (CAH_{10} and C_2AH_8) which form at low or intermediate hydration temperatures (up to about 85°F);

(ii) the cubic hydrate C_3AH_6 which soon appears at higher hydration temperatures.

The above behaviour is explicable on the basis that the hexagonal hydrates, although persistent at low and intermediate temperatures, will convert at higher temperatures (in presence of water) into the stable cubic hydrate.

$$6CA \xrightarrow{\text{hydration}} \begin{cases} 6CAH_{10} \\ or \\ 3C_2AH_8 + 3AH_3 \end{cases} \xrightarrow{\text{conversion}} 2C_3AH_6 + 4AH_3$$

Anhydrous   Hexagonal hydrate   Cubic hydrate stage
cement   stage

The rate of hydrate conversion increases with the hydration temperature and thus the nature of the bond formed in the concrete depends on the degree of temperature reached during the hardening process, and on the duration of that temperature. According to the hydration conditions, it is therefore possible to produce the hydrates entirely in the hexagonal forms, entirely in the cubic form, or as a variable mixture of both. Has this any effect on the performance of the castable?

We know that, in order to obtain the best physical properties from a structural HAC concrete, it has hitherto been considered necessary to keep it relatively cool during hardening to avoid the formation of cubic hydrate. Indeed the conversion of hexagonal hydrates into cubic hydrate has generally been held responsible for any loss in strength or increase in porosity experienced by a structural HAC concrete which has been allowed to overheat during hardening, or which has subsequently been maintained in the hot wet conditions which favour conversion. The "cold" strength of a refractory castable (i.e. before firing) should therefore be similarly influenced by the hydration temperature, yet Cook et al.[2] show that gunned castables, allowed to heat to 180–212°F during hardening, give 1-day strengths which are higher than those obtained by curing with cold water. Wygant and Crowley [1] also state that internal temperature rise caused by the hydration of HAC does not impair strength provided that the necessary water is retained in the mix.

In resolving this, and several other apparent anomalies, it is suggested that the following rather elementary line of approach gives the simplest method of predicting and understanding the specific effect of hydration conditions on the properties of HAC concrete.

Let us regard the physical properties of concretes made with a given aggregate as being determined chiefly by the relation between the *volume* of hydrate produced (X), and the *volume* (Y)* within the concrete which the hydrate is asked to fill. On this basis, the concrete properties are dependent merely on the adequacy with which the hydrate material can fill the allotted space, and it is a necessary corollary that these properties are otherwise independent of the precise type of hydrate present. In other words a concrete bonded with cubic hydrate should have properties at least equal to those of a similar concrete containing hexagonal hydrates—provided that the relation X/Y is the same in each concrete.

However, it is known that any direct conversion of hexagonal to cubic hydrate will reduce the volume (X) because the density of the cubic hydrate is considerably greater than either of the hexagonal hydrates. The ratio X/Y will thus be lowered and, in usual circumstances, a reduction in concrete quality can therefore be predicted. The normal consequences of conversion are hence explained. But it must be remembered that the space which the hydrate material has to fill (Y) is not a fixed quantity. Volume Y is greatest when the concrete has a high water–cement ratio and, in general, the concrete space associated with the use of $W/C = 0\cdot50$ and upwards can be adequately filled only by the more voluminous hexagonal hydrates. By using lower water–cement ratios, volume Y can be diminished to the point where the less voluminous cubic hydrate (together with alumina hydrate) can satisfactorily fill the reduced space. It is therefore predictable that the effects of hydrate conversion upon HAC concrete properties will become less and less as the water–cement ratio of the concrete falls, and this also has been fully proved in practice.[3, 4]

Accordingly, in the case of structural HAC concretes, or refractory castables at the stage before they are fired, the position is as follows:

(i) With mixes gauged at high water–cement ratios, the best concrete properties (as cast) can be obtained only by standard methods of curing and cooling, so that hexagonal hydrates, which can adequately fill the rather large void space, are produced and preserved. The presence of major quantities of cubic hydrate (indicating conversion) in a concrete of this type will always

---

* Assuming a fully compacted concrete, the volume Y can be roughly defined as: $Y =$ (total vol. of concrete—absolute volume of the aggregates). Any unhydrated cement present is counted as aggregate.

be associated with a lower "cold" strength and a greater porosity than could have been obtained by keeping the mix relatively cool during hydration.

(ii) With mixes gauged at low water–cement ratios (rich mixes, gunned mixes, vibrated mixes) excellent properties are obtainable from concretes containing major quantities of cubic hydrate and the presence of cubic hydrate in this type of concrete does not have the deleterious implications mentioned in (i) above. Accordingly, as will be seen in Sections III and IV, in the particular case of refractory castables made with low W/C, there is no reason to avoid conversion during hardening, and membrane curing (with unchecked temperature rise) can indeed be superior to the alternative method of cooling with curing water.

The higher "cold" strengths obtained by Cook *et al.* from castables which were allowed to reach high temperatures during hardening were thus primarily due to the use of relatively low water–cement ratios. In addition, the increased rate and degree of cement hydration at high temperatures more than compensated for any loss of hexagonal hydrate volume caused by conversion during the short-term hardening period (24 hr).

III. THE CASTABLE FIRED TO INTERMEDIATE REFRACTORY TEMPERATURES

We next consider the behaviour of the hardened castable when heated from atmospheric temperature to the point at which thermal solid-state reactions begin between the constituents of the mix. The hydrated cement binder is here submitted to conditions outside the experience of structural HAC concrete and the discussion in this section applies only to refractory castables.

Up to the level of temperature defined, the physical properties of a given castable are still determined by the hydrates, the dehydration products of the hydrates, or the decomposition products of the hydrates, and it is suggested that a study of the space-filling capacity of these various products can lead to the best understanding of castable behaviour in this temperature range also.

We have noted that high-hydration temperatures can reduce the cold strength and increase the initial porosity of castables made with a high water–cement ratio, and that this effect diminishes or disappears as the W/C is reduced. However, the curious fact has long been known that high hydration temperatures are never harmful (and are usually favourable) to the strengths obtained from a castable after firing. Even high W/C mixes which are allowed to overheat, and are therefore partially converted during hardening, always give at least as high *fired* strengths as the same castable which has been cured "ideally", in spite of the fact that the "cold" strength may be greatly reduced by the conversion. Low W/C mixes give much higher fired strengths if they are initially converted and of course their "cold" strength can be quite as high as would be obtained with low-temperature hydration. Indeed the fired strength of such castables is often roughly proportionate to the degree of conversion occurring during hydration.

In the past, this knowledge alone has allowed the general use of refractory castables at widely varying hydration temperatures (and hence in hot climates) without the close attention to water–cement ratio which is found necessary when dealing with structural HAC concrete under the same hydration conditions.

As the hardened castable is heated up in service for the first time, free water is lost from the pores and gels, and also the calcium aluminate hydrates begin to dehydrate. These processes overlap to some extent but, when the temperature of the castable refractory has reached about 1000°F throughout, it may be concluded that all the free water and most of the combined water has departed. Whatever the original composition of the binder—be it hexagonal hydrates or a mixture of cubic hydrate and alumina hydrate—there is always a reduction in binder volume due to dehydration, and therefore some loss in strength on firing to intermediate refractory temperatures. Since initial hydration of the castable at higher hydration temperatures is capable of producing a higher *fired* strength than does the same castable when initially hydrated to hexagonal hydrates, we conclude that, other things being equal, the space-filling capacity of the dehydrated products left in the first case is greater than that in the second case. Once more the assumption is that the strength of a concrete fired to an intermediate refractory tempera- ture does not depend so much on the nature of the cement products as on their volume.

A given weight of anhydrous cement gives a larger volume of hexagonal hydrate than cubic hydrate and therefore low-temperature hydration gives higher "cold" strengths more easily than does high-temperature hydration. But, if these unequal volumes of hydrate give approximately the same volume of dehydrated product on firing, then the fired strengths of the differently cured castables will be the same—and this is roughly the situation found in practice. Consequently, in order to obtain the highest strength from a cast- able which is fired to an intermediate refractory temperature, two conditions should be fulfilled.

(i) The lowest water–cement ratio capable of allowing full compaction should be used during casting. This reduces the space within the concrete which must be filled either by the hydrates or by the dehydrated products, and therefore increases both the "cold" strength and the fired strength of the castable.

(ii) Because of the major reduction in binder volume which will occur when dehydration takes place on firing, it is particularly important that the maximum degree of cement hydration should be reached during the initial hardening period, From the point of view of fired strength, full hydration of the cement present in the castable is more vital than the type of hydrate formed. It does not matter if conversion to cubic hydrate and alumina hydrate occurs, since the loss in volume on dehydration of these hydrates is less than that of similarly dehydrated hexagonal hydrates.

When a castable is hydrated at low temperature, one effect of reducing the water–cement ratio of the mix is to increase the amount of unhydrated cement in the hardened concrete, since the voluminous and impermeable hexagonal hydrates quickly begin to coat and seal off the larger cement particles. Under these hydration conditions the degree of total cement hydration falls with the water–cement ratio and it would therefore appear that the requirements of (i) and (ii) above are incompatible. However, the rate of hydration of calcium aluminate is increased by rising temperature. High-temperature hydration of HAC, whether achieved by self-generated heat or by high ambient temperatures, is therefore capable of increasing the degree of total cement hydration within the limited hardening time which is normally allowed. This higher degree of cement hydration, which results from even short periods of high-temperature curing, has been shown by Tseung and Carruthers.[5]

Of course the rate of conversion is also increased with temperature and, as soon as this commences, the hexagonal hydrates coating unhydrated cement particles are replaced by cubic hydrate of lower volume. More permeable areas, or fissures leading to the unhydrated cement nuclei are thus created and accordingly, a certain amount of "secondary hydration" can take place when conversion occurs in mixes which would otherwise achieve only partial cement hydration.

The final result is that, particularly in a castable gauged with low water–cement ratio, the cement can be more fully hydrated in a limited time, the maximum amount of hydrate material can be formed, and consequently the strength of the castable after firing and dehydration is as high as possible.

The possible effect of the presence of CA_2 in some of the white, pure cements can now be considered. At ordinary temperatures this compound hydrates much more slowly than CA and therefore can make little contribution to the cold strength of the castable at 1 day. Higher temperatures increase the rate of hydration and it is therefore of interest to compare the hydration products of CA and CA_2 when both are hydrated at temperatures high enough to cause complete conversion to cubic hydrate.

$$3CA + 12H \longrightarrow C_3AH_6 + 2AH_3$$
$$3CA_2 + 21H \longrightarrow C_3AH_6 + 5AH_3$$

It can be deduced that the high-temperature hydration of CA_2 yields a greater volume of hydrate material than is obtained from CA, and on our previous reasoning, the fired strength of a castable cured in this way, should therefore be higher when CA_2 is present in the cement. Mel'nik,[6] working with pure calcium aluminates, found that a cement consisting of CA gave higher strengths at ordinary hydration temperatures than did CA_2. This is almost certainly due to the much lower rate of hydration of CA_2 at this temperature level. On the other hand, when autoclaved for 8 hr at 8 atm, CA_2 not only gave a much higher strength than similarly treated CA, but also its autoclaved strength was higher than that obtained by low-temperature or "ideal" curing of CA.

When incorporated as cement in a refractory castable mix, which was then autoclaved, CA_2 gave very high fired strengths which showed little diminution with increasing firing temperatures until these reached 1800°F. Although Mel'nik omits any reference to water–cement ratio, and gives a quite different explanation for the above comparison between the behaviour of CA and CA_2, it seems that all the facts are easily explicable on the theory of hydrate volume which has been advanced above. Indeed, this latter hypothesis predicts that, other things being equal, the highest possible fired strengths will be obtained from a CA_2 cement, incorporated in a castable gauged with a low water–cement ratio, and then steam-cured or preferably autoclaved (in order to produce a high degree of total cement hydration).

The strength behaviour shown by a castable on heating for the first time through intermediate refractory temperatures can be rather variable. As we have seen, the general effect is one of strength reduction with increasing temperature, because of dehydration and loss of binder volume, and any considerable increase in strength obtained after firing, normally takes place only when thermal reaction and "ceramic bond" formation is well advanced. However, there are many factors which can affect the shape of the strength/temperature curve.

Firstly, dehydration of hydrates will have least effect on fired strength when the internal concrete space which has to be filled is at a minimum, and when the maximum amount of hydrate has originally been provided by full cement hydration. These circumstances are likely to be realized by high-temperature curing of a castable placed with a low W/C. Secondly, the dehydration behaviour of the various hydrate materials is quite distinct, and in itself this may have a bearing on the fired strength, particularly at the lower temperatures of firing. CAH_{10} loses two or three molecules of water at low temperatures, or even at low humidities, and then dehydrates in a fairly regular way as the temperature rises. A castable in which the binder consists mainly of CAH_{10} will usually show a marked drop in strength between 200°F and 600°F, a drop which appears more obvious because of the high "cold" strength which this type of bond can give even at high W/C. Cubic hydrate, on the other hand, does not really start to dehydrate until about 450°F and then loses most of its water over a comparatively short temperature range. It is always associated with alumina hydrate, whose dehydration is not complete until about 2000°F.

Thirdly, when the cubic hydrate is present it decomposes at over 1100°F into C_3A_5 (or $C_{12}A_7$) and lime. The latter constituent is difficult to detect in a castable fired to the appropriate temperature, and clearly it is liberated in a very reactive form. In the case of castables which harden at the high hydration temperatures we therefore have the probability of reaction, at comparatively low refractory temperatures, between the decomposition products of cubic hydrate on the one hand and alumina, unhydrated cement, or the finer aggregate particles on the other hand. Consequently it is found that the strength/firing-temperature curves of castables hardened at low temperature are usually of a different type from those of castables in which the hydration temperature rise is unchecked. Castables in which the hydrate has been substantially converted before firing do not show such a sharp initial drop in strength at the lower firing-temperatures and the graph is more in the nature of a plateau sloping gently downwards towards the higher firing temperatures. Solid-state reaction between dehydration or decomposition products of hydrates produce local inflections in this general pattern.

The temperature at which major thermal reaction starts between the aggregate and the cement constituents is much higher than any so far discussed and of course it depends on the chemical nature of the aggregate and on the amount of fluxing impurities originally present in both aggregate and cement. The temperature at which the castable has its minimum strength can therefore vary appreciably, apart from the influence of hydrate type mentioned above. Attempts have been made to increase the castable strength obtainable at temperatures below 2000°F by the addition of low melting fluxes, clays, etc., but in addition to their deleterious effects on ultimate refractoriness, these materials are usually remarkably ineffective. The main principles governing the production of high fired strengths at intermediate temperatures have already been given but further improvement can sometimes be obtained by the incorporation of certain crystal-growth promoting agents or mineralizers. In such cases high fired strengths are produced at temperatures far below the point at which the classical "ceramic bond" would be formed.

IV. THE EFFECT OF HYDRATE STRUCTURE ON SOME OTHER CASTABLE PROPERTIES

It is customary to recommend that refractory castables should be heated up for the first time at a reasonably slow rate, so that any steam formed from the free or combined water can escape without causing explosive spalling. The latter is a rare occurrence with normal castable mixes and usually it can occur only when a castable is suddenly submitted to temperatures well over 2000°F. The recommended rate of first heating is therefore very conservative for normal applications. However, if the castable has a denser and more impermeable structure than usual, the possibility of explosive spalling on suddenly heating the "green" concrete will be increased, and, among the factors which may cause this are the use of a dense non-porous aggregate, a high cement content (implying a low W/C) and a high plastic clay content.

Gitzen and Hart[7] have reported work on a castable, containing tabular alumina and a very finely divided white HAC, which when hydrated at relatively low temperatures (below 60°F) gave a very impermeable product even after oven-drying. It was found that the consequent lower resistance to explosive spalling could be rectified by reducing the cement content or by substituting a cement of normal fineness, or by curing the castable at higher temperatures (preferably 90°F). The mechanism whereby the first two remedies provide a more open internal structure in the concrete is clear. It also seems plain that the high-temperature hydration is effective because it causes a reduction in hydrate volume through partial conversion and, instead of the voluminous impermeable hexagonal hydrate formed at low temperatures, there is produced a considerable proportion of cubic hydrate which occupies less space and has a much lower specific surface. From the discussion in Section II we would expect that the beneficial effect of high-temperature curing for this particular purpose would tend to diminish at low water–cement ratios, and evidence of this is shown in the data of Gitzen and Hart.

The thermal shock resistance of a *fired* castable is intrinsically high, although it naturally varies with the thermal shock resistance of the type of material used as aggregate. With any given aggregate, the thermal shock resistance of a castable is favoured by casting with a relatively high W/C (in practice this usually means that the cement content should not be too high). For mixes placed by gun or by vibration the internal structure produced by high-temperature hydration gives the best fired strength combined with good thermal shock resistance.

The erosion resistance of a fired castable to the cutting acting of solid particles suspended in a gas (as in fluidized-bed reactors) depends chiefly on the properties of the binder. The aggregate plays a less important part but it must have adequate physical properties and a large maximum size of particle is unfavourable to erosion resistance. The latter is closely correlated with the mechanical strength of the castable at the service temperature[8] and once more the highest fired strength should therefore be sought. A castable containing a relatively high cement content, gunned or vibrated into place is indicated. If a high hydration-temperature is permitted by membrane curing, that is no disadvantage with this type of mix and indeed can again be considered advantageous.

Abrasion resistance, or resistance to purely frictional forces, is shown best by a hardened castable in which the exposed surface is mainly covered by fairly large particles of dense tough aggregate which themselves take the wear. The function of the binder is merely to keep them in place. However, it is rare in practice to find an application in which the castable is subjected only to frictional forces and there is usually an appreciable element of erosion. In these circumstances a practical compromise is to use a castable containing a hard, abrasion resistant aggregate, of sand size only, and to place it by the methods described above for obtaining highest erosion resistance.

REFERENCES

1. J. F. WYGANT and M. S. CROWLEY, *Bull. Amer. Ceram. Soc.* **43** (1), 1 (1964).
2. M. D. COOK, C. P. COOK and D. F. KING, *Bull. Amer. Ceram. Soc.* **42** (II), 694 (1963).
3. T. D. ROBSON, *High-Alumina Cements and Concretes.* C. R. Books Ltd., London, 1962.
4. K. NEWMAN, *Reinf. Concr. Rev.* **5** (5), 269 (1960).
5. A. C. C. Tseung and T. G. Carruthers, *Trans. Brit. Ceram. Soc.* **62** (4), 9 (1963).
6. M. T. MEL'NIK and N. N. Shapovalova, *Tsement (USSR)* **28** (4), 9 (1962).
7. W. H. GITZEN and L. D. HART, *Bull. Amer. Ceram. Soc.* **40** (8), 503 (1961).
8. J. F. WYGANT and W. L. BULKLEY, *Bull. Amer. Ceram. Soc.* **33**, 233 (1954).

LINING OF SECONDARY REFORMERS

L. G. HUGGETT

INTRODUCTION

FOR the production of ammonia the function of the secondary reformer is to remove a few per cent of residual methane from the primary gas by combustion with air which also serves to add the required amount of nitrogen to form synthesis gas.

Primary gas and air are admitted at the top of the reformer vessel via a burner and the top of the reformer thus constitutes a combustion chamber, in which temperatures of about 1200°C occur. Owing to the possibility of local variations in the gas ratios, higher temperatures up to about 1350°C are possible. The gas passes through a catalyst bed supported on inert material in the form of small random lumps and out through a branch to the waste heat boiler. The vessel is a vertical cylinder of about 10 ft diameter and 25 ft high, and the top section above the catalyst bed forms a combustion chamber.

Except for the combustion chamber the gas temperature is about 1000°C and this constitutes a fairly light duty as far as the refractory lining is concerned. However, complicating features arise because of the operating pressure of 200 lb/in.² and the fact that a considerable amount of hydrogen is present in the process gas. Allowance must be made for the greater thermal conductivity, due to the presence of hydrogen in the pores in the refractory, when calculating the lining thickness. The gas also contains sufficient carbon monoxide to cause carbon monoxide disintegration of unsuitable iron bearing refractories and for these reasons a lining consisting of low iron refractory concrete based essentially on a mixture of Molochite (calcined china clay) and Secar 250 (calcium aluminate cement) was chosen. The choice of refractory concrete rather than brick for lining the vessel was also influenced by the desire to provide as nearly as possible a monolithic lining in order to avoid overheating of the vessel shell by contact with the high pressure and therefore high heat capacity gases. This requirement applies principally in the section of the vessel adjacent to the catalyst bed because of the pressure drop of about 5–10 lb/in.² which occurs. The purpose of this paper is to describe the factors influencing overheating.

DESIGN OF LINING AND METHOD OF INSTALLATION

The lining in the first vessels installed at Heysham consists of a uniform $8\frac{1}{2}$ in. of a proprietary concrete based essentially on Molochite and Secar 250. (Later vessels are of different design, but the same conditions occur.) Refractory concrete can be installed by casting or by gunning and it has been common practice, especially in the U.S.A., to use the latter method for lining such vessels and similar vessels used in various reforming processes in the oil industry. The method chosen, after consultation with the manufacturers of the cement and the contractors, was designed to minimize the amount of shrinkage occurring in the concrete both in drying and subsequent heating and involved casting in approximately 4 ft square sections. These were cast alternately in each horizontal ring so that some of the shrinkage in the first set of panels could take place before the others were cast.

Some means of holding the refractory concrete to the vessel shell is required. In this connection the term reinforcement is often used, but this is a misnomer since metal used to support the concrete does not strengthen it in the way that it does in normal structural concrete. Continuous mesh is undesirable because of the possibility of forming planes of weakness and the undesirable effects of differential thermal insulation. The preferred method is the use of separate Y-shaped anchors coated with combustible material in order to provide room for thermal expansion, and this is now normal for this type of lining. Differences of opinion exist about the optimum spacing of these anchors and the principle adopted was the use of the minimum possible spacing on the basis that too frequent anchors could cause more harm than good by acting as centres from which cracks could propagate. In the concrete adjacent to the catalyst the spacing adopted for the Heysham vessels was approximately 2 ft horizontally by 3 ft vertically, although in the upper parts of the vessels where the concrete has to be supported against gravity a closer pitch was used. The 2×3 ft pitch is very much greater than that frequently used, especially in the U.S.A., but has, nevertheless, proved perfectly satisfactory.

SHELL OVERHEATING

Emphasis has been placed on the need to provide as nearly as possible a monolithic lining in order to prevent overheating of the shell by contact with the hot gases. One of the first vessels to be built at Heysham did, in fact, overheat and this is now prevented by the provision of water jackets.

Although refractory concretes are described as monolithic they cannot be strictly so because of the shrinkage which has been referred to. Calculations have been carried out by ICI Research Department in order to investigate the possible effects of gaps of various dimensions between the refractory lining and the vessel shell and of the effect of open cracks in the concrete.

It has been found that provided there is good contact between the concrete and the shell, cracks of quite wide dimensions will allow insufficient heat to pass by convection or direct radiation to cause significant overheating. However, if cracks exist and if gaps occur between the concrete and the metal shell a parallel path is provided through which hot gases can flow and cause overheating. Table 1 shows estimates of the vessel shell temperature which can occur locally owing to gaps of various dimensions.

TABLE 1

Gap width (in.)	Shell temperature (°C)
NIL	215
0·020	350
0·030	460
0·055	600

Structurally, cracks of these dimensions are insignificant. The Heysham vessels have been in service for approaching 3 years and the linings remain in very good condition. The extent and width of cracks has not changed markedly since the original baking out and Figs. 1 and 2 show the

FIG. 1

Typical cracks in cast concrete lining after 1 year's service ($\times \frac{1}{5}$).

state after a year's service, with cracks in the cast lining up to about 0·025–0·035 in. wide and in the gunned lining up to 0·040–0·050 in.

In addition to the shrinkage of the refractory lining account must be taken of the thermal expansion of the vessel shell and the effect is cumulative since once by-passing has started this can cause further expansion of the metal and consequently a wider gap and greater flow of gas and therefore still higher temperatures.

FIG. 2

Typical cracks in gunned concrete lining after 1 year's service (× ⅕).

Fig. 3 illustrates the typical expansion behaviour of refractory concrete. Up to about 250°C normal thermal expansion occurs, but beyond this temperature combined water is lost and a net shrinkage results giving a minimum in the expansion curve at 350°C. At higher temperatures further expansion occurs in the usual way. The total expansion at 1000°C is about 0·25 per cent but on cooling after the first heating there is a permanent shrinkage of 0·2 per cent. The shell temperature depends upon the heat lost through the lining. The 8½-in. lining of the Heysham vessels gives an estimated shell temperature of 200–220°C. Fig. 3 also shows the expansion

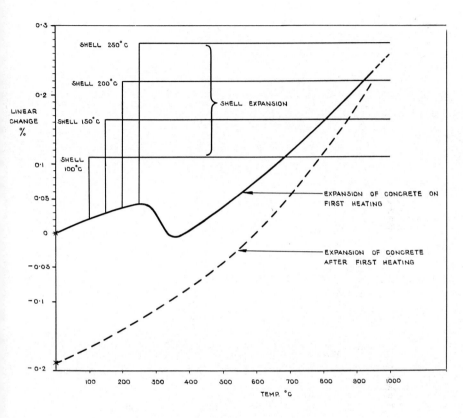

FIG. 3

Typical expansion behaviour of refractory concrete.

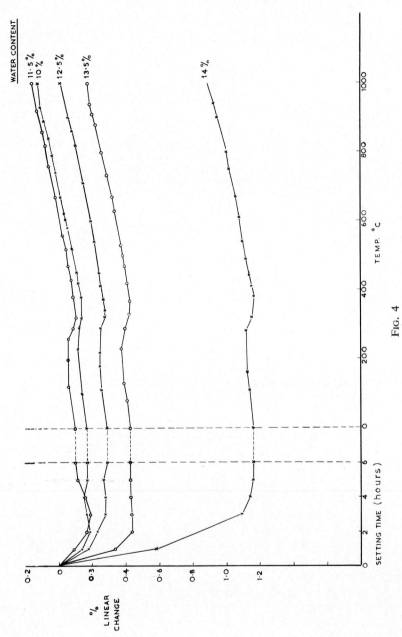

Fig. 4

Setting shrinkage and expansion of concrete.

for various shell temperatures and it can be seen that in each case this is greater than the expansion of the cooler parts of the concrete. Except in the case of the highest shell temperature a zone of concrete lining exists where the expansion is greater than that of the shell and consequently is in compression on the hot face. The strain which refractory materials can accept without fracture is of the order of $0 \cdot 1$ per cent, consequently on this simple basis a shell temperature of 150°C might be considered the optimum since the compression on the hot face should hold the lining tight against the shell without danger of fracture.

Fig. 3 does not give the complete picture with regard to the expansion behaviour of concrete because of the shrinkage on setting. This is illustrated in Fig. 4 where the reference zero is taken to be the fluid rather than the set condition. The fluid to set shrinkage is not strictly a linear shrinkage but in practice may appear to be so if the fluid concrete is cast into a container, when the effect of the shrinkage is a fall in level. If this shrinkage is unrestricted it need not be taken into consideration, but restriction is inevitable to a degree depending upon the method of installation. The upper curves in Fig. 4 are for concretes of very low water/cement ratio, not usable in practice. The two lower curves, which are incidentally widely separated, are for water contents roughly at the limit for concrete placeable by vibration. Some of this large shrinkage is almost bound to appear in the final concrete as tensile strain or cracking because of the restraint on free shrinkage caused by the geometry of the lining and the presence of the metal anchors. Bearing in mind this fact and the considerable variation in shrinkage resulting from a change of only $\frac{1}{2}$ per cent in the water content it can be seen that calculations of the state of stress of a concrete lining could be in considerable error. Thus it would be necessary to incorporate a large margin of error when designing in order to ensure that the concrete is in compression so as to avoid completely the presence of cracks or tensile strain. If this were done failure of the concrete by compression on the hot face would be likely. Otherwise one is faced with the likelihood that cracks or tensile strain will be present and in the absence of a positive bond to the shell small gaps between lining and shell could well appear.

Not only should the design cater for equilibrium temperature conditions but also for the condition during heating up. The maximum compression is produced during this period and, if excessive, results in the effect similar to "pinch spalling" of brickwork where material of triangular section adjacent to joints cracks away. Clearly, if this occurs the strain system is altered.

A method of approach to this problem was examined. Fig. 5 shows calculated temperatures at various time intervals at various points in a lining from hot face to shell, carried out by ICI Chemical Engineering Section, for an $8\frac{1}{2}$-in. lining of concrete with the properties that have already been described and a rate of increase of temperature taken as a uniform 75°C/hr.

From the expansion data and from Fig. 5 the per cent expansion is derived
and Fig. 6 shows the dimensional changes for various times and positions.
The state of compressive strain in the concrete can be seen approximately

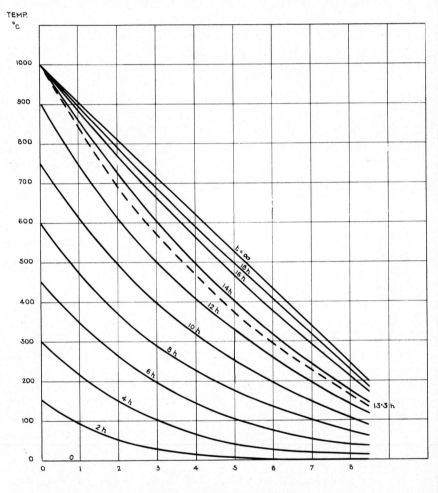

FIG. 5

Temperature distribution through refractory lining. $k = 0.5$ CHU/hr ft °C;
$s = 0.18$ CHU/lb °C; $\rho = 116$ lb/ft³; Thickness = 8·5 in.; U (Outer Face to
Atmosphere) = 2·8 CHU/hr ft² °C; Temp. Rise of Inner Face = 75°C/hr to
1000°C (13·3 hr). All temperatures measured from datum ambient = 0°C.

by comparing the peak expansion with the corresponding shell expansion.
The simple comparison of thermal expansion ignores the elastic expansion
of the shell due to the internal gas pressure. This varies with the shell design

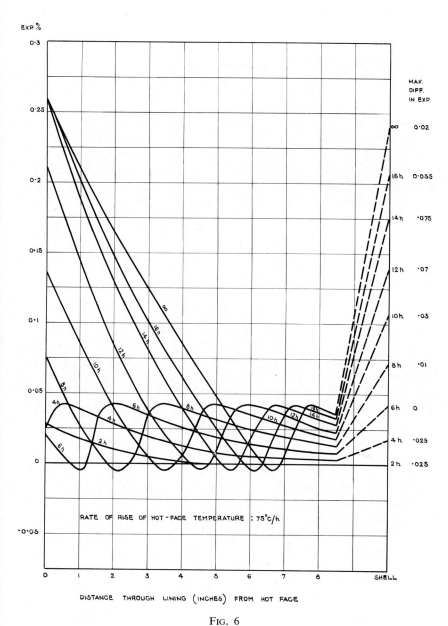

FIG. 6

Expansion of concrete and metal shell at various times from start-up.

but can be as much as one-third of the ultimate thermal expansion of the metal. The effect of the expansion due to internal pressure depends on the stage at which the pressure is applied, but the tendency is to increase the possibility of gap formation and to relieve compressive stresses on the lining. It is concluded that 75°C/hr should not produce dangerous compressive stresses and it appears possible, theoretically, that conditions exist which should just satisfy the requirements of a safe maximum compression during heating coupled with a small permanent compression under equilibrium conditions.

Unfortunately, practical considerations make it virtually impossible to rely on these calculations. If account is taken of the fact that reversals of temperature will inevitably cause progressive slight cracking and crumbling it is questionable how long a lining would remain in its calculated stress conditions. A further difficulty is that concrete is variable in its properties, particularly shrinkage; this property is particularly susceptible to changes in water/cement ratio and curing treatment and it is doubtful whether it could be controlled within limits narrower than $\pm 0\cdot 05$ per cent. A still further factor is the shrinkage which occurs while the concrete is actually setting, i.e.. from the fluid to set condition. This shrinkage is ignored by refractory manufacturers, but nevertheless occurs.

METHODS OF AVOIDING OVERHEATING

It is concluded that for the reasons just given even the most carefully chosen lining thickness cannot be relied upon to prevent conditions arising which will allow gaps to form. The reason for the formation of gaps even when such conditions do arise is uncertain. One possibility may be that thermal expansion of the metal anchors tends to push the lining inwards away from the vessel shell, however, it is possibly unnecessary to look too far for reasons which would account for gap formation since the thermal movements arising in a structure consisting of two materials, of fairly massive scale, without direct physical bonding between the two, are almost certain to produce gaps if there is room for them to appear.

Various methods are utilized in order to avoid this overheating, both in ammonia plants and in the similar vessels used in catalytic reforming and hydrogenation plants in the oil industry. Metal liners are commonly used in the oil refinery vessels which operate at temperatures no more than 500–600°C, but the temperatures are too high to permit this possibility in secondary reformers for ammonia synthesis gas. So-called vapour stops are sometimes used which consist of internal metal flanges running horizontally around the vessel and attached to the shell. These project into the concrete and are designed to prevent the continuous flow of the gas between shell and refractory lining, but, owing to the discontinuity between the metal and concrete and the different thermal expansion coefficients, they cannot be a completely reliable preventive measure.

Records are available of vessels which do operate successfully without overheating and without any special means to prevent gas by-passing other than careful lining procedure. It is claimed, for example, that continuous gunning is one means of achieving this. This is based on the idea that a continuously gunned lining is the closest approach to a truly monolithic lining and the knowledge that gunned concrete is dense. Although much quicker than casting, gunning suffers from some disadvantages. The quality of the deposited concrete is very much dependent upon the operator and owing to the rebound losses is relatively expensive with costly lining materials. The aggregate rebounds preferentially, resulting in a high-cement/aggregate ratio and this can cause a shrinkage higher than that of the corresponding cast concrete.

Continuous casting methods have also been adopted and this method is possibly superior to casting in panels because of the randomness of the shrinkage cracks compared with the regular construction joints which occur in the panel casting method. On the other hand, it is almost inevitable that a wetter mix would be necessary for continuous casting which can offset this advantage.

It is concluded that while there are various means which can be utilized for minimizing the possibility of gap formation and consequent overheating, none of these methods is completely reliable and the simple step of providing a water jacket is the only certain answer to the problem. This method has the two-fold advantage of ensuring that metal temperatures are kept below 100°C as well as restricting the thermal expansion of the vessel shell and therefore maintaining the desirable state of compression in the refractory lining. It has been shown by experiment that a small additional advantage accrues by virtue of condensation of water adjacent to the shell on the inside which will assist in blocking the passage of gas. All the ICI-designed plants have water jackets and these have been completely successful.

REFRACTORY CONCRETE LININGS FOR SECONDARY REFORMERS

T. M. Scott

INTRODUCTION

My Company have many years' experience in the refractory lining of pressure vessels, and in 1961 lined the two secondary reformer vessels for ICI at Heysham. We later lined the secondary reformers at Billingham, and since then have carried out similar work for other companies.

REFORMER PROCESS

Briefly, the gases entering the secondary reformer under pressure consist of carbon monoxide, hydrogen and steam, to which the appropriate amount of air is added to support the desired combustion, this taking place in the conical section towards the top of the vessel above the catalyst. The maximum temperature of the gases at this point is 1350°C. The reaction through the catalyst bed is endothermic; the product gases leaving the reformer at around 900°C consist mainly of hydrogen, nitrogen, carbon dioxide, with a small percentage of carbon monoxide not converted to carbon dioxide in the reformer, and small proportions of methane.

Refractory lining is necessary to reduce heat loss and to reduce the pressure vessel shell temperature to safe limits.

CHOICE OF REFRACTORIES

A great many factors have to be considered, and these are itemized below insofar as they affect the choice between brick and monolithic linings.

1. *The Effect of Hydrogen*

The presence of hydrogen increases the thermal conductivity of both brick and monolithic refractories. A brick lining has a great number of joints, all of which are potential escape routes for the process gases. A monolithic lining is better because it has few joints.

2. *The Effect of Carbon Monoxide*

A refractory of low iron content is essential, whether brick or monolithic, to avoid carbon monoxide disintegration.

317

3. Refractory Strength

Whilst a brick lining can be designed to withstand compressive stresses, tensile stresses cannot be accommodated. A monolithic lining anchored to the pressure vessel shell can be designed so that the stresses are at a minimum and hence gives a more stable lining. Anchoring is difficult and expensive with bricks.

4. Shrinkage Cracking

This must be controlled in order to avoid gas by-passing the catalyst bed. A brick lining will not shrink on heating since the firing shrinkage has taken place during manufacture, but the expansion must be accommodated. In contrast to this a monolithic lining can be designed to accommodate both the expansion and the shrinkage which occurs during the drying out process.

5. Heat Loss

Generally the monolithic lining can achieve the same heat loss with reduced thickness. If this economy is taken into account in a vessel subjected to high pressure where the refractory internal diameter is the governing factor, the saving in expensive steels can be appreciable.

6. Shell Operating Temperature

At first thought it would appear that either construction would meet the requirement. As already pointed out, a lining with numerous joints in different places can only succeed provided the joints hold tight. The chances then of a monolithic lining succeeding must be greater.

7. The Dimensional Accuracy of Lining

A brick lining can be designed and installed with great accuracy, but this is complicated and expensive. The monolithic lining be it cast or gunned into place is obviously much easier and the final result superior.

8. Load Bearing Supports

If corbels or catalyst supports are required, it is most difficult to design these in brick to withstand the loads. A monolithic lining cast *in situ* and anchored to the shell is much more likely to succeed.

9. Refractory Operating Temperature

Bricks and monolithic linings can withstand temperatures equally well provided the mechanical design is correct.

10. Special Process Requirements

If for process reasons, a silica free lining is required, both brick and monolithic linings can achieve this, but the chances are that bricks are more easily obtainable if the highest purity is required.

11. *Comparative Cost*

The points which must be taken into account when choosing a lining are the expected life of the lining, cost of materials required on site, the installation cost, the estimated down time to do repairs, and hence loss of production. The monolithic lining will prove, in most cases, the cheapest in the long run since it is more likely to satisfy the requirements. To repair a brick lining, for example, usually entails removing more bricks than is really necessary to carry out the repair. In a monolithic construction, however, it is possible in most instances to cut out the faulty area and replace.

From the foregoing it will be agreed that a monolithic lining is the better choice, particularly for the application now under consideration, irrespective of whether an inner brick lining is installed or not.

TYPES OF MONOLITHIC LININGS

There are three main types of monolithic linings available:

1. *Plastic Refractories*

This type is not suitable for vessel linings of the type we are considering.

2. *Castable Refractories*

These have a hydraulic setting cement incorporated which gives the refractory high strength in a few hours after casting. The hydraulic bond is replaced by ceramic bond provided the temperature of the lining is raised to $1100/1200°C$. This type is very suitable for casting behind shuttering and provided the shuttering is accurately made, a high degree of accuracy can be achieved. The material, as supplied by the manufacturers, has been carefully controlled quality wise, but it is important to control the water content carefully and to use vibrators to ensure proper compaction.

3. *Gunned Refractories*

These refractories are applied using a pneumatic gun and are similar to castable refractories, but differ in that the aggregate size requires to be smaller thus increasing the surface area of the aggregate, consequently in general the cement content is higher. This, unless steps are taken to prevent it, could give rise to greater shrinkage. The particles in the mix are conveyed to the surface by compressed air, at say 100 ft/sec, and rebound until sufficient thickness adheres to the surface to dissipate the momentum of the particle in compaction. Gunned refractories are, of course, designed to allow for this rebound loss and the resultant placed material is of the correct proportions. The water of hydration is added at the nozzle, in the case of the dry gun technique, and in the mixing chamber, in the case of the wet gun. Particularly in the former, the water added is only sufficient to achieve the best gunning results, but is sufficient for hydration. It follows, therefore, that the resultant concrete can be of good quality. Excellent compaction and increased strength are obtained.

Whilst it is possible to install such a lining of very accurate dimensions, special jigs are required so that contours can be cut back. The degree of accuracy is more difficult to obtain, however, as compared to a cast lining.

TYPE OF LINING CHOSEN

1. Heysham Secondary Reformers

These reformers were 6 ft inside diameter by about 30 ft overall length and had an $8\frac{1}{2}$-in. thick low iron refractory lining. The lining chosen was a castable type, cast behind shutters in panels. The top dome, however, was gunned mainly because of the difficulty in designing suitable shutters.

2. Billingham Secondary Reformers

The final design chosen was a cast low iron refractory lining, provided with corbels to support an internal brick lining. Figure 1 shows the final design. The brickwork on the bottom dome and vessel walls up to the underside of the top corbel, were of standard 42/45 per cent alumina brick. The top cone cylindrical portion above the top corbel was installed using a high alumina silica free brick. The resultant lining achieved the desired requirements, in that a monolithic lining provided the required structural strength but still allowed the high alumina silica free bricks to be installed in the cone to reduce the chances of silica migration. It is perhaps worthy of note that these corbels, spaced at regular intervals, quite apart from reducing the brick load on a corbel, ensured that any gas which found a way behind the bricks, would re-enter the catalyst bed and be processed. The necessary expansion allowances for the brick were of course incorporated in the overall design.

ANCHORAGE AND LAYOUT

Metal anchors are used to retain the refractory in place and to induce the pattern of shrinkage cracking required. Where there is a danger of process gases by-passing a catalyst bed and giving rise to hot spots on the shell, it is essential to form panel joints in such a way that the risk of gas movement through the lining is reduced to a minimum. This can be achieved by adopting keyed or staggered joints. Figure 1 shows a joint adopted for the Billingham reformers. It is interesting to study the behaviour of an individual panel in service. The expansion and contraction of the material is relative to the anchor which rigidly connects it to the shell. The anchor itself will expand in service pushing the panel away from the shell and in certain circumstances would set up a compressive stress in the material. To avoid this, the design of anchor shown in Fig. 1 was adopted in the Billingham vessels and has proved successful elsewhere.

The anchor is made from a milled ½-in. diameter bar opened up in the form of a "V" and screwed into a nut welded to the shell. The anchor was dipped in a bitumastic paint and polythene caps fitted over the tips to provide thermal expansion allowance. To meet the temperature conditions the anchors were made of 18/8 alloy steel.

By thus coating the anchor, it is allowed to expand freely and by adopting the "V" design the direction of expansion is mainly concentrated in the direction of the legs thus eliminating the tendency to force the refractory off the shell.

It is thus possible to adopt larger panels and thereby reduce the number of joints required. Panels can be built around four anchors of dimension equal to twice the anchorage spacing and when shrinkage contraction takes place the material is able to move relative to the anchors, consequently induced tensile stresses resulting in cracking are avoided.

In the case of the Billingham reformers, the panels were cast alternately and Fig. 1 shows the pattern of anchorage, the staggering of the joints, and the alternate panel casting technique. The alternate casting reduces the net circumferential shrinkage of the lining.

A theoretical strain analysis can be conducted by dividing the thickness of the material up into a series of strips parallel to the hot face and determining the mean temperature of each strip. By calculating the algebraic sum of expansions, that is due to temperature rise, contraction and setting, drying and firing shrinkage, the increase in diameter of the shell due to temperature and internal pressure, a pictorial diagram (Fig. 5), can be built up to show the behaviour of the joint in service. From this, it will be seen that the hot face is in compression with a maximum figure at the 1090°C line and that the joints will be open on the cold face half of the lining.

The designer has to decide what compressive strength is permissible between the quarter points and from his knowledge of the behaviour of his materials, so is he able to judge whether to reduce this stress by casting the panels together.

VAPOUR STOPS

Opinion is divided on the effectiveness of vapour stops, some designers insisting that they are essential to avoid the by-passing of process gases behind the lining, whilst others hold the view that they present weaknesses in the refractory lining causing cracking which in turn allows the gases to by-pass the catalyst. Again opinions vary on how far these vapour stops should be allowed to protrude into the lining, since they could give rise to hot spots on the shell local to the vapour stops. If vapour stops are desired, it is possible to design to avoid such troubles but the evidence is that they are not altogether effective.

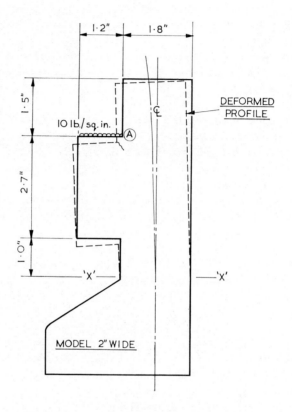

FIG. 3

Billingham secondary reformer—experimental corbel.

DEVELOPMENT WORK

In order to establish a design of corbel, a 1 to 5 scale model was made as shown (Fig. 3) and tested in B.C.R.A. Laboratory. The model was loaded under a pressure of 10 psi and the temperature raised 10°C/min up to 1350°C where it was held for 1½ hr. The load was then increased to 12 psi and held for 1 hr, and under these conditions a slight amount of subsidence was noted at loading point. The procedure was repeated at intervals of 1 hr for loads of 14, 16, and 20 psi with the temperature constant at 1350°C. The test piece had not sheared after a load of 20 psi had been applied for 1 hr.

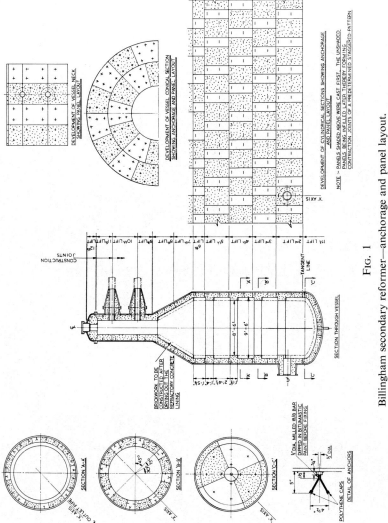

Fig. 1

Billingham secondary reformer—anchorage and panel layout.

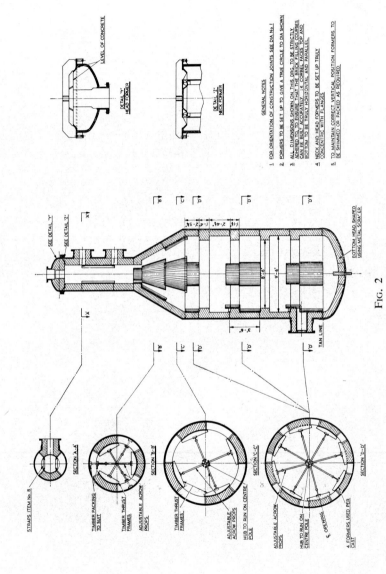

Fig. 2

Billingham secondary reformer—shutter arrangement.

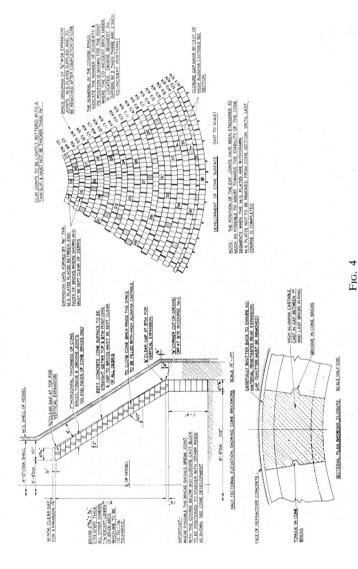

FIG. 4

Billingham secondary reformer—top cone brick arrangement.

STRAIN FORMULA:

$$n = \frac{RT - 2.25s - 1900s}{16}$$

WHERE: n = MAGNITUDE OF CONTRACTION IN THOU/FT IF NEGATIVE
           = MAGNITUDE OF COMPRESSION IN THOU/FT IF POSITIVE
       T = SECTION TEMPERATURE IN °C
       s = SHELL TEMPERATURE IN °C
       s = % LINEAR SHRINKAGE OF MATERIAL AT TEMPERATURE T°C
       R = COEFFICIENT OF EXPANSION OF MATERIAL PER °C
            0·0000053

EXAMPLE:

CONSIDER THE BEHAVIOUR OF THE REFRACTORY CONCRETE JOINTS IN THE CORBEL OF THE REACTOR LINING, WHEN OPERATING UNDER STEADY CONDITIONS

$R = 0·0000044$
$R = 0·0000053$ $0·83$
$t = 170°C$
LARGE PANEL LENGTH = 2·67ft
IN-FILL PANEL LENGTH = 1·33ft

TABULAR RESULTS

SECTION	1	2	3	4	5	6
MEAN TEMP AT SECTION °C	170	400	630	860	1090	1320
SHRINKAGE OF MATERIAL % s_1 (EXCLUDING SETTING & AIR DRYING SHRINKAGE)	ZERO	0·11	0·13	0·14	0·18	0·35
EXPANSION n_1 (THOU/FT)	/	−16	−7	+4	+11	+3
∴ EXPANSION OF LARGE PANEL $2·67n_1$	/	−43	−19	+11	+29	+8
SHRINKAGE OF MATERIAL % s_2 (INCLUDING SETTING & AIR DRYING SHRINKAGE)	ZERO	0·16	0·18	0·19	0·23	0·40
EXPANSION n_2 (THOU/FT)	/	−22	−13	−2	+5	−3
∴ EXPANSION OF SMALL PANEL $1·33n_2$	/	−29	−17	−3	+7	−4

FIG. 5

Strain analysis of refractory linings.

On examining the test piece after cooling, it was found that it had bent about the section X-X. It was concluded that the failure point had been reached when subsidence was first noted, at 12 psi and corresponded to a stress of 40 psi. On the actual installation the corbel would be anchored to the shell near the top of the corbel and would be subjected to a maximum temperature of 1350°C on the hot face only, added to which it would form part of a continuous circular ring. The stresses in the corbel would consequently be much lower and it was calculated that a factor of safety of 4 would exist on the actual installation. As a point of interest a 45° crack developed on the model at the point A due to stress concentrations at the sharp corner. On the actual installation a fillet was formed to avoid this.

The design of the brickwork at the top cone incorporated horizontal joints between the brick rings with each brick tongued and grooved in the vertical plane. The cone thus formed would expand upwards, consequently the appropriate clearance behind the cone had to be increased towards the apex (Fig. 4). To avoid any difficulty with closure bricks a high alumina/low silica refractory concrete was cast in each row.

METHOD OF CONSTRUCTION

Figure 2 illustrates the shuttering arrangement adopted in order that panels could be cast alternately. This method is used quite frequently. The lining was carried out in lifts as shown in Fig. 1. Preplanning is necessary and it is essential to keep the strictest quality control. Each panel must be correctly vibrated to give the necessary compaction, density and strength.

WATER CURING

It is of the utmost importance that adequate curing is carried out during the construction of any cast or gunned monolithic lining. As the refractory concrete sets, a slight contraction occurs, and during this set it is essential that the water required for hydration is retained in the lining. Again, on setting, a temperature increase takes place. It is generally considered that this has no harmful effect unless a very humid, warm atmosphere is in contact with the concrete.

After the shutters are removed, it is therefore expedient to spray the surface with water. This has the added advantage of cooling the refractory should it develop temperature. As a general rule the refractories should be left wet for at least 24 hr after pouring, but, if time allows, a longer period than this would be advantageous.

It is not advisable, however, to spray the surface in the first 2–4 hr with a gunned lining where shuttering is not employed, since such action could easily wash cement from the surface layers of the material so causing spalling.

DRYING OUT THE LINING

It is desirable to raise the temperature of the lining slowly, on first heating, in order to remove the moisture at a controlled rate.

The technique adopted is briefly as follows:

1. The drying equipment consists of external heaters supplying hot gas to the vessel and asbestos sheet baffles internally to distribute the gas flow.

2. Attach thermo-couples to the vessel shell. This enables the operator to observe a rise in the shell temperature coincident with drying of the concrete.

3. Raise the drying temperature in the first instance by 25°C/hr until a temperature of 100–150°C is reached.

4. Hold this temperature for a period of 24 hr to ensure that as much of the water in the exposed face of the lining is driven off slowly.

5. Raise the temperature by 25°C/hr up to a temperature of 450°C to 500°C and hold for 12 hr. This allows the heat to penetrate the lining and remove the moisture in the refractory close to the shell.

6. By raising the temperature to 450–500°C the moisture of crystallization is also removed.

7. Raise the temperature at the rate of 50°C/hr until the operating temperature has been reached.

8. Having held the operating temperature for 12 hr, the lining should then be cooled at a rate of 100°C/hr.

In certain circumstances loose insulating blankets should be placed on the outside of the vessel shell. This economizes in heat and ensures the lining is thoroughly dried. Care must be taken that overheating of the steel shell does not occur, and, if necessary, a portion of the blanket should be removed. This method works out extremely well and is essential on vessels where the operating temperature is low.

Figure 6 shows typical drying out recorded gas and shell temperatures. From this it can be seen that the shell temperature climbs gradually until it approaches 100°C, where it remains comparatively stationary for a considerable time. At 65 hr the shell temperature began to increase more steeply and at this point the lining can be considered to be dry.

The danger of drying out a lining too quickly lies in the possibility of steam forming in the lining and having no ready means of escape, causing the lining to explode with disastrous results. There are occasions, however, when it is just not possible to allow a long period of time drying a lining, but as far as process reactors are concerned, we consider that the drying must be carefully carried out.

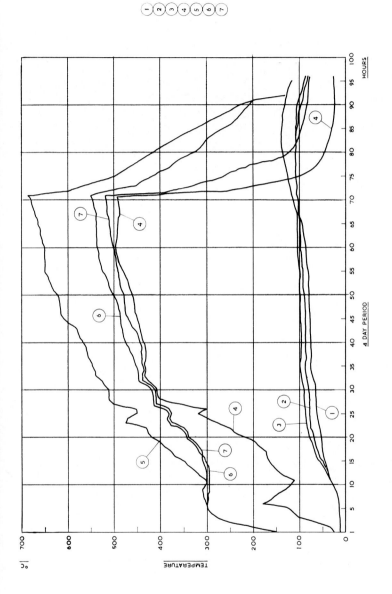

FIG. 6

Graph showing typical temperature recordings during dry-out.

INSPECTION

No. 1 secondary reformer furnace at Billingham was inspected in March 1963. Up to that time the maximum operating temperature had been approximately 750°C on this reactor but the measurements taken of the shrinkage visible on the exposed faces of the bottom corbel corresponded to the firing shrinkage of 0·18 per cent. The reactor appeared to be in excellent condition.

ACKNOWLEDGEMENT

I would like to record my gratitude to the management of the Plibrico Co. Ltd., for their permission to present this paper.

JOINTS BETWEEN REFRACTORY LINED PIPES

L. G. Huggett and W. Green

In the steam-reforming process the gas emerges from the primary stage at about 800°C into a header system and, in the ICI plants, into the secondary reforming vessel followed by a make-gas boiler. Several joints exist where it is necessary to provide a seal between refractory faces. Experience in other plants containing high-pressure high-temperature gases shows that shell overheating can occur with jointed refractory linings. Presumably local pressure differences can occur owing to turbulence in the gas stream which can force gas through the passages. Heat can also be transferred by direct radiation, although this element of heat transfer is small.

It is not possible to guarantee geometrically perfect mating surfaces on a refractory lining and a resilient material is therefore necessary. Several suitable fibrous refractory insulation materials exist which are suitable for sealing simple flat faces. A fibrous silica was chosen initially, in the form of a fabricated blanket made from loose felt sandwiched between woven cloth on the outer faces. The uncompressed thickness is $\frac{3}{4}$ in. and this readily compresses to about $\frac{1}{4}$ in. Because of the compression and partly because of a certain amount of devitrification, the gasket is weak and powdery after the joint has been broken and replacement is necessary. The fabricated gaskets are expensive and experiments are being made using fibrous alumino-silicate materials in the form of felt from which gaskets can be cut. Several proprietary forms of felted fibre are available made from fused china clay and these are all more refractory in air than the silica fibre. In atmospheres containing steam, devitrification takes place roughly to the same extent at about 1000°C consequently the china clay based materials will certainly be satisfactory and cost only a small fraction of the silica fibre gaskets. The proprietary materials vary in physical properties and one of these is more suitable than the rest since it consists of very fine fibres and has a higher degree of resilience and robustness.

PLUG JOINTING

In the secondary reformer itself access is required at the top and the design incorporates a refractory lined lid (Fig. 1) which carries the burner pipe. The refractory lining is designed with a 45° chamfer to prevent a direct radiation path to the metal joint, but this is a refinement which is perhaps not strictly necessary. In the Heysham plants, a slightly different design was used in which the burner pipe was introduced separately but the principle remains the same. In this case the joint in the refractory is cylindrical rather than plane and is therefore clearly more difficult to seal than a plane joint because of the sliding action arising from insertion of the plug. Plugs are also provided near the base of the vessels to facilitate the removal of catalyst. All

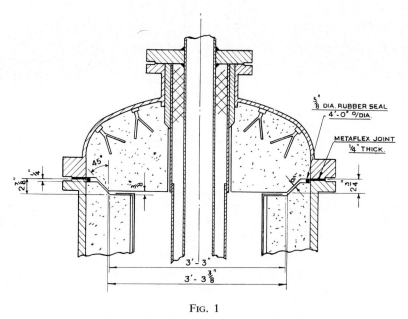

FIG. 1

Flange joint and seal between refractory faces in Billingham secondary reformer.

these joints have, of course, to be broken and remade when access to the vessel is required.

These joints are filled with a cement designed to have a low but adequate strength so that they can be readily broken when necessary. It consists of:

2500°F insulating brick aggregate	4 parts by weight
china clay	1 part by weight
calcium aluminate cement	1 part by weight

When assembling the joint a rubber ring is used to prevent excess cement from squeezing on to the faces of the flanges and the Metaflex gasket used to provide the pressure seal.

The use of the cement in the Billingham and Severnside plants followed its successful use in the Heysham plants. In the Heysham case, the use of a cement seal was virtually essential. In the Billingham plants it has been perfectly satisfactory but a high temperature fibrous insulating material would also be technically satisfactory, and would have the advantage that joints could be made by a fitter only, without the necessity of a bricklayer also.

THERMAL INSULATION FOR
STEAM-REFORMING PLANTS

D. Cooper and R. C. Hall

One of the important features of the steam-reforming process is economy in the use of fuel, so that the efficient thermal insulation of the plant is a prime necessity. Much of the plant is conventional, and where this is so economic thickness of insulation can be derived using a computer programme that is available for the purpose. Some of the equipment is insulated internally, and where junctions occur with externally insulated lines, special construction is necessary.[1] Particular vigilance is necessary to make certain that excess of enthusiasm does not lead to the application of external insulation over mild steels parts that contain internal insulation—the inevitable result is that the mild steel is overheated. At least three examples have been found in practice; fortunately only one was undetected in the construction stage.

Differences from normal practices are mainly in connection with the primary furnace, and the transfer lines to the secondary reformer.

The primary furnace consists essentially of a large and relatively simple box construction, but each furnace unit contains up to 120 alloy tubes, and these protrude through the roof of the furnace and through its base in order to facilitate catalyst changes. The tubes are fixed at their upper ends, but the lower ends move some 6 in. on heating because of expansion. The movement is reversed on cooling. "Pigtails" (convoluted 1 in. diameter tubes) lead from the individual catalyst tubes to a collecting header. The temperature is about 800°C. It is necessary to insulate the tubes external to the furnace up to the junction with the "pigtails", the whole of the length of the "pigtails", and the collecting header. The general arrangement is shown in Fig. 1.

The possibility of insulating the collecting header and each individual "pigtail" connection was rejected in the design stage in favour of a box construction to contain the assembly except for the actual connections to the primary furnace tubes. In the Heysham and Billingham designs the boxes are insulated internally by means of slabs using a certain type of calcium silicate insulation which tests showed to be stable up to 900°C. The slabs have been secured to the wall panels of the box by alloy bolts and to the roof by heat resisting steel mesh. On the whole this system has been successful, despite some minor difficulties arising from shrinkage and cracking of the slabs. It does have some advantages: access is readily available for mainten-

331

ance purposes, the whole of the system can be inspected and it is possible to
carry out the tube isolation technique described by Estruch[2] with the plant
on line.

The application of rigid insulation to the "pigtail" connections to the tubes

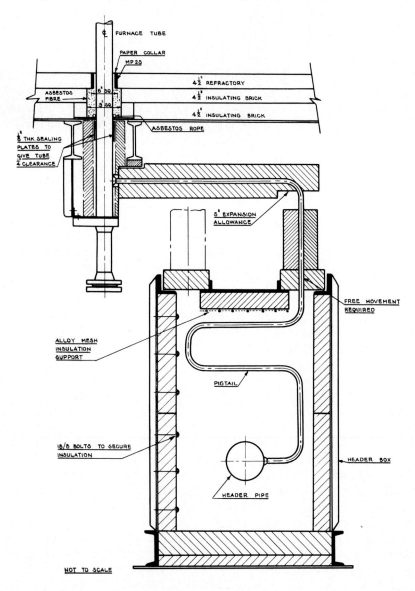

FIG. 1

Insulation of exit pigtails.

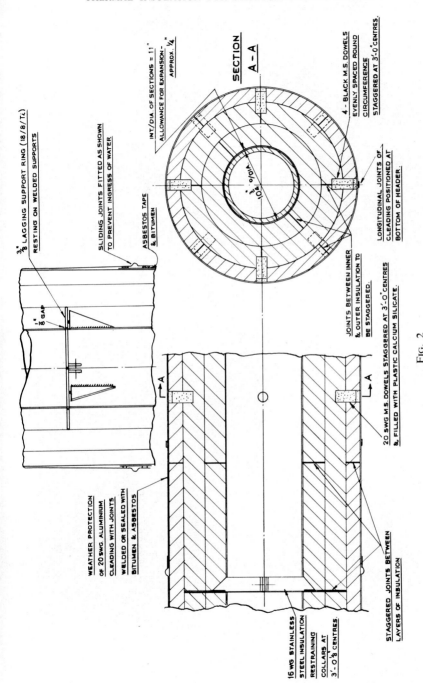

Fig. 2

Method of applying insulation to header pipes.

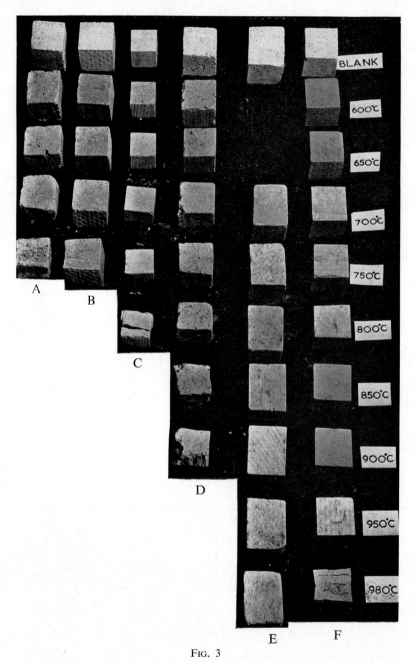

Fig. 3

Results of heating calcium silicates from various sources for 24 hr at the temperatures indicated. (All samples were approx. 2 in. cubes except "C" which were 1½ in. cubes.)

was less successful, but a type of mineral wool resistant to the temperature conditions has been tried in practice and shown to be promising. It is intended to extend the use of this material in the locations concerned.

The transfer lines from the exit headers to the secondary reformers are exposed to the weather and include a considerable vertical length. Externally applied insulation must be designed to cope with radial and with longitudinal expansion. Rigid calcium silicate insulation in two layers was used for the purpose. The material was pre-assembled on oversize formers to allow for radial expansion, and, on the vertical leg support rings were bolted round the lines at intervals of 3 ft (Fig. 2).

Protection from the weather was obtained by means of aluminium cladding with welded seams instead of the asbestos cement normally applied at Billingham. It was considered that there was an element of risk associated with the occasional moistening of the insulation under shut-down conditions, particularly in the presence of marine spray, which could lead to a concentration of chlorides at the alloy surface. Austenitic steels are well-known to be subject to stress corrosion cracking under such conditions; the particular alloy used is very much less prone to this fault. However, in such a key process the elimination of all risk at small cost was considered well worth while.

The insulation of the transfer lines has proved to be efficient and reliable in practice.

APPENDIX

Not all commercially available forms of calcium silicate are suitable for the high temperature duties described. Figure 3 shows the effect of heating trial pieces from a number of sources through a range of temperatures. It is, therefore, important to specify a suitable grade of silicate.

REFERENCES

1. W. D. CLARK and A. W. ELMES, Factors affecting choice of materials and design of units for pressure steam reforming. This volume, p. 21.
2. B. ESTRUCH, Blanking-off reformer tubes during plant operation. This volume, p. 259.

TRANSFER OF SILICA IN THE PRESSURE STEAM REFORMING PROCESS

L. G. HUGGETT and L. PIPER

INTRODUCTION

The steam reforming process depends in part for its effectiveness on the heat recovery system, and, in ammonia plants, on CO conversion plant. At a fairly early stage it became evident that heat recovery efficiency was decreasing because of deposition of solid material in the tubes of make-gas boilers and solid was also depositing in the CO conversion catalyst. The deposit was mainly silica and catalyst dust and from the evidence available it was clear that the silica had been transported in the vapour phase. Transfer of silica had been considered in the design stage and some precautions had been taken. It was not possible to predict the magnitude of the problem nor to consider an entrainment filter in a plant designed to recover maximum possible heat from the system. In high temperature metallurgical processes silica can be reduced to the volatile monoxide which decomposes where the temperature is lower and deposits silica. There is also much evidence in power station technology of the deposition of silica on turbine blades, the silica being transported in solution in steam at very high pressures and coming out as the pressure is reduced. The same mechanism has been studied because of its relevance to silicate mineral formation.

PLANT EXPERIENCE

The first operating plants were at Heysham Works. These incorporate make-gas boilers after the secondary reformers. The deposit accumulated in the tubes over a period of 3 months in distinguishable layers of somewhat different composition, some of which were nearly pure silica. After making due allowance for what appeared to be catalyst dust, it was estimated that the quantity of silica transferred was something over 100 lb. Whatever the method of transfer, the silica must have its origin in material in contact with the process gas stream. All the refractory lining material, catalysts and catalyst supports contain some silica (Table 1), but their temperatures vary considerably and in addition, the physical contacts between the gas and the various siliceous materials are very different. The lining materials are in contact with the gas only on the surface, whereas the catalyst and catalyst

337

TABLE 1

Composition of Materials and Boiler Deposits

Material	SiO_2%
White deposit in boiler tubes	91·9
Grey deposit in boiler tubes	77·7
Refractory concrete lining of secondary reformer	45
Fibrous silica gasketting material	98·7
Secondary catalyst	
(a)	1·2
(b)	60
Catalyst support	
(a) Molochite = Calcined kaolin	54
(b) Steatite rings	64·2
Secondary catalyst	
(a) after use	4·0
(b) after use	47·9

support offer a very much greater area of contact. Although it was evident that dust eroded from the catalysts or from the refractory linings was contributing to the deposits, nevertheless, a process of silica enrichment was taking place, the only possible mechanism being transfer in the vapour phase.

ANALYSES OF CONDENSATE

Samples of water condensed from the process gas at various stages were analysed and found to contain roughly the quantities of silica shown in Table 2 confirming that sufficient silica was present to account for the quantities of deposit observed. It is not easy under process conditions to withdraw samples that are totally uncontaminated with structural materials and finely divided silica which precipitates from solution in the gas when the temperature drops is also liable to be entrained. However, the general picture seems clear, that the major contamination occurs in the secondary reformer. There is little apparent change in the concentration of SiO_2 inlet and exit the make-gas boiler, but there are sampling difficulties and the figures given are the average of variable results. The accuracy of the determination at these points is not better than 1 ppm and a change of this order is sufficient to account for the deposition of 100 lb of SiO_2.

TABLE 2

Silica Contents of Process Gas
(parts per million by weight)

		SiO_2, ppm
Primary reformer	In	0·03
	Out	0·5
Secondary reformer	In	0·5
	Out	3
Make-gas boiler	In	3
	Out	3

TRANSFER AS SILICON MONOXIDE

Transfer of silica as silicon monoxide had been considered in the design stage. The reaction follows the simple equation

$$SiO_2 + H_2 \rightarrow SiO + H_2O$$

Decomposition and reoxidation produce silica again on cooling. Tombs and Welch[1] have investigated the thermodynamics of this reaction and have derived the equilibrium constant as a function of temperature:

$$\log K = \frac{-22,700}{T} + 7 \cdot 37$$

Calculations showed that if the temperature attained was 1100°C and the gas held the maximum possible quantity of SiO then the amount transferred would be less than 1 kg per year. However, it was believed that imperfect mixing of the gas and air could occur locally in the flame of the secondary reformer, and that in consequence temperatures up to 1350°C could be attained in some parts of the top cone. The temperature coefficient of the reduction reaction is high and the maximum SiO_2 transfer could be 180 kg per annum under such circumstance. Accordingly the combustion chambers of the Billingham reformers were lined internally with nearly pure alumina bricks (which incidentally have behaved excellently as a structural material). Nevertheless, silica transfer occurred from these reformers also, and it was evident that a different mechanism was responsible.

TRANSFER BY SOLUTION IN STEAM

No work has been published which shows the solubility of silica in steam at the temperatures and pressures in the steam reforming units, but work has been carried out in connection with the deposition of silica on the turbine blades in power plants operating at very high pressures and with geological studies.[2-6] Extrapolation would seem to indicate that much higher super heat at modest pressures could give solubilities in the right range. Research Department of Agricultural Division investigated the higher temperature regions and obtained a number of values which have been plotted in Fig. 1 together with some of the earlier published results. From these an estimate can be made of the solubility of silica in steam at a partial pressure of 75 psig, the approximate condition in the process.

The straight line plots which are shown are based on the simple assumption of proportionality between the log concentration of silica and the reciprocal of absolute temperature. The estimate of solubility at 75 psig is based on a pressure effect deduced from Straub's figures and involves the assumption that silica forms a hydrate when it dissolves. The pressure effect depends on

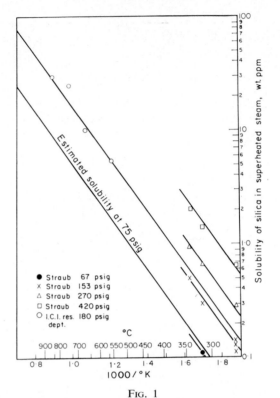

Fig. 1

Solubility of silica at various temperatures and partial pressures of steam.

the number of water molecules combined in the hydrate; making simple assumptions the data indicate a mean value of $2 \cdot 5$.

Thus $$p(SiO_2 \cdot 2 \cdot 5\ H_2O)\ \alpha\ pH_2O^{2 \cdot 5}$$

and since the concentration of silica in parts per million is proportional to $p(SiO_2 \cdot 2 \cdot 5\ H_2O)/pH_2O$ one obtains the relationship.

$$SiO_2(ppm)\ \alpha\ pressure^{1 \cdot 5}$$

Plotting Straub's data with a temperature coefficient consistent with the ICI data leads to an expression

$$\log (SiO_2\ ppm) = \frac{-2300}{°K} = 1 \cdot 5 \log p\ (absolute) + 0 \cdot 1$$

from which the curve for 75 psig is obtained.

It is deduced that at 75 psig, and at a temperature of 800°C the solubility of silica is in the region 5–10 ppm. Thus the samples taken from the process stream were not fully saturated with silica even at the highest values determined. However, when the gas is cooled in the waste heat boiler to about

400°C the solubility decreases to well below 1 ppm and it is therefore not surprising that silica precipitates in the tubes. The fact that the measured values in condensate exit the boiler are about 3 ppm is taken to mean that solid silica is entrained in the gas stream. Confirmation is derived from the fact that the CO conversion units at approximately the same temperature filter out silica in the upper bed. Silica transported in the steam phase ar.d precipitated at lower temperatures has the typical form shown in Fig. 2.

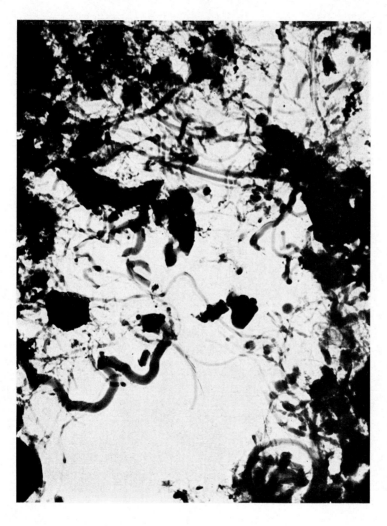

FIG. 2

Typical form of silica precipitated from solution in steam (×25,000).

REMEDIAL ACTION

The indications were that silica was taken into solution in steam in the secondary reformer, but that even so the gas was not fully saturated. Rate of solution is likely to be controlled by diffusion in the gas phase and is therefore dependent on surface contact area. The steatite rings in the Heysham reformers and the calcined kaolin lumps in the Billingham reformers which support the catalyst bed were therefore withdrawn. A small amount of high silica catalyst had been used and this was also removed.

Interesting confirmation of the mechanism deduced was obtained from examination of the steatite porcelain rings withdrawn from the Heysham plant. A surface layer of generally "devitrified" appearance was apparent and this was found to contain only 40 per cent of SiO_2 compared with 58 per cent in the interior. It is also interesting to observe that whereas the high silica catalyst changes from 60 to 47·9 per cent silica on the surface the low silica catalyst actually increases in silica content from 1·2 to 4 per cent. This is no doubt due to the different relative stabilities of silicate compounds and shows that small amounts of silica can be tolerated in suitable combination.

Fabricated rings or other shapes are unnecessary and graded fused brown alumina is now used; this combines the characteristics of low silica content, high refractoriness and cheapness. Precautions are taken against entrained dust by blowing through the system with compressed air before completing the connection to the make gas boiler. As a result of these changes silica transfer is no longer a problem in reformer units.

REFERENCES

1. TOMBS and WELCH, *J. Iron and Steel Inst.*, **172,** 69 (1952).
2. F. G. STRAUB, Steam turbine blade deposits, *Univ. of Illinois Bulletin*, **43,** (59) (1946).
3. G. C. KENNEDY, The hydrothermal solubility of silica, *Economic Geology*, **39,** 25 (1944).
4. G. W. MOREY and J. M. HESSELGESSER, The solubility of minerals in superheated steam, *Economic Geology*, **46,** 821 (1951).
5. T. E. GILLINGHAM, Solubility and transfer of silica and other non-volatiles in steam, *Economic Geology*, **43,** 241 (1948).
6. R. FEITSMA, Solubility of silica in steam, *Mitt. der V.G.B.*, **72,** 170 (1961).

NICKEL CARBONYL FORMATION IN STEAM REFORMING PROCESSES

A. B. DENSHAM, L. S. COOPER and M. W. TANNER

INTRODUCTION

The formation of nickel carbonyl in town gas was discussed in a paper to the Institution of Gas Engineers in November 1963.[1] If the gas distributed contains more than 0·01 parts per million by volume of nickel carbonyl, there is likely to be district trouble as the result of sooting-up of non-aerated burners used in various types of gas appliance.

The carbonyl can be formed from various nickel compounds in contact with gas containing carbon monoxide. At the time of the previous paper[1] no town gas-making plants, utilizing the high-pressure steam reforming process, were as yet in commission. Tests on the ICI plant at Heysham had originally shown 0·1 p.p.m. of nickel carbonyl at the outlet of the primary reformer. However, further tests showed no indication of carbonyl when the Incoloy sampling line was changed, so that the gas cooled in a sampling line which was free from nickel. Dr. Cockerham had also found nickel carbonyl at the outlet of the first and second stages of the pilot plant at the Gas Council Midlands Research Station, Solihull, but this was again attributed to formation in the stainless steel sampling lines and condensers.

The fact that carbonyl had been detected, even if it had only been formed in sampling lines, indicated the need to carry out further measurements, both on full-scale plants and in the laboratory, to see whether there was likely to be any significant trouble from carbonyl in town gas made by the high-pressure steam reforming process.

CONDITIONS FOR CARBONYL FORMATION

The published data on the equilibrium constant:

$$K_p = \frac{P_{Ni(co)_4}}{P^4_{co}}$$

(where $P_{Ni(co)_4}$ and P_{co} are the equilibrium partial pressures of nickel carbonyl and carbon monoxide in atm) as a function of temperature has been reviewed.[1] The results can be expressed by the equation:

$$\log_{10}K_p = \frac{6785}{T} - 18\cdot755$$

where T is absolute temperature in °K. For low carbonyl concentrations (up to a few p.p.m.) P_{co} may be taken as the initial partial pressure of carbon monoxide. The equilibrium concentration of nickel in the gas, which cannot be exceeded is then $P_{Ni(co)_4}/P$, where P is the total gas pressure in atm.

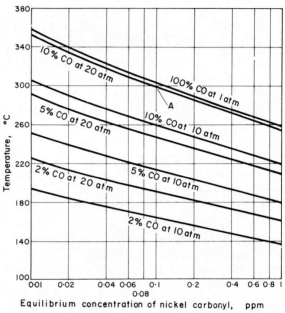

FIG. 1

The effects of temperature, carbon monoxide concentration and pressure on the equilibrium concentration of nickel carbonyl.

Figure 1 shows curves, calculated on the above basis, for the variation with temperature of the equilibrium nickel carbonyl concentrations in gases containing 1, 5 and 10 per cent of carbon monoxide at 10 and 20 atm pressure, and 100 per cent of carbon monoxide at atmospheric pressure.

The curves show that, under the conditions prevailing in high-pressure steam reformers, the temperature is too high (above 400°C) for nickel carbonyl to form from the catalyst in the reactor tubes or from any nickel that may be present in the carbon monoxide converter. Thus it is only necessary to exclude reactive nickel from the gas cooling and washing system.

Figure 1 does not, however, show the optimum temperature for carbonyl formation. Since reaction velocities normally increase with temperature, it might be thought that the greatest likelihood of producing say 0.1 p.p.m. of carbonyl, from gas containing 10 per cent of carbon monoxide at 20 atm pressure would be at a temperature just below the point A on Fig. 1, i.e. about 290°C. In fact we have observed maximum carbonyl formation from nickel-containing alloys to occur at 100–150°C (see below).

Goldberger[2] found the maximum rate of carbonyl formation from finely divided nickel and carbon monoxide to be at 75°C, regardless of pressure. He interpreted his results by supposing that the rate of formation is the product of three terms.

It is difficult to obtain reproducible results from the rate of formation of nickel carbonyl, even from pure nickel. The rate depends very much on the state of the surface and is markedly affected by catalysts and sensitizers, such as sulphur compounds.

Even with an active nickel powder the rate of carbonyl formation drops off with time, presumably because the nickel atoms in more active sites react first.[2] It is only to be expected that this effect will be more pronounced with alloys as used in plant, since diffusion of nickel in the metal will be much too slow to replace any atoms in the surface which may have reacted.

PLANT TESTS

Nickel carbonyl in gas was determined by two methods.[3]
A qualitative glass jet test[1, 3] was also used.

Billingham

The plant at Billingham reforms light distillate for hydrogen production. The converted gas, containing 3.8 per cent of carbon monoxide at 10 atm pressure, passes after preliminary cooling through a low-pressure mild steel boiler with baffles and ferrules of Ti-stabilized 18/8 Cr/Ni steel, across which the temperature drops from 153 to 127°C, while the contact time is about 0.5 sec.

Tests were made on No. 3 unit on the 18th and 19th of February 1964 by means of atomic absorption. The results were:

	p.p.m. of nickel carbonyl
Inlet L.P. boiler	0.003
Outlet L.P. boiler	0.001
After atmospheric cooler	0.001

These figures were all on the limit of detection and well below the permissible limit of 0.01 p.p.m.

Heysham

The plant at Heysham reforms light distillate for hydrogen production. At the time of the tests (1962) there was no carbon monoxide conversion, and no nickel containing alloy was used in the cooling system. The gas leaving the

M

primary reformer at 750–800°C contained 5·9 per cent of carbon monoxide and was at 12 atm pressure.

Tests on No. 4 unit, by the chemical method, on 7th June 1962, showed only 0·002 p.p.m. in the final gas, but 0·10 p.p.m. at the outlet of the primary reformer. The latter was difficult to explain, in view of the high temperature in the reformer, but was subsequently attributed by ICI to the use of a long Incoloy section of sampling line. The gas cooled from 700 to 150°C as it passed slowly down this section, and it was thought that carbonyl might have been forming at the cooler end (equilibrium concentration 31 p.p.m.).

The Incoloy section from the outlet primary reformer of No. 3 unit was subsequently heated electrically to 500°C, and the gas was cooled in an additional silver plated mild steel sampling line. Further chemical tests on the 7th of September 1962 showed no detectable nickel carbonyl at this point, but a qualitative (glass jet) test still showed carbonyl at the outlet of the unheated Incoloy line from No. 4 unit.

These results are included to show the importance of correct sampling.

Hythe

The plant at Hythe reforms light distillate for town gas production. The converted gas, containing 1·2 per cent of carbon monoxide at 12 atm pressure, passes after preliminary cooling through a de-aerator feed water heater (DFWH), with tubes of Ti-stabilized 18/8 Cr/Ni steel, across which the temperature drops from 155 to 132°C, while the contact time is about 0·05 sec.

Tests were made on No. 2 unit, which had been operating for 1 month, by the chemical method, on 17th March 1964. The results were:

	p.p.m. of nickel carbonyl
Inlet No. 2 DFWH	0·01
Outlet No. 2 DFWH	0·006
Final gas	0·003

The final gas showed only a very faint indication of carbonyl by the glass jet test and there had been no district complaints.

Further tests were made on No. 1 unit, which had just been started up, by the atomic absorption method, on the 7th and 8th of April 1964. The results were:

	p.p.m. of nickel carbonyl
Inlet No. 1 DFWH	0·002
Outlet No. 1 DFWH	0·002
Inlet No. 2 DFWH	0·01
(on reduced make)	

The figures for the outlet DFWH and final gas were on the limit of detection and well below the permissible limit. The 0·01 p.p.m. at the inlet to No. 2 DFWH might be due to catalyst dust blown forward to a cooler zone.

Southall

The plant at Southall reforms L.P.G. for town gas production. The converted gas containing 2 per cent of carbon monoxide at 3·7 atm pressure passes after preliminary cooling through a feed water preheater, the second stage of which contains cupronickel (70 per cent Cu, 30 per cent Ni) tubes, across which the temperature drops from 130 to 106°C; the contact time is 0·4 sec.

Tests were made by the chemical method, on the South stream, on the 1st and 2nd of April 1964. The results were:

	p.p.m. of nickel carbonyl
Inlet feed water preheater	0·002
Outlet feed water preheater	0·003
Outlet Vetrocoke plant	0·002
Outlet Vetrocoke plant	Very faint indication by glass jet tests.

Further tests were made by the atomic absorption method, on the North and South streams, on the 3rd, 4th and 5th of June 1964. These showed less than 0·002 p.p.m. at all the sampling points.

These figures are all well below the permissible limit.

Provan

The plant at Provan reforms light distillate for town gas production. The converted gas, containing 3 to 5 per cent of carbon monoxide at 7·5 atm pressure, passes after preliminary cooling through a heat exchanger (A) with stainless steel tubes, but mild steel shells, followed by a stainless steel air cooler. Across this system the temperature drops from 240 to 18°C and the pressure to 6·8 atm, while the contact time is about 8·5 sec.

Tests were made by the Scottish Gas Board, by the chemical and atomic absorption methods, in May 1964. The results were:

| Inlet to A | trace, | 0·005 p.p.m. of nickel carbonyl |
| Final enriched gas | trace, | 0·005 p.p.m. of nickel carbonyl |

These figures are on the limit of detection and below the permissible limit.

LABORATORY WORK

The laboratory work was carried out with specially purified town gas, containing 14–15 per cent of carbon monoxide, at 21·4 atm pressure, and with pure carbon monoxide at atmospheric pressure. Figure 1 shows that pure carbon monoxide at 1 atm should be roughly equivalent to 11 per cent of carbon monoxide at 20 atm.

Work at 21·4 atm

Town gas was deoxygenated, dried, debenzolized, compressed to 700–750 lb/in^2, filtered, and further dried and debenzolized under pressure. It was then passed through a pressure-reducing valve to a stainless steel reactor, containing the material to be investigated.

This reactor consisted of an EN 58B steel tube, of internal diameter 1 in. and 24 in. packed length, with Ermeto end fittings and flexible (BTR Industries Ltd.) high-pressure connections. It was mounted vertically in a tube furnace and could be by-passed as required. The material could be tested dry, or water could be trickled over it concurrent with the gas to produce saturation conditions.

The gas from the reactor outlet was passed through a reducing valve, trap and rotameter, directly to the burner of the atomic absorption spectroscope used for analysis. This burner consumed 18 s.ft^3/hr of gas, so the contact time of gas with the material tested could not be adjusted. However, since the experiments were conducted at constant reactor pressure, and at constant gas rate measured under standard conditions, the contact time did drop as the gas in the reactor expanded due to rise in temperature or humidity. Contact times, calculated on an empty tube basis, were as follows:

> Dry at   20°C   45 sec
> Dry at 300°C   23 sec
> Sat. at 100°C   35 sec
> Sat. at 150°C   19 sec

In order to study the effects of longer contact time, the reactor could be sealed up with gas under pressure and by-passed; the instantaneous instrument reading, when gas was again passed through the reactor, gave a measure of the carbonyl formed during the sealed up period.

The normal method of operation gave results for both long and short contact times. Starting dry at room temperature, gas was passed through the reactor for 30 min while measurements were made of the carbonyl concentration. The reactor was then sealed and by-passed for 30 min, after which gas was again passed through it and an instantaneous value of the maximum carbonyl concentration was obtained. The temperature was next raised about 50°C, and the above procedure was repeated. This was continued until the temperature had reached 300°C. Measurements were then made in the same way while the reactor was cooled in stages.

Measurements were also made under saturation conditions at 100 and 150°C, using short contact times only.

The gas entering the reactor had the following characteristics:

> Carbon monoxide   14 to 15 per cent
> Oxygen   0·01 to 0·04 per cent
> Benzole   2 lb/million s.ft^3
> Water (dry tests)   8 to 16 lb/million s.ft^3

The materials tested were EN 58B and 25/20 stainless steels, Incoloy 800, and 70/30 Cupronickel, containing 11·4, 21·08, 31·5, and 31·2 per cent of nickel respectively. They were mostly in the form of swarf, cut dry on a planing machine, set to give a cross-section of 2/1000 in. by 10/1000 in. The cupronickel was supplied as coarser turnings. In this form the materials would probably be more reactive than as fabricated tubes. The weight of stainless steel used per test was about $0 \cdot 22$ lb, and the weight of cupronickel was $0 \cdot 53$ lb.

The results were far from being reproducible. Maximum carbonyl formation was at about 100°C, but the activity at this temperature was sometimes greatly affected by preheating to a higher temperature. There was also a marked fall off in the rate of carbonyl formation with time, presumably as the nickel atoms in the surface were used up.

For example, a sample of EN 58B initially gave only $0 \cdot 02$ p.p.m. of nickel carbonyl with a 30-min contact time at 100°C, over a period of 15 hr. The temperature was then raised to 300°C and dropped again to 100°C. The nickel carbonyl concentration, with a 30-min contact time at 100°C, rose to $0 \cdot 8$ p.p.m. and dropped continuously to $0 \cdot 1$ p.p.m. over a period of 15 hr; during the same period the concentration for a 40-sec contact time dropped from $0 \cdot 015$ to $0 \cdot 002$ p.p.m.

For this reason only smoothed curves, relying mainly on the higher values, are shown in Figs. 2 and 3.

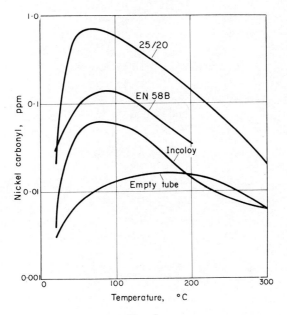

FIG. 2

Formation of nickel carbonyl from various materials in gas at $21 \cdot 4$ atm pressure with a contact time of 30 min.

Figure 2, for a 30-min contact time, shows significant carbonyl formation from EN 58B, 25/20, and Incoloy 800, with maxima at about 100°C. The empty tube showed very slight carbonyl formation at the start and end of the experiments.

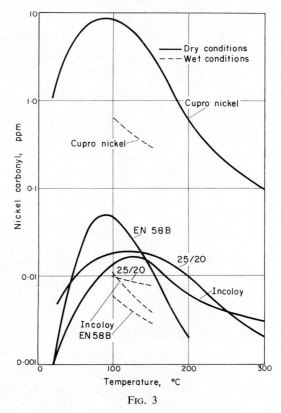

FIG. 3

Formation of nickel carbonyl from various materials in gas at 21·4 atm pressure with a contact time of 20 to 40 sec.

Figure 3, for a 20- to 40- sec contact time, also shows some carbonyl formation from EN 58B, 25/20, and Incoloy 800, with maxima at about 100°C. The maximum figure was 0·05 p.p.m. from EN 58B. It should be pointed out that the reduction in carbonyl formation was by no means proportional to the reduction in contact time.

Cupronickel gave pronounced carbonyl formation.

The effect of water (broken lines) was to reduce carbonyl formation.

Although Fig. 3 does show some nickel carbonyl formation, the contact time of 20 to 40 sec was considerably longer, and the partial pressure of carbon monoxide was considerably greater than would be expected in a normal reforming plant. Moreover, the observed decrease in rate of carbonyl formation with time (see above), would soon reduce the carbonyl concentration to below the permissible level of 0·01 p.p.m. Thus these experiments confirm the results of the plant tests that there is no likelihood of nickel carbonyl formation from stainless steel under normal operating conditions.

Ammonia or filming amines have been used in the gas cooling systems of high-pressure reformers to reduce corrosion of mild steel by carbon dioxide and water. It was thought that ammonia might promote carbonyl formation from stainless steel. A test was therefore made with EN 58B, under saturation conditions as described above, at 125°C. Replacement of the water by N/3 ammonia solution, corresponding to about 50 grains/100 s.ft³ of ammonia in the gas, gave no enhancement of the very small carbonyl formation shown in the bottom curve of Fig. 3.

Work at Atmospheric Pressure

Measurements with pure carbon monoxide at atmospheric pressure were carried out because it was easier to study the effects of minor additions to the gas.

Carbon monoxide from a cylinder was passed through active carbon (to remove any carbonyls), and then through a rotameter to the reactor. This consisted of a Pyrex glass tube, of internal diameter 1 in. and 12 in. packed length, mounted horizontally in a tube furnace. The inlet gas could be humidified by bubbling it through water at 98–100°C; in this case an ice-cooled trap was fitted at the outlet of the reactor.

The gas leaving the reactor was divided into two streams; one was passed through iodine monochloride solution in acetic acid, followed by a wet meter, for chemical determination of carbonyl; the other went to a glass jet for qualitative tests.

The gas rate, measured under standard conditions, was 1 ft³/hr. This gave a contact time of 22 sec for dry gas at room temperature, dropping to about 12 sec at 300°C, and about 10 sec for wet gas at 150°C. No attempt was made to investigate longer contact times.

The normal method of operation was to start by passing carbon monoxide for 1 hr (the sampling time required for the chemical test) at room temperature. The carbon monoxide was then replaced by hydrogen while the temperature was raised about 50°C. Carbon monoxide was passed through the reactor again for 1 hr at the new temperature, and was then replaced by hydrogen while the temperature was raised a further 50°C. The upper limit of temperature was 300°C dry and 150°C wet. If the maximum temperature was not reached in 1 day the sample was allowed to cool down in hydrogen overnight.

The materials tested were essentially the same as those used in the high pressure work. The EN 58B was also tested in the form of wire mesh, and the effect of etching with 10 per cent nitric acid containing 5 per cent of 40 per cent hydrofluoric acid was also investigated.

Apart from cupronickel, none of the materials tested showed any significant formation of nickel carbonyl under dry or wet conditions. The highest individual reading was 0·01 p.p.m. with unetched EN 58B turnings, dry, at 250°C, but in general the results were at or below the limit of detection.

Results for cupronickel are shown in Fig. 4. It will be seen that etching somewhat reduced nickel carbonyl formation under dry conditions, and that there was very little carbonyl formation under wet conditions.

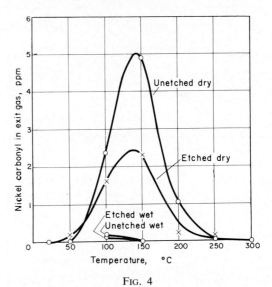

FIG. 4

Formation of nickel carbonyl from cupro-nickel in 100 per cent CO at atmospheric pressure, with contact times of 10 to 22 sec.

Hydrogen sulphide can be a catalyst for nickel carbonyl formation, though it will not normally be present in the gas from high pressure reformers. Tests in which about 20 p.p.m. of hydrogen sulphide was added to the carbon monoxide again gave negative results except with cupronickel. In this case there was a marked increase in carbonyl formation; the results were not very consistent, but etched cupronickel turnings showed an increase from 0·2 to over 50 p.p.m. at 50°C.

Experiments with ammonia, added to the carbon monoxide so as to give a concentration of 40 grains/100 ft³, showed no significant promotion of carbonyl formation from EN 58B under wet or dry conditions.

CARBONYL FORMATION FROM CATALYSTS

The catalyst in a high-pressure steam reformer contains nickel in a highly reactive state, but is normally much too hot for any nickel carbonyl to form.

However, should the reforming catalyst break up and blow forward through the carbon monoxide conversion unit into a cooler zone, there is a possibility of carbonyl formation.

This is illustrated by a single series of tests with a catalyst containing 16 per cent of nickel. The catalyst was crushed to 5 to 10 mesh and packed into a silica tube of diameter 1 in. and packed length 12 in. It was then reduced in hydrogen at 770°C, and cooled in hydrogen. There was an immediate formation of nickel carbonyl when the hydrogen was replaced by carbon monoxide at atmospheric temperature and pressure; the glass jet gave a brilliant yellow flame and showed a heavy deposit immediately. The absorbent solution was quickly spent so that the carbonyl concentrations shown below are only approximate. The carbon monoxide was replaced by hydrogen in between determinations while the temperature was raised.

Temperature, °C	Nickel carbonyl concentration, %
20	7
100	0·37

CONCLUSIONS

1. None of the plant tests showed any significant formation of nickel carbonyl under normal operating conditions.
2. Laboratory tests showed some formation of nickel carbonyl from EN 58B, 25/20 steel and Incoloy 800, but the concentrations were significant only with longer contact times and higher partial pressures of carbon monoxide than would be experienced in plants.
3. Cupronickel showed significant carbonyl formation at contact times approaching those experienced in plants.
4. Neither hydrogen sulphide nor ammonia significantly promoted carbonyl formation from stainless steel. However, hydrogen sulphide gave marked promotion of carbonyl formation from cupronickel.
5. A reduced nickel catalyst was very active in producing carbonyl at temperatures between 20° and 100°C.

REFERENCES

1. L. S. COOPER, A. B. DENSHAM and M. W. TANNER, *J.I.G.E.*, **4** (3), 183–203 (1964).
2. W. M. GOLDBERGER and D. F. OTHMER, *Ind. Eng. Chem. Process Design and Development*, **2** (3), 202–209 (1963).
3. A. B. DENSHAM, P. A. A. BEALE and R. PALMER, *J. Applied Chem.*, **13**, 567–580 (1963).

PREVENTION OF VANADIUM PENTOXIDE
ATTACK OF REFORMER TUBES BY
MAGNESIUM COMPOUNDS

H. KELLER

WHEN cracking tubes are heated with heavy fuel oils, there is great danger that the vanadium often present in these oils will damage the tube. In the case of tubes of heat-resistant 25–20 Cr–Ni steel, there is very rapid formation of scale, particularly at the weld seams, but sometimes in other places, and this can render the tube unserviceable in a very short time. This is caused by the vanadium pentoxide V_2O_5 which is produced in the process of combustion or by the vanadates which are the result of reaction between the vanadium pentoxide and the alkali metals also present in the oil. Both these strongly promote scale formation because they form compounds with the oxides normally present on the steel. These compounds have low fusion temperatures, between 650° and 700°C. The normal protective layer of oxide is therefore removed from the surface of the steel and the "catastrophic" scale formation occurs. An important factor in the rapid rate of formation may be the properties of V_2O_5 as a catalyst in oxygen transfer.

As mentioned above, in the case of 25–20 Cr–Ni steel the damage is particularly apparent at the weld seams. It was found that scale formation was appreciably reduced if all traces of welding slag were removed from the surface of the tube. This includes the very small splashes which may occur on each side of the weld seam.

Tubes which have already suffered scale formation can be repaired by welding. For this operation to be successful, however, mere surface removal of the scale is insufficient. It is necessary to grind off the surface of the steel to a depth of 1–2 mm. This is because the scale forms along the grain boundaries and thus penetrates slightly beneath the surface.

Ferritic steel with 24 per cent chromium, 1·5 per cent aluminium and 1·5 per cent silicon is more resistant to V_2O_5 attack. This steel can only be used in tubes for low-pressure operations, however, because its creep resistance is much poorer than that of austenitic 25–20 Cr–Ni steel.

The most effective method of combating the vanadium pentoxide attack has proved to be the addition of magnesium compounds to the fuel oil flame. Magnesium combines with V_2O_5 to form vanadates whose fusion temperatures are far above the operating temperature of the tube. Thus, no fused layers form on the tube surface.

It would be especially desirable if the magnesium could be added in the form of an oil-soluble compound. This is theoretically possible by using one of the magnesium soaps such as magnesium oleate, magnesium stearate or magnesium naphthenate, but the magnesium from these sources is very expensive. A method usually preferred, therefore, is the use of a solid magnesium compound, especially very finely ground, calcined dolomite which is injected into the flame in the air stream.

Correct alignment of the burners is very important in all cases. As the magnesium vanadate is formed throughout the flame, care must be taken to ensure that the flame direction is as straight as possible. The flame must above all be prevented from impingeing directly on the tubes, as this could lead to the presence of free V_2O_5.

The addition of calcined dolomite has proved a very effective means of resisting attack by V_2O_5. If managed skilfully, no damage due to "catastrophic" scale formation should be apparent even after 6 years. There is, of necessity, an increased amount of fly ash which involves more frequent cleaning of the reactors and the waste heat boilers.

The use of dolomite has a further advantageous side effect in that the fairly large volumes of sulphur dioxide and sulphur trioxide which are normally formed in the combustion process are converted into the sulphate which is a much less dangerous corrosion agent than sulphuric acid.

CORROSION OF MILD STEEL DUE TO IMPINGEMENT IN THE MAKE-GAS STREAM

J. G. Hines and P. Neufeld

INTRODUCTION

The heat-recovery system on the Billingham reformers is shown diagrammatically in Fig. 1. Gas from the shift converter passes successively through a high-pressure boiler, a low-pressure boiler, a feed heater and a gas cooler, catchpots being placed between each item in the line. Corrosion has not been a problem up-stream of the L.P. boiler, as the gas is above the dewpoint, and this paper is concerned entirely with the parts of the plant that operate below the dewpoint. With the exception of one of the bundles in the feed heater this part of the plant was made from mild steel. It was appreciated that the condensate from a gas stream containing carbon dioxide would be corrosive, but experience in other plant indicated that the corrosion rate would be moderate and that it would be tolerable if an appropriate corrosion allowance was included.

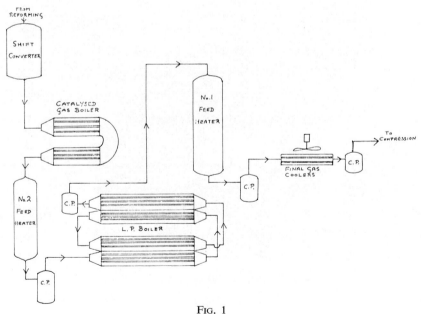

FIG. 1
Billingham steam reforming plant heat recovery system.

357

After a few months' operation hydrogen was found in the steam from the
L.P. boiler on No. 1 Unit, and when the boiler was opened up severe corrosion
damage was found on the inlet tube plates, the inlet tube ends and in the
interstage bends—i.e. in places where condensate droplets impinge on the
metal surfaces. Similar corrosion has subsequently been found in other parts
of the system, and in the other Billingham units. It has also occurred at
Severnside, where the heat-recovery system is generally similar to that at
Billingham, but the Heysham units (where the impingement conditions are
less severe because of differences in design) have not given trouble.

SERVICE EXPERIENCE

The L.P. boilers of the Billingham units are twin tube/tube plate exchangers,
the water being on the shell side. Each exchanger is divided into two passes,
and the four passes are connected by 180° pipe bends, with 90° bends on the
inlet and exit pipes to the whole boiler. The boilers normally receive gas at
150–70 psi, and 150–80°C though the temperature can reach 240°C under
certain circumstances; the temperature falls rapidly until the dewpoint is
reached in the first pass, and then more slowly to 120°C at the exit end. Most
of the heat recovered comes from condensation of steam, and about 2 tons/hr
of condensate are formed in each boiler. The gas velocity is about 60 ft/sec
in the tubes and of the same order in the pipe work. Some regions where

FIG. 2
Inter-pass bend, L.P. boiler, Billingham.

serious corrosion occurred are shown in Figs. 2, 3, 4. Some damage also occurred in the catchpots downsteam of the L.P. boilers, and in the first feed water heaters (Fig. 5). Each feed heater is a steel vessel containing two bundles of finned tubes arranged one above the other, the tubes in a bundle being wound as concentric spirals joined to headers by unfinned tubes. The lower bundle handles non-deaerated water and is of copper, but the upper, which handles deaerated water, was mild steel. Gas enters the top of the heater at about 125°C, and leaves at 80–90°C, while feed water enters at ambient and is heated to 90°C in the copper bundle and to boiler temperature in the steel bundle. The external surfaces of the steel bundles have been severely attacked, particularly the distributor pipes which are more exposed to impingement effects than are the finned tubes. The copper bundles have not been attacked from the gas side, and the steel shell of the feed heater has suffered only moderate damage. Some corrosion has also occurred in the distributor pipes to the gas cooler.

FIG. 3
Inlet tube plates of second and fourth passes, L.P. boilers, Billingham.

Corrosion damage is confined to the mild steel surfaces, and is severe only where it is associated with impingement of water droplets carried by the gas stream. The distribution of serious damage and of the rate of penetration through the system is complex, and appears to be caused almost entirely by differences in the severity of impingement from place to place. The extent of the damage varies considerably over quite short distances; thus on the L.P. boiler the inlet tube plates were very severely attacked where the stream of high velocity droplets ejected from the interstage piping impinges, but only moderately damaged elsewhere. Three types of corroded surface were met.

(i) In regions sheltered from high velocity impingement the surfaces are covered by a black shiny scale of magnetite and ferrous carbonate, and the penetration rate falls to an acceptable low level. (Estimated at 0·03 mm/yr from electrochemical measurements.)

(ii) Under moderately severe impingement the black scale is broken down locally leading to pits with smooth, almost polished surfaces. These pits often show marked directional effects, extending in the direction of the local droplet stream.

(iii) Under severe impingement conditions the protective scale does not form and uniform metal wastage occurs at rates of up to $\frac{1}{2}$ in./yr. Under these conditions weld metal is attacked less rapidly than plate.

Fig. 4
Detail of Fig. 3.

FIG. 5
Distributor pipes, mild steel first feed water heater, Billingham.

FIG. 6
Mild steel thermocouple sheaths: No. 1: Inlet L.P. boiler; No. 2: Between
second and third pass; No. 3: Exit fourth pass.

These three types of attack are illustrated in Fig. 6, which shows thermocouple sheaths from an L.P. boiler.

The thickness of the black film in the sheltered areas decreases progressively through the system as the temperature falls, as does the rate of penetration in regions where the film cannot form. In intermediate conditions the effect of temperature is less clear, presumably because it is obscured by the effects of variations in gas velocity.

The Billingham reformers are used to make either "H gas" or "N gas", typical compositions (ignoring water) being:

	H gas	N gas
Carbon dioxide	22%	16%
Carbon monoxide	2·5%	4%
Hydrogen	74%	64·5%
Nitrogen	0·5%	15%
Methane	1·0%	0·5%

N gas contains a little less carbon dioxide than does H gas, and also contains traces of ammonia produced by reaction between hydrogen and nitrogen on the steel surfaces. The condensate from N gas may thus be marginally less acid than that from H gas, and this possibility caused some confusion initially. The Heysham units operate on N gas duty, and had run for more than a year when the first trouble was encountered at Billingham on a reformer that had been mainly on H gas. It is now known that there is little difference in pH between condensate from the two duties, and there is no material difference in corrosion behaviour either, although the H gas condition is marginally more damaging. The Heysham units are of a design different from the Billingham and Severnside units, and the difference in behaviour appears to be associated with geometrical differences. Nevertheless it is reasonable to suppose that a more alkaline condensate would be less corrosive, and attempts have been made to control the corrosion by adding ammonia to the gas stream. No convincing effect on corrosion rate or condensate pH was obtained within the limits of the tests done.

PROTECTIVE MEASURES

When the damage to No. 1 L.P. boiler was discovered various protective measures were put in hand. The tube plates were sprayed with 18/8/Ti, and this was reinforced on the inlet tube plates by baffle plates in 18/8/Ti with ferrules which protrude about 12 in. down the tubes and protect their inlet ends. The baffle plates are bolted to the tube plates. The boiler header boxes and interstage pipe bends were also lined with 18/8/Ti sheet, as have been parts of the distributor pipes on the feed heaters and gas coolers. These measures were taken in the spring of 1963 on No. 1 Unit, and similar precautions have been taken on the other units. The first boiler treated in this way ran for a further 14 months before failure occurred due to penetration of the tubes, at the ends of the ferrules. The stainless steel sprayed coating was begin ning to show signs of loss of adhesion also.

No attempt has yet been made to protect the finned tubes in the steel feed water bundles, although the distributor pipes have been protected with stainless steel. Here again attack has been concentrated at the edges of the protective sheaths, presumably because of the added turbulence at these points.

Fig. 7

Test plates on tube plate L.P. boiler, Billingham.

EXPERIMENTAL WORK

Two sets of experiments have been done. In the first, test plates of various materials are bolted to the baffle plates on the inlet tube plates of the L.P. boiler. The test plates are 5 in. square, and provided with four holes corresponding to the tubes that they cover (Fig. 7). The second set of experiments have been done in a test rig which takes a side stream from the gas inlet the L.P. boiler on No. 1 unit. The rig allows specimens to be exposed to a gas stream at controlled temperature, pressure and velocity, and also permits injection of ammonia into the test gas stream. The arrangement of the test rig is shown in Fig. 8.

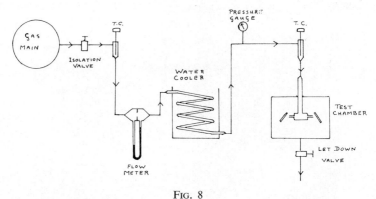

Fig. 8

Side stream test rig.

Fig. 9

Mild steel test plate as in Fig. 7.

RESULTS

One set of test plates has been examined after 6 months' exposure. Five metals were tested, Inconel, Ni-o-nel, FV560 (20% Cr, 2% Mo), an 80/20 cupronickel and mild steel. The first four showed negligible corrosion, although the cupronickel showed signs of preferential removal of nickel which is, however, not considered to be serious. The mild steel plates showed typical impingement pitting, of severity consistent with their position. The pits show marked directional effects (Figs. 9, 10, 11) and it is interesting that the direction of pit growth (and presumably of droplet travel) changes markedly over distances of an inch or so.

Table 1 shows results obtained on a variety of materials in the side stream rig. None of the metals tested showed significant corrosion, and if these results are combined with those from the test plates and with service experience on 18/8/Ti it is clear that all metals or alloys that might reasonably be used to replace or shield mild steel have satisfactory resistance. Aluminium itself is resistant, but aluminium spray on mild steel is not; this is not unexpected as condensate can penetrate the pores in the sprayed coating and react with the steel underneath. Sprayed 18/8/Ti did not show failure after 5 weeks in the test rig, nor in the first 6 months of its service on the L.P. boilers. After 14 months' service on the L.P. boilers however, as already stated, it did show signs of loss of adhesion and evidently is susceptible in the same way as sprayed aluminium, but to a lesser degree.

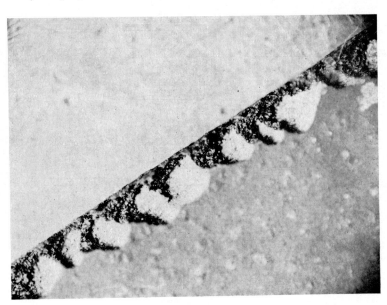

Fig. 10
Detail of Fig. 9 ($\times$ 7).

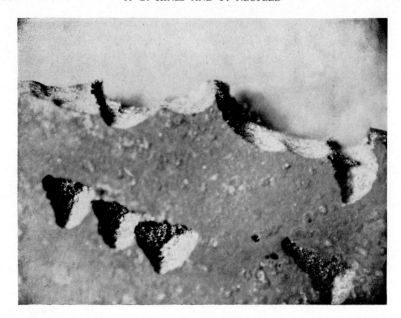

Fig. 11

Detail of Fig. 9 (×7).

TABLE 1

Tests in side-stream test rig

Material	Max. corr. rate mm/yr	Duration of test weeks
FV560	Nil	1
18/8/Ti	,,	1
13% Cr	,,	1
99·5% Al	,,	3
Nickel	,,	3
Copper (deox.)	,,	3
Al-brass	,,	1
Sprayed 18/8/Ti on M.S.	,,	5
Sprayed Al on M.S.	Blistering	5
Sakaphen Si14E on M.S.	,,	3
Sakaphen Si14EG on M.S.	Nil	9
Ensecote H/T on M.S.—I	Blistering	3
Ensecote H/T on M.S.—II	Nil	3

Conditions:

Condensate pH	6·5	Gas temp. at nozzle °C	110–15
Vel. at nozzle ft/sec	45	Reformer duty	N+H
Gas main temp. °C	150	Pressure psi	150–70

Three types of resin coatings on mild steel were tested. Two of these, Sakaphen Si 14EG* and Ensecote H/T† appear to be satisfactory. The first Ensecote specimen tested failed in 3 weeks, and was returned to the manufacturers who suggested that the original coating had been incorrectly applied. A further specimen, with correctly applied coating, proved satisfactory, and replacement tube bundles coated with the system have been installed in No. 1 unit.

Table 2 lists the results of tests on mild steel in the side stream rig. These tests were intended to determine the effect of ammonia additions to the gas stream. The liquor (30 per cent ammonia) was added to the main gas stream at the rates shown, but proved insufficient to appreciably affect the condensate pH except at the maximum obtainable injection rate. Results on the test specimens were somewhat erratic (Fig. 12), most showed an irregular region of attack immediately opposite the impinging jet, the rest of the surface being covered with the carbonate–magnetite scale. The maximum measured rate of penetration out of six specimens is taken as the criterion of attack. While the results indicate that ammonia additions sufficient to give a pH of perhaps 8 or 9 in the condensate may well be beneficial they can hardly be taken as conclusive evidence. Attempts to inject ammonia liquor into the side stream test rig have been unsuccessful to date, due to equipment failures. They did, however, show that to obtain a pH range 8–9 would require of the order of 250 l/hr of ammonia liquor to be injected to the make-gas stream.

TABLE 2

Tests in Side-Stream Test Rig

Material	Max. corr. rate mm/yr	Con- densate pH	NH₃ liq. injection gall/hr	Vel. at nozzle ft/hr	Gas main temp. °C	Gas temp. at nozzle °C	Reformer duty	Pressure psi	Duration of test weeks
Mild steel	7·5	7·0	5	33	150	110–15	H	150–70	1
Mild steel	12·7	7·0	5	33	150	110–15	H	150–70	1
Mild steel	Low	7·0	12	33	150	110–15	H	150–70	1
Mild steel	6·0	7·0	12	55	150	150	N	150–70	1
Mild steel	3·8	7·5	24	47	150	110–15	N	150–70	1

DISCUSSION

Rapid attack of mild steel due to impingement by steam condensate droplets in a high velocity stream is of course not a new phenomenon. Attack is often found in wet steam lines, particularly at bends. The presence of CO_2 in the make-gas has, however, led to the unusual feature of unusually rapid attack associated with the breakdown of a protective film in unusually mild impingement conditions.

* Not at present available in this country.
† Newton Chambers.

It is fortunate that none of the common engineering materials except mild steel appears to be susceptible to attack. Ammonia additions do not appear to be a satisfactory means of reducing the severity of the attack, as except in ammonia plants the quantities required would be prohibitive. Even in an ammonia plant the ammonia injection would be more than 1 per cent of the total make, which would seriously affect the plant's profitability. Careful design to minimize velocities and turbulence does not seem to be a very fruitful field either. Trouble usually occurs at bends, welds and changes of section, where local velocities may be much higher than the nominal velocity. It is not practical to eliminate such features, and though no serious work has yet been done to investigate velocity effects, it seems likely that the nominal velocities would have to be drastically reduced in order to obtain any benefit, perhaps to 5–10 ft/sec. Such a large increase in the dimensions of equipment would be necessary that this solution too must be rejected.

FIG. 12

Mild steel specimens from side stream test rig.

It is, therefore, necessary to use either protected mild steel or a resistant metal as constructional materials wherever impingement by condensate droplets is possible. So long as they are properly applied, non-metallic coatings such as Sakaphen Si 14EG and Ensecote H/T seem to be satisfactory, though we have no really long-term experience of these as yet. They also have the defect of being mechanically weak and easily chipped.

Sprayed 18/8 stainless steel is suitable as a temporary protective measure, and may be expected to give good service for several months. Due to its porous nature, however, in time sufficient corrosion of the basis steel will have occurred to affect the adhesion of the coating. It is not, therefore, suitable for permanent protection.

Loose or metallurgically-bonded linings of any stainless steel, copper alloy, nickel base alloy or aluminium would give adequate protection to mild steel equipment that is at risk. Two possible causes of trouble must be noted, though neither has caused any trouble in practice.

The high nickel alloys might be susceptible to attack by the CO content of the make-gas, if temperature conditions were right. This does not seem to be a problem with austenitic steels, and measurements have shown no carbonyl formation in the Billingham L.P. boilers.

The condensate will inevitably contain some traces of chloride, and under adverse conditions of drying out this could conceivably cause stress corrosion cracking of austenitic stainless steels. No cracking has been experienced to date, and in designs of future plants and in maintenance work this possibility has been considered so remote that it has been ignored.

CONCLUSIONS

Mild steel is the only common constructional material that has been found to suffer rapid attack in the make-gas stream of steam reforming plants. This is due to impingement by condensate droplets which contain dissolved CO_2. It is not practical to prevent this attack either by reducing the velocity of the stream or by injecting ammonia.

Long-term tests show that all the stainless steels and many alloys of copper and nickel are suitable as materials of construction, either solid or as protective sheeting over mild steel. Shorter tests also indicate that aluminium alloys and some non-metallic coatings are satisfactory.

CORROSION IN CENTRIFUGAL AIR COMPRESSORS

R. Erskine and A. F. Hall

INTRODUCTION

Pressurized air is injected into the secondary reformer in order to reduce the methane content and to provide nitrogen in the correct proportion to be combined with the hydrogen produced in the primary reformer. In early steam reforming plants the air compressors were required to deliver at 180 psig pressure, but with increasing size of plant and development of the process, the delivery pressure has risen until it is now 450 psig with a capacity of 15,000 ft³/min and a power consumption of 4000 h.p. Centrifugal air compressors are used for the purpose as technically and economically suited for the task. The relatively high compression ratios are necessarily associated with high tip speeds and with high stresses in the impellers. It is therefore necessary to use high strength steel for fabrication purposes, with a minimum U.T.S. of 60 tons/in.² in order to accommodate peak stresses. The compression ratio per impeller that can be attained with steels of this type is, in practice, about 2 : 1.

The use of high tensile steels raises problems associated with ductility and with propensity to hydrogen embrittlement. The risk of hydrogen embrittlement is very real in industrial atmospheres where condensed water from the air contains corrosive agents. Corrodents can have effects in other parts of the machine besides the impellers, for example, the shafts, casings and cooler systems. This paper discusses the various locations in which damage occurs and remedial actions that can be taken.

CONDENSATION

The relative humidity of air in the United Kingdom averages 85 per cent. If the air is compressed adiabatically the relative humidity decreases, but if the compression is isothermal the relative humidity increases. The power required for a given output is a function of gas temperature and the size of the machine is a function of gas density. It follows that in a multi-stage machine consisting of a number of impellers in which the compression is adiabatic, efficiency is improved if the inlet gas to each stage is cooled from the preceding exit temperature. Condensation occurs in the upper stages of compressors operating at pressures higher than 100 psi. Thus in the multi-stage machines operated in connection with reforming units, air in the first

371

stage is above the dew point, in the second it is around the dew point, but in the third and higher stages the air falls below the dew point, and condensation occurs.

The air in industrial atmospheres contains sulphur dioxide and ammonia, and it is found in practice that condensed droplets contain ammonium sulphate, which is an active corrodent. Evidence collected during the last 2 years shows that the parts of the compressor most severely affected varies with the type and location of the machine. Corrosion has been experienced on shafts, coolers, compressor casings and impellers. Operational difficulties have occurred in consequence as follows:

    (1) Corrosion of labyrinths in shafts has permitted by-passing with consequent loss of efficiency.

    (2) Corrosion of casings and coolers leads to build-up of dirt in impellers with loss of efficiency and the risk of out-of-balance forces. Plant may be shut down because of excessive vibration.

    (3) Corrosion of impellers has caused complete mechanical breakdown.

It would be possible to install equipment to clean the inlet air, but such equipment is expensive and cumbersome and its efficiency may decline from time to time. It is also possible, at the expense of efficiency, to operate above the dew point. The alternative, which has been adopted, is to use corrosion-resistant materials where necessary.

REPAIR OF COMPRESSOR SHAFTS

The process air for one of our plants at Severnside is provided by a four-stage single-shaft compressor with labyrinth seals between stages. After 6 months' operation it was found that the shaft and impellers had suffered corrosion, the most serious effects being on the shaft between first and fourth stage impellers and between the second and third stage impellers. The designed clearance of the machined section to accommodate the labyrinth seals is 0·006 in., but as a result of corrosion the clearance had increased to 0·024 in. The efficiency of the machine was reduced and there was impingement attack at the back of the first stage impeller.

A corroded shaft can be built up by nickel or chromium plating or by metal spraying. These methods require considerable dismantling and there was some doubt about the adhesion of sprayed coatings in service. The first repair to a corroded shaft was by means of sprayed stainless steel and it served successfully for 12 months. In the meantime accumulated experience had suggested that a filled epoxy resin could be used and machined to the required tolerances. Test pieces were prepared which proved that adhesion was excellent whether the amount of build-up was 0·040 in. or only a few thous. It was possible to turn the applied coating down to a feather edge without risk of breakage.

An epoxy coating has the advantage of corrosion resistance and impermeability. It can be applied on the site without removing the impellers from the shaft and if simple instructions are followed there is no need to employ specialist firms with the possible consequential delays. The shaft now in service (life to date 5 months) was repaired by means of resin and subsequently machined, the complete repair taking a total of 3 days.

It is known that similar procedures are followed in aero engine repairs with complete success.

PROTECTION OF INTERSTAGE COOLERS

If corrosion of cooler casings is anticipated it is not difficult to take preventive measures. The surfaces concerned are shot blasted and a modern stoving type resin applied. Where adequate protection has not been provided and experience shows that corrosion occurs there is greater difficulty. However, satisfactory results have been achieved by shot-blasting the corroded surfaces and then applying a cold curing solvent-free epoxy coating.

Until recent years corrosion in the tube bundles was either accepted and the bundle renewed when necessary or it was constructed in an expensive alloy steel. Four or 5 years ago resin coating of mild steel tube bundles was developed in Germany. Considerable scepticism existed about the value of this system especially when applied to the outside of tube bundles. However, service experience has now established resin coating of tube bundles both internally and externally as a reliable process and acceptable for this type of duty.

COMPRESSOR CASINGS

Corrosion of a compressor casing may not in itself be serious but the corrosion products help to foul the machine. Since there is always pitting as a result of the corrosion there is loss of smooth contours which detracts from the efficiency of the machine. The normal operating temperatures are such that it would be desirable to use stoved resins for the protection of the casings, the diffusers and the diffuser supports. However, stoved coatings cannot be applied successfully to castings that normally contain some porosity and it is therefore necessary to use cold curing epoxy resins. Particular care must be exercised to limit the thickness of the applied protection. Differential expansion of the base metal and the coating can lead to separation if the thickness of the resin is excessive.

Resin coatings of this type have been successful. Inspection after 12 months' service shows no build-up of dirt, no evidence of ageing, and satisfactory adhesion.

CONSTRUCTION OF IMPELLERS

The impellers used in commercially available air compressors are of the shrouded type, i.e. front and back shrouds with vanes between. Rivetted or welded constructions are available which can be subdivided as follows:

RIVETTED IMPELLERS

1. Vanes milled out of back shroud. Rivet holes drilled through vanes.
2. Rivets machined out of vanes.
3. Vanes made out of sheet, either U-type or Z-type.

WELDED IMPELLERS

1. Vanes welded to front shroud, back shroud press fit.
2. Front and back shrouds with one-half vane on each, then butt-welded together.

1. *Experience with Rivetted Impellers*

Following the failure of each fourth-stage impeller in three six-stage compressors operating at Billingham after only 1200 hr operation a detailed metallurgical examination was made of the broken parts. The 13 per cent chromium steel wheels were of rivetted construction, the rivets being integral

FIG. 1

Cracking at root of rivet ($\times 500$).

with the blades. The examination showed that the failures in some rivets had been initiated at the roots by stress corrosion cracking and propagated by corrosion fatigue. Other rivets had failed by corrosion fatigue. One example of the type of cracking found is shown in Fig. 1. Since cracking would be liable to occur if a very small amount of corrodent reached a rivet, any method of protection used had to be 100 per cent effective. The complex shape of the impellers and the very high tip speeds (about 1000 ft/sec) posed a major problem and time available for a solution was extremely short.

The first system considered was the application of a stoved resin coating to the assembled impeller. It was known that a firm in Germany had succeeded in applying coatings to impellers of similar size and it was also known from British aero engine manufacturers that these coatings were stable at high speeds. The solution would have been satisfactory if the problem had been one of general corrosion over the whole wheel, but the crux of the matter was the very small gap which necessarily existed between the wheel discs and the blades which had to be sealed to prevent corrodent reaching the root of the rivets.

In applying a stoved resin coating it was known that the most difficult task would be to seal that gap because the air trapped would tend to blow holes in the coating during stoving even if it bridged it beforehand. If applied successfully the coating would be weak at the vital point and any relative movement of the discs and blades during running would break the coat. Nevertheless a wheel was coated for test purposes and the coating contractors succeeded in making an excellent job. The impeller was fitted to a shaft and ran 5 per cent over-speed for 1 min. Examination showed that the coating had split at the roots of several of the blades and it was decided that the method of protection was unsuitable for this particular duty.

At the same time another method of protection was under consideration. This called for the use of a resin cement to be placed, before rivetting, between the edge of the blades and the wheel discs. On rivetting most would be squeezed out but the residue would effectively seal the roots of the rivets. To be successful the cement had to have the following properties:

(1) A "pot" life of at least 24 hr to allow complete assembly and closing of the rivets of an impeller whilst the resin was still soft.
(2) The ability to withstand the heating process to which the impellers were subjected when fitted to the shaft. (This could be as high as 300°C for a very short period.)
(3) Suitability for a service temperature of 180°C.

A programme of testing was devised and a suitable resin selected. The resin was a hot cured epoxy resin which set cold but did not fully cure until stoved. The use of a resin cement during the assembly of the impellers meant a modification of the normal workshop practice and it was necessary to draw up a sequence of operations which had to be strictly followed.

A complete rotor for one machine was built using the technique, and has now been in service for 1500 hr.

The same technique has since been used in the building of impellers for two different types of compressor. In these cases the blades were integral with one of the wheel discs. All impellers are subject to overspeed tests after construction, a procedure which usually causes some permanent deformation of the impeller. In the case of impellers built using the technique described the amount of deformation has been reduced, indicating that the resin adds to the stability. This method of constructing impellers is the subject of a patent application.

2. *Experience with Welded Impellers*

The third stage welded impeller on an air compressor at Heysham was found to be cracked after 5000 hr running. The impeller was cracked in three places at the periphery all closely adjacent to fillet welds.

The impeller was made from 1% Cr-Mo steel with a carbon content of 0·34 per cent. A macro-section through a cracked region (Fig. 2) showed the crack to be in the heat-affected zone of the fillet weld where the hardness was about 320–40 HV as compared with a general hardness of 250–60 HV.

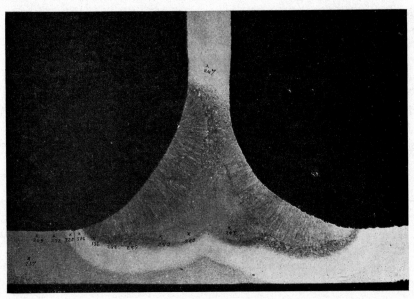

FIG. 2
Macrosection through fillet welded vane ($\times$ 5 approx.).

Samples of deposit from the impeller were analysed, and shown to be mainly ammonium sulphate, and water extract of the deposits gave pH values of 2–3.

It is well known that if low alloy steels with a hardness exceeding about 220 HV are subject to corrosion, the atomic hydrogen arising from the cathodic corrosion reaction enters the ferrite lattice and causes embrittlement. The presence of an acidic deposit on the impeller provides these conditions readily. The proportion of hydrogen evolved which enters the steel depends to some extent on the impurities in the corrosive environment, e.g. traces of some sulphur compounds poison the evolution reaction and increase the amount of hydrogen entering the steel. The tendency of a given steel to embrittlement is greater the higher the strength of the steel.

It was therefore clear that the impeller had failed by hydrogen embrittlement of the heat-affected zones in the fillet welds of the impeller. It is quite possible that if these zones had been at a lower hardness level, i.e. nearer 220–40 HV than 320–40 HV, the cracking would not have occurred. However, the post-weld heat treatment applied by the maker did not lower the hardness of the heat-affected zone. The maker was not prepared to adopt the higher temperature necessary to effect this on the grounds that it could cause general softening of the material as well as possible distortion. It therefore became necessary to consider alternative materials.

It was obviously necessary to choose a material with sufficiently high strength yet good resistance to hydrogen embrittlement. The material chosen was the martensitic precipitation hardening steel Firth-Vickers FV520B. It was known that in the 60–70 tons/in.^{2} tensile range the susceptibility of this material to hydrogen embrittlement is low. The same cannot be said of the other materials considered, such as 16% Cr–2% Ni and 16% Cr–2% Mo. In the former the combination of poor ductility and corrosion resistance make it suspect for this duty. With the latter the corrosion resistance might be adequate, but the ductility is low at the 60–70 tons/in.^{2} level and might well lead to cracking.

It was considered that since we were dealing with a range of environments of varying severity and since the consequences of failure were so serious we should standardize on the best material available. It was accepted that the use of a precipitation hardening steel might involve some commercial and technical problems, but it was decided to proceed.

There was experience in another Division of ICI where welded FV520B impellers in the 60–70 tons/in.^{2} condition had given 5 years' satisfactory service in a centrifugal air compressor operating below the dew point. In addition there was good experience within this Division and outside ICI with rivetted FV520B impellers in coke-oven gas exhausters.

The welding fabrication of FV520B involves careful attention to the specified procedure. However, there is adequate experience to show that the techniques involved can be carried out by competent fabricators. Some difficulty was encountered with respect to suitable metallic-arc welding electrodes because there was insufficient practical experience with develop-

N

ment-stage electrodes. This matter was resolved and it is now possible to specify and obtain the weld metal properties required for the welded impellers.

As a general rule the use of argon-arc welding is to be preferred because of the advantages of weld cleanliness. However, argon arc welding is not always applicable to impeller fabrication.

The Division is now committed to the use of FV520B stainless steel for both welded and rivetted impellers for air compressors in a variety of machines at various sites. There is no doubt that in some of the atmospheric environments in which we are concerned, FV520B is the only one of the steels which have been considered which possesses adequate resistance to hydrogen embrittlement. It has therefore been decided to adopt the policy of using FV520B steel for impellers for which high strength steels are essential.

CONCLUSIONS

At first sight this is a field where one would not expect a great deal of trouble, but the information in this paper will leave little doubt that this is not the case. Experience has shown that the condensate from industrial atmospheres can be very corrosive and can do considerable damage. Steps must therefore be taken to guard against these adverse effects of this corrosion by the use of suitable materials, since it is not an economic proposition to operate the compressors to prevent condensation.

CORROSION PROBLEMS ON FINNED AIR-COOLED HEAT EXCHANGER TUBING

A. F. HALL and R. ERSKINE

INTRODUCTION

The use of air-cooled heat exchangers is, under certain circumstances, an economic alternative to water cooling and a number of such exchangers have been used on reformer units. The chemical engineering aspects of cooling have been covered in many papers but it is perhaps not so well known that certain air coolers have suffered severe corrosion which can limit their usefulness unless appropriate steps are taken. The coolers used on both the Heysham and Billingham plants have not been entirely satisfactory and action has had to be taken to protect these from corrosion by means of various coatings.

PROBLEMS ASSOCIATED WITH FINNED TUBING

Although a wide range of finned tubing is used in air-cooled heat exchangers, those used by us have mainly aluminium fins. These are either strip wound on to a mild steel tube or attached integrally to aluminium tube.

The industrial atmospheres in which the air-cooled heat exchangers are used are aggressive to aluminium, containing as they do moisture droplets, acid fumes (SO_2 and chloride) and dust. The corrosion normally takes place as pitting, layer or other forms of localized attack and it is most likely to occur in the presence of droplets of polluted water. The bottom row of finned tubes usually contains the coldest fluid and droplets of moisture which disentrain on the bottom row do not evaporate quickly. The damp acidic dust lies on the fins and naturally causes corrosion. It is found in practice that the bottom row corrodes much more than the upper rows, presumably because the first row removes most of the water droplets and holds most of the dust.

The corrosion of the aluminium fins can be very serious, to the extent of reducing the useful fin length by more than half. The type of corrosion which can occur is illustrated in Figs. 1 and 2 as compared to a "good" fin in Fig. 3. In the first two cases the finned tubing was exposed at ambient temperature to a fairly aggressive atmosphere for about 1 year, the third tubing being maintained about 25°C above the others in the same environment and was found to be free from corrosion.

Differences in the composition of the aluminium can have some effect on the corrosion resistance of the fin material, but it has been found in practice that this is not significant and that the commercially available materials all behave in much the same manner.

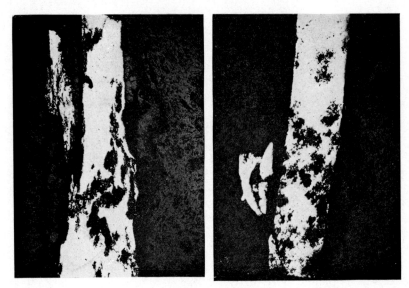

FIGS. 1 AND 2

Corroded fin tips (1 year's exposure to industrial atmosphere ($\times 28$).

Thus, it is a natural consequence of using aluminium finned exchanger elements that the first row of tubes is bound to suffer some corrosion and becomes clogged up with corrosion product and entrained dust.

There are two ways in which the bottom row of tubes can be protected.

(1) The use of a disentrainment mesh just below the bottom row.

(2) The provision of a protective coating over the bottom row of tubes.

The use of a disentrainment mesh of aluminium turnings has been tried with a good measure of success. The mesh disappeared after 6 months' service, acting as it does in a sacrificial way. The use of stainless steel mesh is to be tried. Method (2) has been used quite extensively.

THE PROTECTION OF ALUMINIUM FINNED TUBES

The problem of protecting aluminium finned air-cooler tubes is not only of selecting a coating to withstand the conditions, since almost any paint would offer some degree of protection, but one of application. In some quarters, coating the inside of 30-ft long tubes of small diameter is regarded as an easier task than that of coating the fins.

It is at once obvious that a coating cannot be applied by brush, and, since one fin tends to mask another, the difficulties of spray application are considerable. The simplest method of coating is by dipping the whole tube into a bath of paint. Not all paints are suitable for dip application and for this particular case the viscosity must be such that a paint film is applied evenly by dipping and air bubbles trapped on the surface should be an absolute minimum. It is probable that many paints could be produced which would satisfy this condition by thinning with solvent. With many such paints, solvent washing would be a problem, i.e. as the solvent evaporated it would tend to wash the paint off the fins.

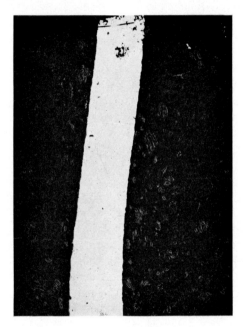

Fig. 3

Fin tip (maintained about 25°C above ambient) after 1 year's exposure (× 32).

The paint selected must in addition wet the surface properly when applied by dipping and the dried film must have reasonable adhesion to aluminium. It is usual with new aluminium to apply a "conversion" coating (e.g. chromate or phosphate chemical pretreatment) before painting, in order to improve adhesion, but this is not practicable in this case. The applied paint film must not be too thick otherwise the performance of the heat exchanger would be seriously affected.

It seemed evident that a number of systems based on synthetic resins would be satisfactory, but many of these would need to be hot cured and the problem of stoving 30 ft tubes was considered an undesirable complication apart from being very expensive. A suitable coating appeared to be a two-pack polyurethane system which, when tried, proved to be successful. A two-coat system was adopted; the first coat was a chromate primer, the second a clear lacquer. The system of coating was as follows:

(1) The tubes were degreased by dipping in trichlorethylene.
(2) The tubes were dip coated with the polyurethane chromate primer. After dipping, the surplus material was allowed to drain for a short time. Any bridging between the fins was broken with a jet of compressed air.
(3) Within 24 hr of applying the priming coat the clear varnish was applied by dipping. A longer time between coats is undesirable since it would mean loss of intercoat adhesion. Again it may be necessary to break any bridging with a jet of air (this is not a serious problem).

The total film thickness obtained was 0·002 in. For reasons stated earlier it is only considered necessary at present to coat the bottom row of an air-cooled heat exchanger. Calculations showed that the effect on the performance of the exchanger of this coating would be negligible. The overall reduction in capacity (heat duty) would be 1 per cent and the increase in the air pressure drop would be 0·5 per cent with the power consumption of the fans virtually unchanged.

Two units have now been built with the bottom row of tubes treated in the above manner. The first of these has been in service for about 12 months and is proving satisfactory. The cost of coating the tubes was about $2\frac{1}{2}$ per cent of the cost of the units.

Although it was anticipated that this treatment would be successful, there remained the problem of units that had already been assembled. Experiments were done which demonstrated that this coating could be applied to the lower half of the bottom row of tubes of units already assembled. At that time another Division of ICI had an air-cooled heat exchanger which had been built but not commissioned. In order to obtain a direct comparison between coated and uncoated tubes it was decided to attempt to coat part of each bank of this unit *in situ*. The procedure adopted was as follows:

(1) The tubes were steam cleaned and allowed to dry.
(2) Degreasing was carried out by spraying with trichlorethylene.
(3) Priming coat of polyurethane was applied by spray gun.
(4) Polyurethane lacquer was applied by spray gun.

The coating applied in this way was, of necessity, much less perfect than that applied by dipping. Nevertheless, when this exchanger was examined after 6 months' service there was virtually no evidence of corrosion on the treated tubes whereas there was corrosion on the untreated tubes in the same exchanger. Furthermore the dirt build-up was less on the treated surfaces than on the adjacent unprotected surfaces.

CONCLUSION

The aluminium finned tubing used in air-cooled heat exchangers is liable to severe corrosion in industrial atmospheres. This can cause a reduction in efficiency unless appropriate steps are taken. One method of combating the corrosion by coating the tubes has been used with considerable success.

HEAT RESISTING RUBBER CONNECTORS

L. T. Butt

There have been few applications for rubbers in steam reforming plant. However, flexible connectors for the combustion air headers and downcomers to the light distillate burners were required, and since these operate at only 130°C, an elastomer was a possibility (Fig. 1).

Fig 1

Flexible connector.

Four elastomers were potential candidates for the job: "Viton",* silicone rubber, "Hypalon"* and polyacrylic rubber. The normally quoted continuous operating temperatures (Centigrade) for these materials are, respectively, 200°, 200°, 130° and 160° and at first sight it would appear logical to employ "Viton" or silicone rubbers. "Viton" connectors would be considerably more expensive than the same article made from "Hypalon" or polyacrylic rubber. Silicone rubber is intermediate in price, but this elastomer has the additional disadvantage of relatively poor physical properties. For this reason "Hypalon" and polyacrylic rubber were the two materials selected for detailed

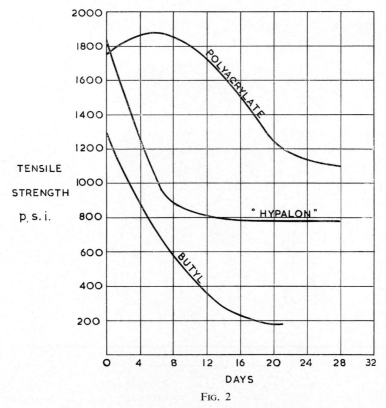

Fig. 2

The effect of heat ageing at 130°C on tensile strength of "Hypalon", polyacrylate and butyl rubbers.

examination in the laboratory. In addition we examined butyl (the most heat-resistant general purpose rubber) as a comparison and also various samples of neoprene on cotton and asbestos offered by suppliers as a standard material for such purposes.

* Trade marks of Du Pont Co.

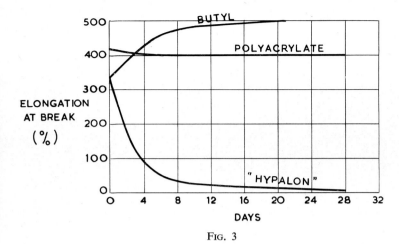

Fig. 3

The effect of heat ageing at 130°C on elongation of "Hypalon", polyacrylate and butyl rubbers.

All samples were placed in an air oven at 130°C, and some were removed for physical testing at intervals of 7 days over the period of a month. The neoprene/fabric samples had aged within 7 days to such an extent that they were rigid and need not be considered further. Figures 2 and 3 show the variation of tensile strength and elongation at break of "Hypalon", butyl and polyacrylic rubbers during 28 days' exposure to the test temperature. It will be noticed that the rate of fall-off of tensile strength shown in Fig. 2 is lowest in the case of polyacrylic rubber and that the percentage of original strength retained at the end of the test period is greatest.

More significant still for a duty where flexibility is essential is the effect of exposure to heat on the elongation. In Fig. 3 it can be seen that the fall in elongation of polyacrylic rubber over the test period is relatively small, on the other hand "Hypalon" after 7 days no longer retains a serviceable proportion, having hardened considerably. In the case of butyl, the ultimate effect of heat degradation is to increase the elongation, as shown, and although this is associated also with its becoming plastic rather than elastic, it is evident that in applications where flexing occurs this is to be preferred to a decrease in elongation and embrittlement.

The final selection of polyacrylate rubber for the connectors was the only possible decision in the light of this work. Its employment for this duty has subsequently proved to be successful using an asbestos fabric as reinforcement.